Bryan Do

The Very Civil Engineer

1768-1855

Bryan Donkin

The Very Civil Engineer
1768-1855

Maureen Greenland

Russ Day

Phillimore Book Publishing

2016

Published by

PHILLIMORE BOOK PUBLISHING

www.phillimorebookpublishing.co.uk

ISBN 978-0-9934680-1-8

bdba@holmesfield.plus.com
B.D. Book Associates

Contents

List of Illustrations

ILLUSTRATION ACKNOWLEDGEMENTS

Illustrations have been provided by kind permission of the following institutions and individuals:
Dacorum Heritage Trust, Berkhamsted and Mr A.J. Ward: 8
Derbyshire Record Office, Matlock: 19, 21, 22, 35, 41, 42, 43, 59, 62, & 63
Institution of Civil Engineers, London, 13, 14 & 47
Kent History and Library Centre, Maidstone: 4
London Metropolitan Archives, City of London: 33
Newcastle City Library: 57
Northumberland Archives, Woodhorn, Ashington: 1
Royal Society, London, 56
Southwark Local History Library and Archive, London: 39
Wellcome Images, Wellcome Collection, London: 23, 24, 25 & 26
Mrs Alice Bentley: 2 & 38
Private collections: 32, 46, 54 & 55

Most of the remaining illustrations are from out-of-copyright publications, mainly from the nineteenth century and referenced in this book. Some have been in general circulation for so long that it has been impossible to trace their source.

Acknowledgements

Thanks are owed to the many helpful librarians and archivists up and down the country who have patiently put up with our niggling queries, but especially to the friendly and knowledgeable staff at the Derbyshire Record Office, where the Donkin collection is held. If it had not been for the good sense of Terry Woodhouse, former Managing Director of the Bryan Donkin Company, this book might never have happened: he saved from destruction many of Donkin's priceless personal and company records.

Family records, too, have been invaluable: several members of the Donkin family have been particularly generous in sharing their knowledge and documents of the family's history. We would also like to acknowledge the help of Bernard Jones in the final stages of the book, and Ann Kingdom of the Society of Indexers for her skilful work. Not least, the support and advice of Andrew Illes of Phillimore Book Publishing has been greatly appreciated.

Preface

Dangling from a crane, a dirty old machine soared skywards through the roof of a Chesterfield factory and down onto a truck, to rattle off down the bypass to Sheffield for restoration by the authors. After much gentle removal of the hard covering of grime, and the careful renovation of damaged parts, Bryan Donkin's beautiful rose engine emerged in all its glory of mahogany and brass. Children who were invited to turn the handle were intrigued by the complicated patterns that this geometric lathe could produce; onlookers marvelled at the beauty of its whirling cogs and engineers stood in silent admiration.

Discovering that the rose engine had been made for the serious purpose of protecting bank notes from forgery was the first step to research that led to a PhD. Curiosity was aroused about the man who had built the unique machine; finally, after thirty years, this book tells Bryan Donkin's story. So diverse were Bryan Donkin's talents that a comprehensive study would require a book twice as long, which could be daunting for the person on the Bermondsey omnibus to read. While Donkin's pivotal contribution to the Industrial Revolution has become obvious, there is still scope for further research into this brilliant man's achievements. Fortunately, some of Donkin's own diaries, notebooks and letters have survived to illuminate his life and his world. Magazines and books of the early nineteenth century have helped to set the scene in graphic detail, too; even Government reports of the day have their moments of humour and poignancy.

Teasing out the details of the life of this one man, born a child of the Enlightenment in the eighteenth century and living through the first half of the nineteenth, inevitably brings into focus many different aspects of Georgian and Victorian life and the changes that took place during that time. The impact of steam power influenced the proliferation of new inventions and trades. As a multi-faceted civil and mechanical engineer, Donkin was able to embrace the challenges of these innovations, working out processes from start to finish, making his own tools for specific purposes, applying his lively mind to solving practical problems and making things with skill and precision.

Bryan Donkin did not throw his weight about or brag about his achievements. Although he was highly thought of by his peers, historians have not given him the recognition he justly deserves … until now.

… he was the most advanced mechanical engineer of the time.
George Escol Sellers, *c.*1884

I
Foundations

A voyage of discovery was about to begin. In March 1768, plans were afoot for the launch of an exciting expedition to the South Seas to witness and record the transit of Venus, the rare occurrence when the planet passes between the earth and the sun. The Admiralty acquired a Whitby-built collier to convert, and renamed it *Endeavour*. With up-to-date equipment and the botanist Joseph Banks on board, Lieutenant James Cook commanded the voyage that would take him round the world to the largely uncharted lands of the Southern hemisphere, where he explored New Zealand and Australia. The civilised world was expanding.

England and France had fought for years to gain territories and establish their empires; progress had been made by Britain in colonising Eastern Canada and parts of India in the face of French opposition. Back at home the country had been ruled for eight years by George III, who had already shown signs of the illness that gave him the reputation of madness. There was unrest in the country, sparked by food shortages and rising prices. Riots were incited by John Wilkes, a flamboyant radical MP.[1] In his writing and speeches, he had repeatedly attacked the King and the Government and was arrested for seditious libel. To avoid his sentence, he fled to Paris, where he stayed for five years until the beginning of 1768, returning to create more mayhem.

England was on the verge of momentous changes: the beginning of the Industrial Revolution was starting to shift the population from the countryside to the towns; mechanisation of farming activities not only drove country people from their traditional work on the land, but inspired the development of machines for the production of goods in the cities. James Watt, who had struggled for years to harness the power of steam, finally finished constructing a steam engine to his satisfaction in 1768 and prepared to patent it to drive a water pump. Hargreaves' newly invented spinning jenny enabled sixteen spindles of cotton to be spun at once, greatly increasing the production of textiles. The new turnpike trusts meant that some roads were paid for by users, enabling the owners to keep them in good order, so travelling was speedier. Canals were being built to move heavy goods more efficiently. On the land, improvements in farming methods brought better use of the fields; instead of letting land lie fallow, turnips, swedes and grasses were sown, in turn providing fodder for animals and food for the fast-growing population.

The Arts flourished. Robert Adam, influenced by his four-year visit to Italy in the previous decade, was translating the forms and motifs of the ancient monuments of Rome and Pompeii into decorations for walls, ceilings and mantelpieces in the great houses of England. In March 1768, he was working on designs for the entrance hall at Osterley Park and the dining room at Syon House, amid on-going projects at Harewood House, Keddleston Hall and Kenwood.[2] The age of Neo-classicism had begun in the 1750s, replacing the opulent ornamentation of the Rococo era with a cool, restrained style inspired by classical architecture. Joshua Reynolds, at forty four, was painting portraits of the great and the good, adapting his style to reflect the new taste for Greco-Roman art; he was also gathering together artists to form the Royal Academy, and was elected as their first President when it formally opened later in 1768.

In Vienna, an opera called *Bastien et Bastienne* was performed; it was composed by the talented twelve-year-old Mozart. Here in England, Thomas Arne, composer of 'Rule Britannia', was the leading composer of his day. Another 'first' that year was the publication in Edinburgh of the Encyclopaedia Britannica. *The Good-natured Man*, a work by the poet and playwright Oliver Goldsmith, was first produced at Covent Garden in January 1768, but it was not a great success, unlike his acclaimed *She Stoops to Conquer*, performed three years later. Goldmith's friend Dr Johnson had earlier sold copies of Goldsmith's *The Vicar of Wakefield*; it included a piece of verse, *Elegy on the Death of a Mad Dog*, which ended with the immortal words: 'The man recovered from the bite; the dog it was that dy'd'.

The Age of Enlightenment was firmly established; ingrained concepts and ways of thinking rooted in tradition and religion had given way to curiosity and logical scientific thought. For three years, in Birmingham, a group of strong, intelligent men had met whenever the full moon shone, to share their philosophies, to experiment with minerals, to study light and air, and to talk of mechanics and steam power, canals and clocks.[3] They were The Lunar Society, eventually a dozen in all, headed by Erasmus Darwin, the portly doctor and inventor; among the first members were the enterprising manufacturer Matthew Boulton, James Watt, the cautious but brilliant Scottish engineer, and Josiah Wedgewood, a fine potter who found fame and fortune through his empirical research. The group they gathered round them were men of vision and free thinkers who, spurred by the developing public interest in nature, technology and the sciences, and gaining confidence from each other, pushed out the boundaries of knowledge. At the same time, another group, headed by the esteemed engineer John Smeaton, was meeting every Friday evening at the Queen's Head in Holborn, London; three years later, the discussion group became the Society of Civil Engineers, the first professional body to focus on their common interest.

It was a propitious time for a budding engineer to arrive on the scene. In a hamlet in Northumberland called Sandoe, lived John Donkin and his wife Jane (née Soppitt). On 22 March 1768, a son was born to Mr and Mrs Donkin, and christened Bryan. The exact place of Bryan Donkin's birth remains a mystery. Whereas Bryan's older siblings were born 'at Sandoe', Bryan and the younger children were born 'at Fountain Hall'.[4] There is no evidence of a Fountain Hall in or around Sandoe; the best guess for Bryan's birthplace is Fountainhall near Leith in Scotland, where perhaps Jane Donkin had family or friends who looked after her when the child was born. Young Bryan was baptised in the parish church of St John Lee, not far from Sandoe, on 18 April 1768.[5] Mrs Donkin already had her hands full with two sons and two daughters – William, aged eight, John a six-year-old, Ann four, and little Jane, the youngest at two years old. Mrs Jane Donkin was thirty-two years old when Bryan was born; she went on to produce three more children – Mary, Henry and, when she was forty, Thomas. Most of her life was given up to childrearing, as was the norm for women at that time.

John Donkin, Bryan's father, was described as a 'gentleman'.[6] At that time, a gentleman was defined more by demeanour than by pedigree.[7] A man's bearing, his dedication to the public good, and his education gave him a standing in society above the working class. (With due deference, he was referred to by a close relation as 'Mr D'.)[8] John had worked as land agent for William Errington, the previous owner of the stately home at Sandoe, Beaufront. In his will, Errington recommended that his executor should 'continue the working of the mines, collieries and smelting mill, which I now do, and recommend him to continue John Donkin in the management of the same'.[9] John seems to have been a level-headed, intelligent man, a conscientious land agent to the brothers John and Henry Errington. Faith in God guided his life.[10] Before Bryan was born, his father was a subscriber to a book on ecclesiastical law; clearly he was a thinker as well as a very able practical man.[11] John was a wise choice for the post of manager of land and property; with his ear to the ground, hardly a deal would have been struck without his prior knowledge.

Bryan Donkin's parents, John and Jane, were cultured people 'of good education and taste', who gave their children every encouragement.[12] As a young boy, Bryan was physically brave, and loved climbing, which often alarmed the adults around him. His talents showed themselves early in his boyhood, when he amused himself by making thermometers and 'many ingenious trifles' in a little workshop, presumably set up for him by his father. At the age of eight, he was taken by his father to see an old flour mill on the Tyne at nearby Corbridge, and surprised his friends by making a perfectly correct drawing of it when he returned home. Apparently, this was the first indication to his father of Bryan's flair for mechanics. Fascination with the movement and power of water, which became an important element in Bryan's later life, was already firmly established at an early age: the house where he lived was near a source of constantly flowing water, which he channelled by means of pipes and wheels to turn a spit for roasting food over the fire. Neighbours were amazed at the contrivance and the Donkin household received many visitors who came especially to see it. Later, when Bryan's eldest

1 *Map of the Sandoe area, 1769.*

sister Ann (who was five years older) complained that her spinning wheel was not functioning properly, the budding engineer's advice was 'You should examine it … to find out the cause'.

Even at play, Bryan's early interest in practical science came to the fore; one of his amusements was to rig up an electrical machine to make little puppet men and women dance to music, while his eldest sister, Ann, kept time with a wand. The ability to generate an electrical charge through a small hand-wound machine had been discovered decades before.[13] This form of electricity was known to be able to attract tiny balls made of cork, or pith from an elder tree, so that they would jump.[14] A popular toy in the early nineteenth century was a development of that principle: substitute the pith balls with tiny figures made of the same material, and it becomes a puppet show of electrified jumping dancers. From about 1800 (or possibly earlier) kits were sold that included a manually-operated machine and pith puppets.[15] How Bryan Donkin found out about the phenomenon in the 1770s can only be guessed at, but when he was ten years old, the *Gentleman's Magazine* recorded experiments by Benjamin Franklin, reported to the Royal Society, which included dancing pith balls.[16] At any rate, Bryan's electrical entertainment, with a musical accompaniment, was so successful that the villagers were invited to a performance, which they found 'quite magical'. No doubt, young Bryan realised that there was more to it than mere magic.

Sandoe (now spelt Sandhoe) was a wonderful place to grow up in. It lay a mile or so to the north west of Corbridge; Hexham was about the same distance away. Watling Street, the great Roman road, ran to the east side of Sandoe, meeting Hadrian's Wall, and to the west the old turnpike road led from Hexham northwards. Immediately to the north of Sandoe lay the moorland of Stagshaw Bank, crossed by lanes and punctuated by lead mines. Twice a year, on the day before Whit Sunday and on July 4th, a massive fair was held on this wild land. Here cattle were traded, craftsmen brought their wares, and people were attracted from far and near to exchange livestock and enjoy the event – the usually quiet village of Sandoe was full of people trekking through to Stagshaw Bank and back. Bryan's uncle bought a pair of 'pumps' there one year, from a Darlington shoemaker's stall.[17]

Hexhamshire (as the area was known) had seen tragedy though; only seven years before Bryan's birth, in 1761, the terrible Hexham riot had devastated families in the town and outlying villages. Feelings had run high at an attempt to conscript for the militia by listing all eligible men and choosing them by a balloting system.[18] Labourers, tradesmen, servants and pitmen, some with their wives and children, gathered in the town centre to protest on the day of the ballot, and were confronted by a detachment of the North Yorkshire militia in front of the Moot Hall. After four hours of argument, the angry mob advanced with staves and clubs, and was brutally bayoneted and shot down by the soldiers. Fifty or more died, including two children and an Anthony Brown of Sandoe, and more than three hundred suffered awful wounds: a man from Chollerton lost an ear and a finger, and many of the victims never worked again.

In the mid eighteenth century, Sandoe was little more than a cluster of buildings. Dotted around the surrounding countryside were grand houses – Sir Edward Blackett, baronet, lived at nearby Aydon Castle, and Mr Gibson, whose family of lawyers spanned the centuries, lived not far away at Close House. Much of the region lay in the parish of St. John Lee, an area about seven miles long and four wide. The parish church stood on the ridge at Acomb, high above the flood plain of the Tyne. Here it was that several members of the Donkin family, including Bryan, were baptised, and the churchyard still bears evidence of the deaths of local residents of Bryan's era, including seven members of the Donkin family.

On the fringe of the hamlet of Sandoe was Beaufront, first recorded as a mere tower in 1415 when defence from marauding Scots was necessary. Beaufront was owned by the Errington family from 1587, and in Donkin's time was the home of John Errington, whose brother Henry lived at Sandoe Hall, just across the lane

2 *Church of St John Lee, drawn by a member of the Donkin family.*

below the High House where members of the Donkin family lived later. Beaufront was a substantial mansion when Bryan was young, but when the ancient buildings became the property of the Cuthbert family in 1835, they were transformed into the romantic castle that still stands today. Below the terrace the land sloped down the gentle hillside towards the Tyne valley, and the garden of Beaufront gave way to landscaped areas planted with beeches and other trees; a fine beech tree planted there had grown to the height of 144 feet by the twenty-first century. John Errington spent £20,000 on improving the magnificent gardens, fruit walls, hot house, plantations and walks.[19] Bryan's uncle witnessed the development of the walled garden at Beaufront in 1770; the tall brick wall was topped with flat white stones, which followed the elegant curves and corners of the wall as it changed level and arched across the wooden entrance doors.[20] The large estate of the Erringtons provided work for both Bryan's father, John, and his uncle.

Henry Errington, born in 1740, was the younger brother of John Errington, and lived at Sandoe Hall, while his elder brother resided at Beaufront. As a young man, he embarked on the grand tour like many of his contemporaries; during a sojourn in Rome he met Laurence Sterne, the novelist, and contributed to his fellow traveller's bills while in Italy. At twenty nine, he married Maria, the widow of Sir Brian Broughton, who chose to be known as Lady Broughton except in Sandoe, where she answered to the name of Mrs Errington. The couple also spent time at their estate at Red Rice, near Andover in Hampshire, as well as staying in their London home in Cleveland Row, Queen's Park, built for them in the year after their marriage. When in Sandoe, Mrs Errington threw herself into village life, and devised a scheme for helping the local economy.[21] She bought flax and employed local girls to spin, using a newly invented multiple spinning wheel (on which twelve girls could produce yarn together); she paid the girls and sold the yarn. Mrs Errington also had a number of ordinary spinning wheels, and taught the individual children to spin when they were strong enough, readying them for employment. While she was living the rural life, her husband was sometimes elsewhere; he had a London life, too.

John Donkin's status as land agent gave him some standing within the communities of Hexham and Corbridge, with responsibility for leasing the farm buildings on the estate, hiring managers for the lead smelting mills at nearby Feldon Foot and Corbridge and overseeing their production, as well as managing the livestock and land. He supervised the maintenance of the roads and bridges, and was in overall charge of the finance and organisation of his employer's land; occasionally he attended court on behalf of John Errington. He had to organise the cutting of wood and its preparation and carriage for use as pit props in the lead mines on his master's territory and inspect the work in the mines; and receive payments for lead ore that was sold. In the course of his duties, he often had to hire a horse to travel as many as seventy miles from home, in all directions, to review lettings and make repairs to buildings and waterways.[22] If a tenant farmer died, it was John Donkin's duty to re-let the farm and sell the stock, to collect money owed to the deceased and pay off any debts.[23] If part of the Errington estate were to be sold, it was John Donkin who organised the sale. He sometimes acted as a trustee when landowners died, responsible for advertising the sale (or letting) of land, property and stock, including shares in lead mines.[24] At one point, he felt that his tasks were becoming onerous, and submitted a request to the local court 'to make what Allowance may be thought reasonable or such as usually made on such Occations [sic]'; it sounds as if he deserved a little extra cash. He did, however, have the means and enterprise to build a brewery in Hexham, providing a good living for his family. In the late 1770s, John Donkin undertook the responsibility of becoming one of three commissioners in connection with the Enclosures Act, calling meetings for 'persons' who had claims to common ground in the areas of Corbridge and Fourstones, in preparation for dividing up the common lands often used by villagers for grazing their few animals.[25]

Although over three hundred miles from London, Hexham was no backwater when it came to keeping abreast with modern developments in transport, and when a canal between Carlisle and Newcastle was proposed in January 1794, there was no shortage of good local men willing to subscribe to a survey of the planned route, each donating at a level that befitted their individual status and position in society. John Bell, a tanner of Hexham gave a guinea; John Donkin & Company of Hexham Brewery a modest five guineas, and Colonel Beaumont (through his agent, John Blackett), ten guineas, while the Duke of Northumberland, who with his massive interest in coal mining had the most to gain from a canal, contributed £25.[26] Several schemes were put forward and rejected; the first of these was by Ralph Dodd (who later, as engineer for the Thames Archway Company, made the first failed attempt at building a tunnel under the Thames).[27] Eventually John Sutcliffe put forward a scheme, the first part of which would run from Stella, the last navigable landing point on the Tyne, westward through eighteen locks to Hexham, seventeen miles away, and from there onward to Carlisle. No doubt the canal from Hexham to Stella would have been a boon to local trade, not least to Henry Errington, who had his own wharf at Stella, from where he transported 'pigs' of lead smelted at his mill at Feldon. (Four pigs of lead had been stolen from the wharf in May 1790 – a reward of 10 guineas could be claimed from John Donkin.) John Donkin too, with his personal holdings in lead mines, ships, farms and of course, the brewery, stood to gain from the project.[28] Alas, the canal scheme failed to get parliamentary approval and was never built. Had it gone to plan and joined the 'East and West Seas', it might easily have brought into question the necessity of building the Caledonian Canal some eighteen years later.

As a child, Bryan must have absorbed knowledge of his father's work. William, his eldest sibling, was being groomed to follow his father into the same employment, and Bryan, being a bright child, would have picked up and stored much information from their experiences and conversations.

Bryan had at least three uncles, and aunts Elizabeth and Peggy. One uncle, William, was the black sheep of the family: described as a 'wild child', he supposedly ran off to India as a young man and worked as a wharfinger (or harbourmaster); when encountered there by an English traveller, he refused to make contact with his family and was never seen again.[29] Another of Bryan Donkin's uncles was the headmaster of Tynesdale Public School in Newcastle in 1750.[30] Of Elizabeth, little is known; she did not marry.

Another uncle – whose name is not known – was a copious diary writer: he will be called 'Uncle Donkin' here. He had a relatively easy life, supervising some of the work on the estate, but with plenty of time to himself. His responsibilities included calculating and dispensing the pay to the labourers in the fields, the lead mines and the smelting mills, in co-operation with John Donkin.[31] As well, he saw to the maintenance of walls and banks on the estate, measuring up for materials and carting stones for repairs, and was not averse to helping with the haymaking. He had recently moved back to the area from Cotherston, a village near Middleton-in-Teesdale, in Yorkshire.[32] There, his work on the estate of a lady landowner had been similar, but even less demanding; he had pottered about, visiting friends, sometimes doing a little thatching or haymaking, checking work at a local mill and fishing in the local beck. Once, he took part in the ancient ceremony of 'beating the bounds', riding his horse 'Galloway' round the muddy countryside in the rain, with a lawyer and several other local gentlemen, looking for the stones that marked the perimeter of his mistress's land. The event took all day, riding on rough paths, 'through mosses, and myres [sic], and waters, over hard and slippery stones, up one hill, down another'. At the end of the day, there was food and ale, and Uncle Donkin carried a great can of punch out to the locals who had gathered to witness the event.

Uncle Donkin's calligraphic skills were put to good use for transcribing leases and agreements, meticulously writing letters and copying quotations from books for local people. Uncle Donkin passed on his skills and knowledge to a handful of local boys, who occasionally came for tuition, returning the next Saturday with their completed homework. When not engaged on a task for the estate, he stayed at home and read 'good' poetry from *Fables for Ladies* and perused articles, old magazines and the local paper. He was keenly aware of national politics as well as local gossip. He disapproved of gaming, cards, horse racing and the theatre and even some of his brother's pastimes. In Hexham one November night, well-to-do people gathered to take part in an event that he described as 'a scene of refined folly, or perhaps more properly, polite and fashionable sin'; he lamented that it was a shame that such scenes of intrigues should ever be practised in Christendom, and was secretly pleased when the bad weather was so severe the next morning that the Gentry were prevented from going home. He frequently walked by himself and visited neighbours, but seemed, in his forties, to be somewhat of a loner. Uncle Donkin missed his friends from Cotherston, and in the prime of life, he was without a particular male or female companion. Nevertheless, he was not immune to feelings of the flesh, and once, at least, was aroused by the sight of Molly, a servant at the Hall, doing the mangling.

The driving force in Uncle Donkin's life was religion. As he walked through the fields and lanes, he mused on the Resurrection, the glory of God and the sinfulness of Man; sometimes he took a religious book to read as he walked. When down in the dumps, he could be revived by reading a text from the Bible; but biblical readings often caused him to reflect on his own sins and the iniquity of Man, and made him miserable. At home, he read sermons, but he rarely attended church: his was an intensely personal faith. Uncle Donkin's piety was probably due to the influence of John Wesley: for thirty years, the evangelical Anglican preacher had travelled the country on horseback, converting thousands to Methodism. Wesley worked tirelessly to win the vast crowds over to his brand of Christianity with his enthusiastic sermons on sin and personal salvation. Uncle Donkin almost certainly heard Wesley preach. John Wesley first came to Newcastle in 1742 and returned no less than thirty-six times to ensure that his rules for Methodism were being carried out. Four of his visits were to Hexham.[33]

It was to Uncle Donkin, this sensitive, introspective and fanatical man, that young Bryan as a toddler was sometimes entrusted.[34] His uncle was clearly capable of looking after the little boy for half a day now and then. On one occasion he carried the two-year-old to Corbridge, where, with Bryan's seven-year-old sister Ann and his Aunt Elizabeth, they waited for a considerable time for the stage coach to Newcastle.[35] Uncle Donkin spent most evenings at John Donkin's house, and was there on the evening before the birth of Bryan's sister Mary, who was born in the small hours of 16 January 1771.

Although the surrounding countryside was a working landscape, the estate was a pretty place, with native deciduous trees – the oak, ash, alder, willow, elm, birch and hawthorn – interspersed with banks of gorse, and green pastureland scattered with meadow flowers. The land was ploughed by man and horse, continuing the tradition of arable farming that had prospered in the area since medieval times. In summer the cereal crops were still harvested entirely by hand, men scything in a staggered line, the womenfolk and small children following, gleaning the fallen corn behind the reapers and gathering it in sheaves; each was tied with a plait of straw and stood on end to form stooks. When thoroughly dry, the sheaves were pitched onto horse-drawn drays and taken back to the farm to be threshed, again by hand. Hay, too, was scythed, and pitch-forked into stacks. Cattle grazed on the low ground near the river, and on the hills shepherds in their brimmed hats and knee breeches guarded their small flocks from foxes, their crooks at the ready and sometimes piping a tune to ward off boredom.[36] Rural scenes like this, later immortalised in nursery rhymes and children's books, seem idyllic now, but life was rarely easy for the workers. The labourers of the area were poor; they kept a few sheep or a cow, and perhaps some geese, or a couple of straw beehives –

but they were not necessarily ignorant.[37] The cottagers, living in their thatched stone huts with their tiny vegetable plots, were often able to read their Bibles and exchange stories and songs.

It was common for the small farmers in the area to supplement their income with a second occupation from their rented land. Coal lay close to the surface and some farmers paid miners to excavate the ground. William Errington of Sandoe, one of the family of local landowners, had a team of colliery workers and took on apprentices: one boy, John Ursop, had to be discharged in January 1765 because he was already bound to another master.[38]

The Tyne's banks were a natural playground for children, where they climbed the overhanging trees and fished with rods. They made mischief, riding astride tombstones, scrumping apples and swinging from trees.[39] Fun was to be had, but life could be hard; the poor had to be resourceful, scraping a living from the land. The poorest resorted to busking by the roadside, or begging at the gates of the big houses.

Crossing the river where there was no bridge or ferry was a challenge. Some achieved it on horseback, by rowing boat or even on stilts, and others struggled through the current with burdens – provisions or family members – on their backs.[40] The first bridge over the Tyne at Hexham had been built in the late 1760s, as the result of a petition by inhabitants of the area.[41] The Tyne was a notoriously fickle river, subject to violent flooding. In September 1770, Uncle Donkin saw it rise higher than ever before in his life, and crossed the bridge with trepidation. Little more than a year later, in the November before Bryan Donkin's fourth birthday, the beautiful six-span bridge was swept away by a huge flood; happily, although many houses and estates around Hexham suffered considerably, no lives were lost.[42] The foaming waters caused more devastation and drowning as they crashed towards the coast, demolishing more bridges and causing numerous deaths in the Newcastle area. The six-span bridge down the river at Corbridge, which was built on Roman foundations, survived the terrible flood, but the residents of Hexham and the surrounding countryside had to manage without a bridge for several years.

By 1775, plans were underway to replace the bridge, but the nature of the ground posed problems. Shifting gravel made the river bed unstable, and the ground where the first pier of the bridge was to be built was found to be 'a quicksand and full of bubbley [sic] springs'.[43] A trial timber pile, driven into the ground at two and a half inches per stroke of the ram, went into the ground 26 feet without stopping, a sure sign that the earth below was sandy and insecure. A better site was found, half a mile downstream, and after another survey and an Act of Parliament in 1777, work began. During that year, when Bryan was nine, his father was deeply involved. John Donkin's responsibility came about because the proposed bridge was within the estate of Beaufront; it was Henry Errington, the landowner, who put forward the plan. As Errington's land agent,

John Donkin was able to add his own proposal, to make a road to connect the north end of the intended bridge to the Alemouth Road, the turnpike road that ran north from Hexham.[44]

The architect was John Smeaton, a man regarded as the father of civil engineering, and highly respected in his time.[45] Best known for designing the Eddystone lighthouse and seeing it through to its successful completion in 1759, he was no stranger to large structures. The Calder and Hebble Canal, the Ripon Canal, and the bridge in Perth had all been built to his design, as well as the Coldstream bridge that linked Scotland to Northumberland across the River Tweed; work was in progress on the bridge in Aberdeen when Smeaton undertook the building of the Hexham Bridge. It was John Donkin who first approached Smeaton, on behalf of Henry Errington. Errington financed the development to the tune of £5,700, and spared no expense in sponsoring a strong and beautiful structure. It became known as Mr Errington's Bridge.[46] A masterpiece in stone, the nine arches of the finished bridge spanned the Tyne proudly and was an asset to the local people.

With his father's involvement in the project, young Bryan Donkin must have watched, listened and learnt as the great piers and arches of the bridge took shape. When Smeaton's diving bell plunged into the swirling water and the heavy stones were lowered into the foundations, he would have noticed the effect on the ever-changing flow. He witnessed its progress for four years and was thirteen when it was completed in 1781.

While the bridge was being built, another structure was under way on the north bank of the Tyne and in 1779, an advertisement appeared in the *Newcastle Courant*:[47]

> To be let for an Inn
>
> and entered upon in spring next, all that new erected, completed and well finished building, pleasantly situated on the north of the Tyne, adjoining the new bridge now building across the river, near to the market town of Hexham.
>
> Mr Potter at Bridge-end will shew [sic] the premises and for further particulars; apply to Mr Donkin at Sandoe or Mr Jasper Gibson at Hexham.

The main structure was a handsome building three storeys high, with a steeply pitched roof, its gable end facing the road; to the North, a similar two storey building stood, and in between, there was a square malting building.[48] Two years later, not only was the building an inn, but a brewery too, and a new venture for John Donkin: together with Jasper Gibson and his brother Reginald, James Liddell and William Harbottle, (known as Billy), Bryan's father signed a deed of partnership in the brewery business in 1781.[49] The following year William Winship paid a bond of £100 to enable him to draw ale from the Hexham Brewery, as did several other local innkeepers; this tied them to having ale, liquors and spirits supplied to them on a regular basis. Although profits in the early years must have been hampered by the lack of a bridge to the main part of the town, the John Donkin & Co Brewery was the larger of the two breweries in the town, and grew to be prosperous.[50] The consortium also owned shares in the brewery's farm, where, in twelve years, a herd of Leicestershire sheep grew to 'near five hundred breeding ewes and gimmers [young sheep], fifty ewe lambs and upwards of twenty rams' before they were sold.[51] These hefty sheep were money-spinners for the breeder; they were also easily fattened even on 'indifferent pastures'.[52] The Leicestershire sheep would have gobbled up the waste products from the brewing process.

The new bridge had a short history. When Smeaton inspected it in January 1781, he was satisfied that it was safe; so were Mr Errington and everyone involved in the building. In February 1782, a flood caused the water to back up behind the Hexham Bridge, higher by three feet or more on the west side than on the east. John Donkin, who had been asked by Smeaton to keep an eye on the bridge, noted that the flood, far from damaging the bridge, had rounded and compacted the protective stones round the base of the pillars, providing extra strength to the foundations.[53] At the beginning of March, John had inspected the bridge again and found no sign of injury or decay.

Disaster struck on 11 March 1782. Thick snow had fallen throughout the previous night, and in the morning heavy rain, driven by a strong wind, was sponged up into the snow and the mixture poured into the swollen river, causing the water to rise five feet higher upstream of the bridge than on the seaward side. Worried by the storm, John sent his son – probably William – with stonemasons, and followed in time to see the bridge disintegrating. First, tiny grains of limestone fell from the south wall of the bridge, and then followed splinters of stone, while a crack appeared in the fourth arch. A pillar started to shake and the third and fourth arches collapsed. As John and his son turned away in horror to go home, two more arches fell. John Donkin told Smeaton later that '... it was not above a couple of minutes between first perceiving the mortar dropping out of the joints of the soffit and the fall of the arch, and six more were down in half an hour'.[54] By evening most of the bridge had been destroyed.

John Smeaton was mortified. Had he known that such a quantity of water could ever have accumulated in the river, he would not have hazarded his reputation as 'an artist' on building the bridge. He had taken into account the shifting riverbed, and allowed for a force of water amounting to 900 feet a minute. No-one was to blame for the freak conditions – if there had been an hour's respite in the snow and rain, the water would have been dispersed downstream, reducing the velocity from 1000 to 900 feet a minute, and the bridge would have been saved. During the recriminations and legal wrangling after the event, when the talk was of rebuilding the bridge, Smeaton admitted to John Donkin that the episode had convinced him that 'I was mistaken and that I might be so again'.[55] The following year he put in an estimate for the reinstatement of the bridge, but he begged John Donkin to 'consider whether you may not stand a better chance by employing some other able engineer who has got the horrors of the River Tyne painted upon his imagination'.[56] Eventually, in 1795, the bridge was rebuilt by the county surveyors, Robert Thompson and William Johnson.[57] That Hexham Bridge still stands today.

This terrible event, witnessed by his father and brother, could not have failed to influence the young Bryan Donkin. Conversation at the Donkin dinner table was surely dominated for a while by the technical detail and the drama of the scene. Smeaton stayed at Sandoe during the enquiry into the disaster, and no doubt contributed to the speculation over the ruined bridge. Bryan, with his capacity for absorbing knowledge, would have soaked up the stories and facts for use in his later life.

Smeaton's relationship with John Donkin was not harmed though, and the great engineer was called in to design new machinery for the brewery at Hexham Bridge End that Bryan's father owned. Smeaton sent the rolled-up drawings from London by the London Fly, addressing the package simply to Mr Donkin at Sandoe, to be left at the inn until called for.[58] An explanation of the sketches was in the letter: for the proposed horse-driven treadmill, improvements would be made by constructing a wheel with 112 cogs and adjusting the length of the arm. Grinding oats with two horses would double the amount of oats ground in an hour. Machinery was needed for drawing water from a new well, and a 'trundle' or roller, for driving the wort pump that produced the brewing liquid.

Less than eight miles away to the east of Sandoe, near the small town of Prudoe, was Eltringham. There, in a homestead named Cherryburn, lived the Bewicks, a farming family.[59] At the time of Bryan Donkin's birth, their fourteen-year-old son Thomas was newly apprenticed to an engraver in Newcastle. Thomas was a bright, but wilful teenager. Much of his childhood was spent playing in the countryside near Cherryburn, on the south bank of the Tyne. Although he was sent to the school at Mickley, he found it hard to concentrate; bored, the young teenager filled the spaces on his slate with drawings, and misbehaved. Thomas often played truant till home time, amusing himself by building dams and floating homemade boats on the Tyne, tormenting oxen until they ran into the water, and once riding bareback on a runaway horse. He fished until midnight and killed animals and birds for sport; but he developed into a young man with a love of nature and a talent for drawing. The epiphany for the rebellious boy came when he saved a hare as it fled from the hunters, only to be persuaded to hand it over to a farmer, who promptly broke its legs and sent it limping off to make more sport for the dogs. Thomas's emotion was overwhelming. Later he held a dying bullfinch that he had stoned, and was overcome by its beauty: that was the last bird he ever killed. At every opportunity, he drew pictures of the wildlife and country scenes that he saw every day, at first scraping on wood or stone, or chalking on the flagstones near the hearth, and later with pen and ink or brush and colour.

3 *Leicestershire sheep belonging to John Donkin.*

Once apprenticed to the engraver Ralph Beilby in Newcastle, he developed the art of engraving on wood; his first efforts saw publication in the year of Donkin's birth, 1768, albeit as mathematical diagrams in Charles Hutton's impenetrable book, *Treatise on Mensuration*. An early commission was for an engraving of the route of the proposed Newcastle to Carlisle canal, for Ralph Dodd. His unique ability, though, was to capture the fine detail of an animal, bird or scene on a tiny block of wood, cutting intricate designs across the end grain at different depths to produce shades from white through greys to black, when printed. He became the unsurpassed master of the craft, and illustrated several works, notably the *History of Quadrupeds* and the *History of British Birds*, both substantial works, and the first of their kind. Part of the time, Bewick worked from his old family home, and again enjoyed the pleasures of the countryside round Eltringham. As Bryan Donkin grew into his teens, Bewick was making weekly visits from Newcastle to Cherryburn, where he fished, and relished the changing seasons. For a short time, his work took him to London, which he hated – 'I would rather be herding sheep upon Mickley bank top, than remain in London, although for doing so I was to be made the Premier of England'.[60] He could not wait to return to his beloved Northumberland. He wrote that he 'became known to most of the villages on both banks of the Tyne'. Bryan, too must have known the area well: perhaps their paths crossed. One of the illustrations in Bewick's *History of Quadrupeds*, is of a Leicestershire sheep, standing by a fence on a bank; on the engraving are the words 'Sandoe, 22 Dec. 1788' and the monogram TB; the sheep he drew was almost certainly from John Donkin's brewery. Was Bryan perhaps there on the day it was sketched?

Although from quite different family backgrounds, both the young Donkin and Bewick thrived on the Tyneside air, and both 'made good' in their later careers. Oddly, Bewick and Donkin were later involved in a professional controversy, on different sides, where neither was to blame.[61] Both Bewick and Donkin would have been in sympathy with the sentiments expressed by Mark Akenside, a Newcastle man and a contemporary of Bryan's father. Akenside's long poem, *The Pleasures of Imagination*, was so popular that it was translated into several languages. One section, 'Early Influences', describes his love of Northumberland:

O ye Northumbrian shades, which overlook
The rocky pavement and the mossy falls
Of solitary Wansbeck's limpid stream,
How gladly I recall your well-known seats
Belov'd of old, and that delightful time
When all alone, for many a summer's day
I wandered through your calm recesses, led
In silence by some powerful hand unseen.

Nor will I e'er forget you: nor shall e'er
The grave tasks of manhood, or the advice
Of vulgar wisdom, move me to disclaim
Those studies which possess'd me in the dawn
Of life, and fix'd the colour of my mind
For every future year.

2

Father's Footsteps

At the age of eleven Bryan had his own Latin primer, which any adult of today would find a challenge.[1] The family had enough money to pay for a private education, so Bryan may well have had a tutor to give him grounding in the essentials of education; it could even have been Uncle Donkin. Certainly, by the 1770s, there were small local schools (like the one that Bewick attended) as well as smaller private groups, where both sexes were taught by members of the clergy, gentlefolk, or intelligent young ladies. In the churchyard at St John Lee lies the body of a schoolmaster, Robert Elliott of Acomb, who died in 1789 at the age of fifty; it is quite possible that he had a hand in Bryan's early education. In Hexham, the grammar school had been established in the reign of Queen Elizabeth I, and in Newcastle there was a Mathematical School, established by Charles Hutton, which would have suited Bryan.[2] The town also boasted a long-established grammar school where, as in most schools, the three R's and Latin were the basic curriculum: it may have been the school where his other uncle was head teacher.

Undoubtedly a bright boy with natural curiosity, Bryan was brought up in an intelligent and caring family where reading and writing were part of everyday life. He was familiar with the workings of a large estate and had grown up watching his father, his uncle, and now his brother William attending to the various tasks that their work involved. Suffice it to say that, by the time he reached manhood, Bryan's knowledge of country matters and his skill in mathematics enabled him to take up the offer of a post, following in the family tradition, but far from home.

Bryan Donkin's first job was as a bailiff in the service of the Duke of Dorset, in faraway Kent. His employer was John Frederick Sackville, the 3rd Duke of Dorset, who at the age of twenty-four had succeeded his father to become the owner of the massive country house and estate of Knole. Later described by his descendant, Vita Sackville-West, as 'soft, quiet and ingratiating', the Duke of Dorset was also an attractively romantic and elegant character, who enjoyed the good things of life, including cricket.[3] After his first year as master of Knole the Duke set off on the Grand Tour, taking with him his mistress Mrs Anne Horton (otherwise known as Nancy Parsons), and an entourage of entertainers, travelling through France and Italy, buying expensive works of art and statues. (Horace Walpole later described Sackville's mistress as 'The Duke of Grafton's Mrs Horton, the Duke of Dorset's Mrs Horton, everybody's Mrs Horton'.)[4]

Back at home his fortune dwindled with money spent on improving Knole, furnishing the house with new silverware, making repairs inside and out, putting in new floors and making alterations to the windows. After a couple of years his Nancy was swapped for Mrs Elizabeth Armistead, who in turn was supplanted by the adoring Lady Betty Hamilton; but John Frederick was in no hurry to take on the responsibilities of marriage.[5] There were scandals. Lady Betty married Lord Derby but remained the Duke's lover.[6] For six years John Sackville was England's Ambassador in Paris, a post that allowed plenty of scope for lavish entertaining and enjoyable frivolity, to the extent that the impending war with France was hardly mentioned in the letters that the Duke wrote to his friend the Duchess of Devonshire at Chatsworth; the storming of the Bastille seemed to pass him by. It was even hinted that he became the lover of Marie-Antoinette. In Paris, he became besotted with an Italian ballerina, Gianetta Baccelli, whom he installed at Knole in a private tower with her servants; both Joshua Reynolds and Gainsborough painted her portrait. Lady Derby was forsaken for Gianetta. As a result of one of these liaisons, a son had been born. Master Sackville was educated at a boarding school, where his fees amounted to £30 a year, plus extras including haircuts, writing lessons – as well as paying for copy books, paper and pencils – and more for heating the school, pocket money, and a servant.

4 *Knole*, c.1780.

Bryan Donkin started work at Knole in September, 1789.[7] Earlier in the year, the Duke of Dorset finished his term of office in Paris, returning to live more permanently in the great grey, turreted house at Knole, while acting as Steward of the Royal Household – a position that included keeping an eye on the wayward young Prince of Wales, who was later to become George IV. Gianetta Baccelli and the Duke had separated by the end of the year and the Duke, now in his mid-forties, began to settle down.[8] With his personal steward, Mr Gardiner, at his elbow, he ran his estate efficiently.[9] After his father's death, his first act had been to invite a great gathering of neighbours and tenants to a party; he was generous with his wealth. The local poor came for food at the 'poor door', and were supplied with meal (at ten shillings a stone) to keep them going. At Christmas, the tradesmen's apprentices – the young shoemaker, the trainee maltmen, the hatter's boy and many others – received a shilling each for their Christmas boxes, as did the dancing boys and the drummers, while the beadle and the man from the coal wharf had 2s. 6d. each.

The Duke's personal finances were looked after by Stephen Woodgate. This man also had an overview of the estate's accounts, for such things as tithes paid on small pieces of land and the expenses other than bills settled in cash. As 'bailiff', young Donkin's duties were mainly concerned with the financial side of running the house, the garden and the park, paying the quarterly and half-yearly bills presented by the local tradesmen. One of his first acts was to simplify the way the account book was laid out; otherwise the job was fairly routine. Most of the staff at Knole received a quarterly wage: Bryan earned £20 a year, the same as the housekeeper Mrs Fartier but less than Mr Beattie the gardener, whose salary amounted to £30 a year. The other servants received much less: top of the list was Peter Potter the gamekeeper, at an annual wage of ten guineas, and the carter Soloman Brigden, who received £10; but only £6 a year could be earned by the dairymaid and the housemaid, and Richard, 'the Boy', had to make do with £4. John Dunks laboured in the park, 'grubbing' hedges, chopping wood and cutting down the gorse and was given a shilling or two for such jobs. Casual labourers were employed in the park and in the garden, costing the Duke £60 or more a quarter. Limestone had to be burnt in the lime kilns, there was hay to be stacked, and when venison was taken to the London house, it cost two shillings for the man, a shilling for the turnpike fees, and a shilling for the horse's expenses.

Bills, sometimes ill-spelt but more frequently well written, were presented by the baker, the butcher, the ironmonger and other purveyors of food and goods, and from workmen who repaired locks, built walls and mended fences. Donkin recorded them all and arranged the payments. Every quarter or six months the bills poured in, for 'ratt traps', buckets, new breeches for the under-groom (at £1 5s. 6d.), six quires of paper (£2), tea, coffee, black lead for cleaning stoves, leather collars for the horses, vegetable seeds for the garden, and everything else needed to keep the huge establishment in good order. One day, the grocer-cum-general storekeeper supplied three dozen eggs, six balls of packthread, six pounds of best butter, and six 'yello' chamber pots. Best Seville oranges were bought in quarter-chests. A half-year's bill from the butcher alone, for beef, mutton, veal and lamb, came to over £60. Other household expenses were jotted down by the housekeeper, Mrs Fartier: she paid the weekly washerwoman and the sweep, and bought small amounts of oranges and fish, as well as all the equipment needed for the day-to-day running of her domain. She also received letters and parcels for His Grace. In those days long before postal reform, mail was paid for on receipt and was quite expensive at sixpence for a parcel and up to five pence for a letter. The estate boasted a brewery; the brewer bought in huge amounts of malt. The sums spent on malt, the housekeeping, the stable and outdoor expenses, and clothing for the servants were all about equal, while the maintenance of the house – repairs, decorating, building and so on – cost almost three times as much.

Income came from tenant farmers who paid rent, and from the locksmith, the ironmonger and two other traders who paid 15s or £1 per annum to rent sheds in the market. Produce from the home farm was sold: four fat bullocks went for £60, and Donkin claimed five shillings for his expenses at the market when he went to collect the money. A small profit was made by selling excess fruit from the garden, and apples from the orchard were sold for about a shilling a bushel.

Bryan had his own room, with all expenses paid. When two of the tiny squares of glass in his window broke, the sum of threepence was paid to the glazier; when he was ill, the apothecary was paid a shilling to give him a purge and a medicinal draught. All the servants were well looked after; the apothecary regularly prescribed stomatic powders and fomentations to members of the household, from the lowliest chambermaid to the gentry themselves. He could also extract teeth. Some of the servants were even inoculated, a risky business five years before Jenner's trials with vaccinations against smallpox.

Bryan was on good terms with the Duke, who asked his advice on how to deal with maggots on sheep, and on managing game on the moors; Bryan's response was to write to Northumberland to ask his father, who sent messages through his daughter Mary, and a recipe involving powdered brimstone mixed with oil to spread on the backs of sheep in order to prevent maggots from hatching.[10] (If they did breed, they should be cleared out and the skin dusted with dry mould or powdered lime; or turpentine could be poured through a quill put into the cork of a bottle 'but this must be used with caution, as too liberal a quantity may occasion the wool to fall off'.) On 4 January 1790, only seven weeks after Donkin's arrival at Knole, the Duke married an heiress, Arabella Cope, who was half his age. The new Duchess wanted to find 'a bit of spar' – for medicinal purposes perhaps – yes, the Donkin family would try to procure a piece for her. Arabella soon established herself at Knole, ruling with a rod of iron.[11] In no time, the Duke was persuaded to reduce his lavish spending and the sparkle went out of life at Knole. Their three children were brought up strictly, for Arabella was severe. The Duke became morose, fretful and bad-tempered over the next few years; he finally lapsed into deep melancholia and died in 1799, at the age of fifty-four.

By this time, Bryan Donkin had moved on. In February 1791 a memorandum from Mr Gardiner, a senior member of staff at Knole, decreed that the butcher and baker should submit their bills weekly, and the other tradesmen (such as plumbers, blacksmiths, masons and other experts) on a monthly basis; and that 'no Servant in the House, or Stables, do presume to Order any Article from the above Tradesmen, without first acquainting Mr Donkin or Mrs Fartier of the necessity of such thing being had, and having their Consent – this order extends to the Apothecary's Bill as well as the other Bills not mentioned here'.[12] Perhaps bored with the job or disillusioned by the new regime, or possibly because he disliked the Duchess, young Donkin, at twenty two, decided to leave Knole. By then he must have realised that in spite of the deep-rooted tradition in the Donkin family for giving service as a land agent or steward on a great estate, his interests truly lay elsewhere, somewhere that demanded the real mechanical skills and creativity that he had to offer.

It has been said that his father's old friend, John Smeaton (who built the ill-fated Hexham bridge in Bryan's youth) started Bryan Donkin on his career as an engineer; it may be true, but Smeaton died in late 1792.[13] He had withdrawn from active business in 1785; his small project for the Hexham Brewery must have been one of his last. His health began to decline but he continued to write accounts of his inventions and works, and corresponded with his friends until he suffered a stroke in September 1792, while walking in his garden. He died about six weeks later. He could have been influential in Bryan Donkin's future, or contacts at Knole may have prompted Donkin to move to another part of Kent to take up his new post. Whatever influences were at work, the upshot was that Bryan Donkin found himself working at the Dartford manufactory of John Hall, millwright. His move to the South was permanent, but he never lost sight of his roots, and throughout his life was constantly drawn back to visit his family in Northumberland.

The 1790s were a time of change for Bryan Donkin. On 17 November 1792 his mother died at the age of fifty-seven. Jane Donkin had brought up eight children; when she died, William, the eldest, was thirty three and not yet married, but following in his father's footsteps as land agent on John Errington's estate at Sandoe. Her second son, Bryan's brother John, was a schoolmaster, and already had two baby boys, John and tiny Bryan, who was to live for only a few years. (Even amongst the relatively affluent Donkin family, infant mortality was not unknown, and John and his wife Jane were particularly unfortunate, losing three children out of the nine who were born to them.) Bryan's three sisters all lived in Sandoe and did so all their lives: Ann celebrated her twenty-ninth birthday the day before her mother died, Jane was twenty-six, and Mary twenty one years old; Henry was nineteen and Thomas, the youngest, was only sixteen. Bryan had

5 *John Hall* (1764–1836).

reached the age of twenty-four, and a new life was about to start in earnest.

In Dartford, he began work with John Hall, a man who would help to shape his life. Donkin became a sort of apprentice to Hall, but certainly not in the sense that a teenager would have been, with all the attendant restrictions and prohibitions imposed by his employer. 'Gentleman apprentices' – men from noble country families, usually sponsored by their father – normally worked for three years in their chosen establishment, to learn a trade or profession; Bryan Donkin's agreement was similar, but on terms agreed between the two men. A solicitor drafted the document in February 1792, and sent it to Bryan 'at Mr Hall's' addressing him as a millwright at Dartford, Kent.[14] Called 'Articles of Agreement' rather than 'indentures', the draft rules of the arrangement stipulated that in return for a sum of money (to be specified) paid in hand, John Hall agreed to 'teach and instruct, or cause to be taught and instructed, the said Bryan Donkin in the art, trade and mystery of a millwright in the best and ablest manner he can in the several respective branches which he now carries on, in the course of three years, or any shorter period as may be hereafter agreed on'. If John Hall were to die before the agreed time was up, his pupil's money would be refunded.

Hall was just four years older than Donkin, and had lived in the Dartford area for about seven years when Donkin arrived. John was a bright chap, who had served an apprenticeship as a millwright at Portal's paper mill in Laverstoke, Hampshire, where his father had held a senior position.[15] He first found a job in the village of Hawley, near Dartford, where a mill was being repaired, and did so well that he was recommended for other such jobs in the area. In 1785, at only twenty-one, he started his own business as a self-employed blacksmith in a shed in Lowfield Street, Dartford, tackling repairs and maintenance jobs for the local mills (mills that ground corn, and produced paper, oil and gunpowder) as well as making metal gadgets and fitments for houses, and shoeing horses.[16] By the time Bryan Donkin joined him, he had set up his own factory in premises in Waterside, on land originally belonging to the ancient Dartford Priory. His engineering activities and work as a millwright flourished, and as the years went on his manufactory grew to encompass heavy engineering of all sorts. From the early years of the nineteenth century, Hall's bill heads alluded to his firm as engineers, steam engine manufacturers and millwrights, iron and brass founders.

Religion played a large part in John Hall's life. He was such a keen Methodist that he established a church in the village of Dartford by converting two cottages on the corner of Priory Lane, Waterside, into a chapel that was opened on New Year's Day in 1794. [17] Bryan Donkin was one of the founder trustees. Together, they tried to establish a Sunday school, but those were early days in the movement towards education in that form and it failed, to be resurrected in 1813 by other Methodists.[18] The chapel quickly became too small, and the new Waterside Chapel was built in 1798 at a cost of £700. Living nearby was Peter Brames, a descendant of a wealthy Dutch family, who had bought the lease of the manor house and the adjoining Priory garden, cultivating the land as a market garden. [19] He, too, was a Methodist, and had allowed part of his substantial house to be used by the Sunday school. Not only were John Hall and Peter Brames friends and fellow Methodists, but when Bryan Donkin came to Dartford, John was newly married to Brames's daughter Sarah. Within this circle of friends it probably came as no surprise when, on 30 August 1798, Bryan Donkin married Sarah's sister Mary, and so became John Hall's brother-in-law. Mary was the ideal wife for Bryan, and his affection for her was deep and lasting; she was intelligent, capable and self-sufficient. Their first child was born the following June. Mary Ann was Bryan's pride and joy. By then he was well established in his new career.

One of Donkin's old notebooks, written during his years with Hall, gives an idea of his interests and his ability to absorb knowledge from every source and record it for future reference.[20] At 8.30 a.m. on Christmas Day in 1796, he recorded the temperature in Dartford – 33 degrees below freezing! Weights and measures fascinated him: the weight of a guinea coin, '8 pecks = 1 bushel', the specific gravity of tin is 7.291 ... Collecting information came automatically to him, be it about the speed of sound, the length of a day, the strength of a beam of wood, or the method of measuring the contents of a pipe. He made notes on how to calculate simple interest, and formulae to work out the measurements of a parabola and the speed of 'falling bodies': his grasp of mathematics was phenomenal. He would see a report of a machine in Nicholson's Journal and write down the salient facts; he kept an eye on details of Boulton and Watt's steam engines and noted in 1793 the sizes of the cylinders and the diameter of the pipes, the number of strokes per minute and the rate of horse power.[21] Later in the notebook he compared the newer version of the steam engine, its performance and the amount of coal consumed in an hour.

He took the same approach when visiting Messrs Kingsford's Mill near Canterbury in 1801, where he recorded every detail, including the exact amount of water that passed over the gate and the depth of the water, and noted that three pairs of grinding stones, measuring 4 foot 2 inches in diameter, ground 96 bushels of wheat in six hours. These observations were written in the same notebooks as more personal matters. Little did he know that centuries later, the world would be privy to the fact that he owned '13 shirts, 6 cravats, 9 nightcaps, 11 worsted stockings, 7 cotton ditto, 9 handkerchiefs and 2 prs understockings'.

Working alongside John Hall, he would have practised his developing engineering skills by acting as Hall's assistant. One of Hall's projects during that time was the building of a windmill. Wheat and barley were crops that were grown extensively in Kent. In the summer of 1795, there was a scarcity of wheat, and a community venture was decided upon, so that the inhabitants of Chislehurst could grind their own small quantities of corn to order.[22] A group of local gentry agreed to finance the building of a parish mill on part of the common, and to allow the poor to bring their sacks of grain and stay to watch it ground and dressed to their liking. John Hall laid the foundation in early summer, 1796, and the mill took more than a year to complete. It was a well executed and handsome windmill with a cap of bent planks and good weatherboarding. John Hall's bill amounted to £1765, plus £214 for the miller's house and £44 for fencing. The mill was a real boon to the people: two days a week were set aside for the poor to use it, paying four pence a bushel for the grinding, and twopence for finishing, Then it was free for the proprietors' use on the other days – a truly co-operative enterprise. No doubt Bryan Donkin took an interest and probably contributed ideas to the project; through visits to mills, he increased his knowledge of their structure and workings.

Soon after Donkin joined the firm, the generous Hall apparently advanced him £250 as capital to set himself up as a maker of moulds for the process of making paper by hand.[23] Certainly, Donkin went into partnership with James Davis in the mould-making business, which continued for ten years. For a small fee, Mr Brames carried paper moulds in his wagon, for Donkin and Davis.[24] The work of constructing the wood and wire frames to hold the paper pulp was not demanding in itself, but the experience of running a business with an older man stood Donkin in good stead for the future. Coupled with the knowledge of the workings of the many paper mills in the Dartford area, this mould-making experience set him on the path towards the development of his life-long career. It is doubtful that Donkin played an active part in the business in the latter years of the partnership; he was too busy with more exciting things.

With Mary pregnant with their second child, the couple rented a house from a Mr Ellis in March 1800. Bryan gave Mary about £4 a week.[25] He put a knocker on the front door, latches on two inner doors, a bolt on the door at the foot of the stairs, and locks on cupboards.[26] The house was lacking in storage space, so he fitted shelves in the washhouse and the garret, as well as in the closets in two bedrooms. The baby boy was born six months later, and named Bryan after his proud father.[27] On the 20th of the same month, Donkin's father died, at the age of seventy-three.[28] He was buried with his wife in the churchyard of St John Lee, near Sandoe. In his will John Donkin left, as part of his large legacy, shares in the Hexham brewery and farms to Bryan and his brother Henry.[29]

A welcome letter came in December 1802, with news from the North from Bryan's brother Thomas in Sandoe. Following family tradition, he was working for Mr Errington, and had several queries and comments about recent events.[30] He had dispatched four firkins (probably of ale from the family-owned brewery at Hexham) – the equivalent of nine gallons (forty-one litres) or a barrel; they had been loaded onto the sailing ship *Formosa* in Newcastle for shipment to the port of London. Thomas hoped they had arrived. A threshing machine was being made for the estate, probably locally; these horse- or water-driven machines for separating the grain from the chaff had originated in Northumberland, and were patented by Mr Andrew Meikle in 1784, but that had not stopped local mechanics making their own versions.[31] Thomas had been experimenting with a cutter to remove the beard of the barley. He had seen a part of a thresher that was supposed to do the job – it was like a cylindrical grater that revolved in a concave sheath – but it only succeeded in cutting the grains into fine bits, so it was no better than flailing by hand. Had Bryan any better ideas?

Their poor brother Henry was also at Sandoe, in pain and suffering badly from piles, for which there seemed to be no remedy, except to have the offending excrescence cut off. Henry was very weak from loss of blood but had an appointment in a few days with Mr Ingham, an eminent, top-class Newcastle surgeon.[32] Mr Ingham would perform the operation 'if the weather be suitable'. Their eldest brother William, on the other hand, was doing well: he had bought an estate of about 800 acres, for £3500, at Walden, not far from Sandoe, and let it for £160 per annum. Rents were astonishingly high because people seemed to be 'farming mad', out-bidding each other in the most unfair manner. William was already the owner of several properties and land in the area, which he let to local farmers, including Mr Chicken at nearby Bankfoot, and made a good living from the rents. Thomas was sad that old Mr Harbottle, a family friend, had been turned out of the rented 'Grainge' Farm by its owner so that it could be sold, and thought the old man should have been allowed to live out his life there; Mr Harbottle appeared very low spirited, and Thomas thought the move would kill him. Rents were rising apace, and people were unfairly gazumping each other in the race to make money from them.

Thomas also sent a drawing of two cogs, a wheel and a frame, with an enquiry about how to draw cogs the right shape – which mathematical book did Bryan use? In Northumberland, he said, the millwrights had no fixed rule, and everyone had 'a whim of his own brain'. It was important that Bryan (if he had time) described his method so that Thomas could learn to draw them properly, and prevent cogs being made that caused friction and wear. Thomas was learning French, so that he could read useful French books that had not been translated. Clearly he was a bright young man who could turn his mind to anything. He asked how Bryan's chemistry and paper machine were getting on. He had heard that Bryan was excited by his progress on the development of his huge new project, and probably would not have had much time for dabbling in chemistry. Thomas ended his letter by sending his love to Bryan, Mary and the little folks; they were Mary Ann, the toddler Bryan and baby John. Sadly, little Bryan died the following year.

Three years later, Bryan's sister Ann suggested that the five-year-old John, and perhaps his sister Mary Ann too, should come to live in Sandoe for a while because 'till John is eight years old he would be as well here as anywhere else' – safely away from the smoke and grime of London, with his aunts in Northumberland.[33] John certainly made a happy life for himself in London in his adult years.

Under John Hall, Bryan learnt fast. As a millwright, he was in his element. His natural ability to understand the movement of water, combined with his innate feeling for mechanics, led him to take out his first patent (No.2730, 2 August 1803). It involved bubbling super-heated steam into a series of inverted buckets attached to the periphery of a wheel, rather like a small mill wheel, the entire apparatus being submerged in a tank of boiling water. The upward thrust of the steam, caught in the succession of buckets, caused the wheel to rotate – it was mechanically inefficient, but a cheap alternative to the steam engines available. It may have eventually contributed to the development of the steam turbine. A description of his invention was considered important enough to be described in *The Athenaeum*, an odd little six-monthly magazine 'of literary and miscellaneous information' covering among other subjects, classical disquisitions, original poetry, obituaries and the prices of grain.[34] In the same year, Donkin had an article published in *Nicholson's Journal*, presenting a table of the radius of gear wheels with different numbers of gear teeth, demonstrating his facility with arithmetic.[35]

While living in Dartford, Donkin made at least one barometer, which was sent to Mr Errington in Sandoe.[36] The design of the wooden case was standard for the time, and may have been bought ready-made, but the words 'Bryan Donkin, Dartford' engraved on the face indicate that the inner workings were constructed by him. For the barometer, he earned three guineas, and proved another of his talents. However, it was his early brush with the paper trade, combined with a stroke of fortune, that changed his life from millwright to engineer.

For hundreds of years, paper had been made by hand, out of rags. Before the twelfth century, the treated skins of sheep, goats or calves had served as a surface on which to write books and documents in the western world while, in the East, papyrus – a fibrous plant – was flattened, woven and pressed into sheets.[37] Later, experiments were made with other materials for paper-making – leaves and bark of palm tree species, the pith of the cocoa-tree, fibres of yucca and aloes, as well as nettles, mallow and above all, flax and hemp. By the eighteenth century, most paper was made with rags, mostly imported from Europe, but later from as far afield as America and Russia. The increase in cotton production in England, due to new inventions by Hargreaves, Arkwright and Crompton, meant that a ready supply of cotton waste was available from the mills towards the end of the century.[38]

Monthly editions of *The Universal Magazine* of 1762 gave accounts of the contemporary methods of making sheets of paper.[39] The best paper was being made from linen rags; the finer the thread, the more easily it could be whitened. The process began with sorting and preparing the cloth; women sat with boards on their laps, ripping the seams and stitches with a long sharp knife, detaching buttons and scraping off dirt. The cloth was cut into pieces with a blade or with knives attached to a wheel, and the rags thrown into graded boxes according to their texture and newness – this was an important stage that could affect the quality of the finished paper. Next, the rags were pushed through holes in the floor to a room below, and then into a large stone vat, into which water flowed from another tank, filling and draining it eight or ten times a day for ten days. A fermentation process then took place; methods differed according to the amount and quality of the rags, but all involved leaving the sodden rags to rot and heat up for several weeks, turning and mixing them now and then. Then, in the water mill, purified water ran through the troughs of the pulpy mass to wash it and a mechanism of wooden hammers reduced it to a finer and more consistent pulp. An addition to the process in the early eighteenth century was the Hollander beater, a machine for breaking up the fibres; this allowed the rags to be beaten and churned, cut and mashed with metal bars, under running water, in a wooden tub. By the end of the century only one paper mill was still using the wooden stampers, although it seems that paper mills had generally been slow to adopt this mechanical aid.[40] The final vat, where the paper was made, was heated by a small fire in a cylinder in the side of the container.

The sheets of paper were made using a forme or mould, which consisted of a wooden frame with a sieve-like mesh of brass wires stretched over the top, supported underneath by thin wooden ribs. To make the paper, a second removable frame, known as the deckle, was placed over the mould to strengthen and contain it, by the 'dipper' at the vat, who deftly slipped the mould with its deckle under the surface of the pulp in the vat, scooped up the right amount of pulp or 'stuff', and shook it this way and that. The wires filtered out the water, leaving the fibrous mass on the surface of the mould, held in by the deckle. The trick was to make an even layer of the required thickness, filling the mould to the sides; the shake was crucial and demanded considerable skill. The dipper pushed the mould along a board to drain for a moment at the far end of the vat; then he immediately placed the deckle on another mould and dipped the next sheet. Meanwhile, the 'coucher' turned the mould upside down onto a felted woollen cloth, making a growing pile of sheets of paper sandwiched between felts. The stack was placed under a wooden press, and the water squeezed out; the paper was peeled off the cloths, pressed again, and hung up to dry. Finally, each sheet was 'sleeked' to polish the surface. Teams of women pressed the edge of flint 'sleeking-stones' across the surface of the smaller pieces of paper. Larger sheets were moved and pummelled under heavy iron hammers driven by the water wheel, or beaten

6 *Paper-making by hand*, 1762.

with hand-held hammers. After final checks for cleanliness and consistency, the paper was gathered into quires, and made up into reams.

There were variations in this time-honoured process, and gradual improvements. In 1768, the year of Donkin's birth, James Whatman introduced into his Turkey Mill, near Maidstone, a double deckle that he had come across in Holland. This mould meant that two large sheets of writing paper could be made at once. It was Whatman, too, who had first introduced 'wove' paper – a leap forward in the quality of paper, creating a surface that was far smoother and more uniform than 'laid' sheets, making a much better printing and writing surface.[41] Whereas the wires of the mould for laid paper were all parallel, the wove wire was constructed from a warp and a weft, resembling weaving. Joseph Bramah, a man of many ideas, patented a hydraulic press that speeded and simplified the drying of the stacks of paper.[42] Drying rooms began to be heated, and the metal hammers for glazing the paper were gradually replaced by heated rollers that produced a more even surface.[43]

Industry was changing, and at the turn of the century, Bryan was ready to take his part in its rapid progress. The Industrial Revolution was beginning to have its effect on the craft of paper-making. The time was ripe for full mechanisation of the process.

3
Trials and Triumphs

Rival schemes would vie for the prize of capturing the market in machines for making paper but, as with many industrial processes, the original idea came from abroad. Its inventor was a Parisian, Nicolas-Louis Robert.

Robert was born in Paris in December 1761.[1] He was a clever but rebellious child with no liking for school work; he was eventually articled to a notary. This work was equally disagreeable to him, and he left for a short but distinguished spell in the army. Still unsettled, Robert was taken under the wing of his elder brother, who was already well established as a scientific instrument maker. Most of their work was for the scientific institutes of Paris, and one particular customer was Tesar Charles, Professor of Physics at the Sorbonne. Professor Charles was working on a project to produce a balloon in direct competition with the Montgolfier brothers' hot air balloon. In 1783, Charles called upon the Robert brothers to work on a different idea, a balloon that was filled with hydrogen (a lighter-than-air gas) and sealed. They achieved it in just ten weeks and their balloon, made of rubberised silk and filled with hydrogen, flew unmanned over twenty kilometres to the village of Gonesse, where terrified villagers, thinking it was the Devil, destroyed it with pitchforks and scythes. Little over three months later Tesar Charles, with Nicolas-Louis Robert as co-pilot, took to the air in their hydrogen balloon, only twelve days after the Montgolfiers had achieved the first manned flight. The professor returned to academic physics, leaving Nicolas-Louis Robert to pick up the pieces of his career as a scientific instrument maker.

A few years later, Robert secured a good job as a proof reader for Pierre François Didot, an important printer and paper mill owner. When Didot senior died, his son Léger Didot became boss of the paper mill at Essonnes. In January 1793, King Louis XVI went to the guillotine and the revolutionary fervour was at its height. Didot's mill was the main source of paper for the temporary paper money ('assignats'), issued by the revolutionary government at this time, when spiralling inflation created a need to print daily huge numbers of these 'bank notes'.[2] Paper was taken by Didot poste-haste by the cartload, still damp from the mill, to be made into bank notes and signed by the revolutionary authorities during the night. On the following morning these assignats of ever-increasing denominations were issued to the public, while Didot was left to return from Paris in his empty cart with just a small bundle of notes under his arm for his pains, to face the sarcastic humour of his workforce.[3] Gaining confidence from the general unrest, the paper workers, truculent at the best of times, were quick to down tools and disrupt production.

At twenty-six, the inexperienced Léger Didot was no match for the workforce; he plucked Robert from his comfortable job in Paris and installed him as 'clerk-inspector of workmen' (in modern terms a 'works manager') at the mill at Essonnes. The task proved difficult even for the former sergeant major and he soon began to put his inventive mind to replacing this unruly crew with machinery that would need far fewer workers. It would also cut out the demarcation between the different craftsmen (the vatman, coucher, pressman, etc), at the same time de-skilling the process.

Robert's first experimental paper machine was built between 1793 and 1796 and 'was no bigger than a bird organ and produced paper no wider than common tape', – far too small for normal use.[4] Didot was throughout this period sceptical, saying 'it would never be brought to perfection'. However, when Robert succeeded in making paper in long lengths, his interest was aroused and he authorised the mill's carpenters, smiths and millwrights to work under Robert's direction to produce a larger machine (a working model). Within months, this new model was completed and Robert, after the working day, continued his experiments. By 1798 he was making paper of sixty one centimetres width and twelve to fifteen meters in length. The paper was thick and thin, the edges tended to fray and no consideration had yet been given to the problem of drying such long lengths. Despite these difficulties, the prospect of eventual commercial success gave Robert the nerve to apply to the French Minister of the Interior for a free patent for his invention. In his application of 9 September 1798, he freely acknowledged the material help he had received from Didot, but it is quite clear that the impecunious Robert looked forward to gaining a patent as the means of lifting himself once more and throwing off the shackles of running Didot's troubled mill.[5]

Robert's long and arduous task was recognised by the government, and he was given a national award of 3,000 francs, 'in the way of encouragement'. Robert used just over half of this money to file his patent and on 19 January 1799 it was granted. The remaining money was far from sufficient to develop and exploit the invention. Didot, ever the shrewd businessman, made Robert an offer of 60,000 francs to buy sole rights to the patent; 6,000 francs in cash and the rest in instalments. The deal was struck and Robert did receive the first 6,000 francs, but negotiations broke down and Robert initiated litigation. When the case of Robert v. Didot was finally heard, the court ruled that the patent and the machine were the sole property of Robert, but that Didot should be reimbursed for the expenses incurred in the development of the project.

A stalemate ensued and once again a compromise had to be found. In March of 1800 a deed of sale was drawn up, which transferred to Didot all the rights to the patent including access to the patent drawings; the deal also included a new machine to be built by Robert. The agreement was that Didot would pay 27,400 francs for the patent and the equipment: 2,400 francs as a first payment and the balance to be paid in instalments once the machine was producing paper at Essones. Robert kept his side of the bargain and built the machine, but received no further money after the initial instalment and there is no evidence of his further involvement in its development. Indeed, the devious Léger Didot had probably hatched his plans to get a new patent taken out in England before the signatures on the agreement with Robert were dry.

For it was England, rather than France, that was ever breaking new ground in her headlong pursuit of mechanisation. The second stage of the Industrial Revolution was well under way. James Brindley, under the patronage of the Duke of Bridgewater, had pioneered the canal system, which by 1800 criss-crossed the country connecting the centres of manufacture with London, the major cities and the seaports, dramatically cutting the cost of transporting raw materials and fuel to far-flung manufacturing towns and reducing the price of finished goods reaching a growing market. He was credited with the creation of eight new canals, which gave Britain the chance to unlock the potential of her world-changing abilities.[6] The steam engines of de Savary and Newcomen (both West Country men), used only as pumping engines to drain deep mines, had been transformed by James Watt and were now increasingly being employed as the motive power in Britain's mills and factories. Said Boulton to Watt in 1781: 'The people in London, Manchester and Birmingham are all steam-mill mad'.[7] By the turn of the century, steam tugs were in use on the Forth Clyde Canal, and in 1803, Richard Trevithick designed and built a steam dredger, which was used to dig out London's new East India Dock. [8]

For Didot, getting a British patent was not a possibility, because he was a Frenchman and the two countries were at war. So he had to rely on his English brother-in-law, John Gamble. Gamble held a situation under the British Government in the office of Captain James Coates of the Royal Navy, who was the British Commissioner for the exchange of prisoners of war.[9] In this capacity, Gamble had no difficulty in obtaining passports and travelled freely between Paris and London. Didot found a willing ally in Gamble who, for a share in any eventual profits, agreed to take out an English patent in his own name. Gamble left Paris in March 1801, carrying with him copies of the specifications and drawings of Robert's French patent, along with samples of paper made on Robert's machine.

Before enrolling the patent Gamble needed financial backers for the essential development of the machine, in order that it could be offered to the British paper-makers as a viable alternative to the traditional hand method. Through letters of introduction from Captain Coates and fortuitous meetings and contacts, first in Dover, then in London, Gamble was introduced to Henry and Sealy Fourdrinier, the senior partners in one of London's leading wholesale stationers, Messrs Bloxham and Fourdrinier of Sherbourne Lane. Gamble, recounting the events, said: 'They were much pleased and astonished with the rolls of paper they saw, and stated they would be happy to purchase a share in the patents'. Gamble lodged his application for an English patent on Robert's design on 23 April 1801 and the patent (No.2487) was granted in October of the same year. Between the two dates, Gamble returned to Paris in order to have copies made of Robert's drawings. While there, he also made arrangements to have the working model shipped over to England, where, it was thought, it would help in the further development of the project. Gamble does not explain how this was achieved. He only says: 'After much trouble and expense, the model arrived in London', but does not elaborate. He and his personal luggage had diplomatic immunity, but a machine measuring 2.4 metres long by 1.3 metres wide is very hard to conceal. Did they break it down into its component parts to be smuggled individually? Did it arrive via a neutral port on a non-aligned merchantman, or was it simply transported like any other contraband, shipped on a dark night under a heavy tarpaulin? We may never know.

Late in 1801, the machine was transferred to John Hall's factory. Hall was millwright to the Fourdriniers, who had acquired a small interest in hand-paper-making with the purchase of Frogmore Mill, near Apsley in Hertfordshire. Firmly established and well regarded for its engineering excellence, Hall's works was the obvious choice as a base in which to carry out the experiments and trials on the paper machine. Didot took advantage of a short truce in the hostilities between Britain and France (the Peace of Amiens) to cross the Channel, and joined Gamble at Hall's manufactory where, funded entirely by the Fourdriniers, they jointly managed the project. John Hall's men put the machine together and made minor alterations under the direction of Gamble and Didot but after six months no progress had been made. Hall later said:[10]

> It was put together by Mr Gamble's instructions and directions, and it would not make a single sheet, nor half a sheet of paper ... I was aware that a series of experiments seemed to make it less capable rather than more capable of performing the making of paper ... I went to town to explain to them [the Fourdriniers] my idea, which was, that I was only picking their pockets and advised them to desist.

Hall presented his bill of just over £300, and withdrew from the project. Léger Didot, who had observed and worked alongside Robert while in France, and John Gamble, the patent holder, proved to have little understanding of the process.

The patent drawings of Gamble's machine of 1801 were drawn in France, and were a direct copy of Robert's original design, but with metric measurements replaced by feet and inches. In spite of eight years of inventive thinking-time, the machine was still a very simple mechanism.[11] It is best explained by describing how the 'stuff' – the mixture of water and pulp – was transformed into a length of paper. This tiny machine was built almost entirely from wood, and powered by a labourer turning a simple hand crank. Central to the machine was a large

7 *Model of Robert's papermaking machine.*

oval vat, or stuff chest, which was supported by a substantial wooden framework. At one end of the vat, partially immersed in the stuff, rotated the drum, shaped rather like a miniature water wheel; when rotated it lifted the stuff from the vat and deposited it onto an inclined board. A simple cover over the paddle wheel was the only means of preventing the pulp being thrown out in all directions. From there the pulp slid onto the machine wire, an endless web of fine wire mesh (rather like a horizontal roller towel), which was stretched over two wooden rollers, one at either end of the machine. There was little control over the thickness and quality of the paper. The hand crank gave motion through a fixed gearing system to these rollers and the rest of the machine. As the forming sheet of paper was carried forward, water drained from it through the wire gauze back into the vat below. More water was squeezed out by a pair of felt-covered rollers, the 'couch rollers', placed near the end of the vat. The paper was taken up and wound onto a removable roller; when full, this roller was taken off the machine and the paper was passed through a separate set of hand-wound rollers, (rather like a mangle) to squeeze out more water before being taken to the lofts for drying. This rudimentary machine copied the action of the vat man and the first part of the coucher's work only, and could only produce unfinished, wet paper. Nicolas Robert had certainly sown the seed for the mechanisation of paper-making, but much greater refinement was necessary.

Bryan Donkin to the rescue! Although he was established as a paper mould maker, he was still working for Hall and had risen in the firm to become the foreman.[12] (In the nineteenth century this title would have carried far more weight than its twenty-first century interpretation, being more of a hands-on works manager.) In June 1802, with Hall's blessing, Donkin took control of the project. He later stated, in the 1807 enquiry: 'We commenced a series of experiments, some of which succeeded, and others failed'.[13] It is however evident that Bryan Donkin, this self-effacing engineer, impressed the Fourdrinier brothers with his diligence and tenacity, bringing the freshness of his intrinsic skills to bear on this demanding project. Within six months under Donkin's guidance, enough progress had been made to induce the Fourdrinier brothers to take the bold step of investing in a custom-built factory dedicated to the further development and eventual manufacture of paper machines.

Work on building the factory was started under Donkin's direction in April 1803.[14] Bermondsey was chosen for the site; it was at that time in the Surrey countryside, south of London, with cheap land and good access to the river for the transport of heavy goods. At the same time, probably using Hall's works as a base, Donkin started work on a new machine that incorporated all the improvements he had made or suggested to that point. This machine was a massive twenty-seven feet in length by four feet wide and its design features and improvements were protected by a second patent, taken out just eight months later, in December 1803. More work was needed, but success was already in sight. The hope of a speedy conclusion, which would bring the continuous paper-making machine to the market, induced the Fourdrinier brothers to convert Frogmore Mill, in the Gade Valley, Hertfordshire, in order to commence full-scale paper-making trials. The new machine was erected there in March 1804. Of the first trial, Donkin said: 'Our first assay of this machine gave us the pleasure of seeing many of the attempted improvements completely successful, but yet very far from being perfect'. Despite Donkin's modesty, his innovation is universally recognised as the first practical paper machine in history.[15]

In just eleven months, Donkin had planned and overseen the building a new factory, constructed the much enlarged and improved paper-making machine, and had managed the conversion of the Frogmore Mill driving gear to power this singular and novel machine.

Donkin's machine was used as a test bed to try out the many improvements and inventions that continued to be made until full commercialisation in around 1812. But the ultimate goal was to produce a universal machine, a machine that could make any grade of paper from coarse wrappings, through tissues for the Manchester cotton trades, to printing and fine writing papers. To this end, trials and experiments were pushed forward at breakneck speed, and after three intense months of tireless work by Donkin, the Fourdriniers were so impressed by the modifications and refinements that they readily commissioned a second machine. Work was started in June 1804 and the new paper-making machine was set to work within the year at another Fourdriner-owned mill, Two Waters, not far from Frogmore.

8 *Two Waters Mill,* c.1820.

During the early stages of running the business Donkin's approach to book keeping was casual; his personal accounts were mixed up with work expenses. Entries in his little account book for September 1804, included, for instance a circular saw for cutting paper into quires, bacon for Mrs Hall, a new hat, paying a bricklayer, and window blinds.[16] October's expenses were equally varied: for carting timber, a book on Smeaton's Eddystone Lighthouse, a leather pipe for Frogmore and Mrs Donkin's housekeeping among many other items. In November, he paid for a barrel of files from Sheffield, his brother Thomas's groceries, and the two guineas for his subscription to the Society of Arts, as well as a pair of gloves and two handkerchiefs, property tax on the 'shop' account and sundry other necessities. He bought a horse in December (£30), together with a whip, spurs and harness, and a 'lanthorn' for the stable; just before Christmas he provided meat for the men's suppers and a Christmas box for Mr Hall's foundry men. Meanwhile, his income was carefully noted: during that quarter, payments poured in from the Fourdriniers, to the tune of £1,178, to be spent on setting up the paper machine business.

Up in Sandoe, Bryan's sister felt aggrieved. Not realising the time-consuming nature of his work, she had invited him to stay, and had received no reply.[17] The latest local news was that their servant, 'our poor Nancy', had been deserted by her false swain, and had been recommended to Lady Broughton (Mrs Errington) as a maid for the London house. The timid girl had set off to Newcastle to sail to London, but Ann feared that she would get lost between the boat and her destination, especially as the girl really wanted to go to Bryan's house, where she would feel safe. If she did ever arrive, would Bryan treat her with kindness and make sure she reached the Erringtons at St.James's? Nancy had been given directions, but was in such a state that Ann doubted that she had understood them. Six pounds of thread for Bryan was part of her baggage: Nancy had said she would take it wherever she went. The good news in the letter was that their Henry and Thomas were coming to stay for a week or two, for the Stagshaw Bank Fair. Thomas had been very ill all spring, and Mary had been much alarmed about him at one time; he was still weak, but they thought 'his own air' in Sandoe would bring him back to health.

Northumberland was a world away. Donkin and the Fourdriniers were now under pressure from rival inventors. Joseph Bramah presented a patent in 1806, but the greatest challenge came from the enigmatic paper maker and inventor John Dickinson.[18] His 'suction roll' machine would continue to be a serious threat until he recognised the superiority of Donkin's technology and bought a 'Fourdrinier' machine for his own use.[19]

The basic design of Donkin's 'Fourdrinier' machine, patented in 1807, was the blueprint for future paper-making machines for generations to come (Patent No.3068). The patent drawings show the many improvements that were incorporated. With his active and fertile mind, Donkin had in fact adjusted many of the machine movements and eliminated wherever possible those parts of the process that could prove troublesome to a labour force unfamiliar with mechanical devices. The machine was much stronger and, although the base frame was still a timber construction, all the stanchions and wire frames were machined at the Bermondsey works from iron castings. Distances between rollers and other moving parts could now be set precisely within this rigid frame. This eliminated the problem of vibration or humidity levels altering the set of the machine. Now the machine could be set precisely to produce paper of predictable thickness and quality.

Donkin had approached the project in the manner of a mature development engineer. He recognised that the many parts of the process needed to be controlled independently of each other. Although driven by a single power source, intricate mechanisms ensured that every operation from stirring the stuff to the winding up of the finished paper was separate, enabling each part of the process to be speeded up or slowed down at will. Much thought was given to the 'shake', the sideways motion of the wire in imitation of the vatman's action. In Robert's machine, this was very irregular and often caused tears or breakages in the paper. Donkin recognised that the shake was the most delicate part of the process and altered it so that the power and number of shakes per minute could be adjusted to suit the nature of the pulp being used. Each of these elements of the machine could readily be set for the production of a particular quality of paper. Extracting

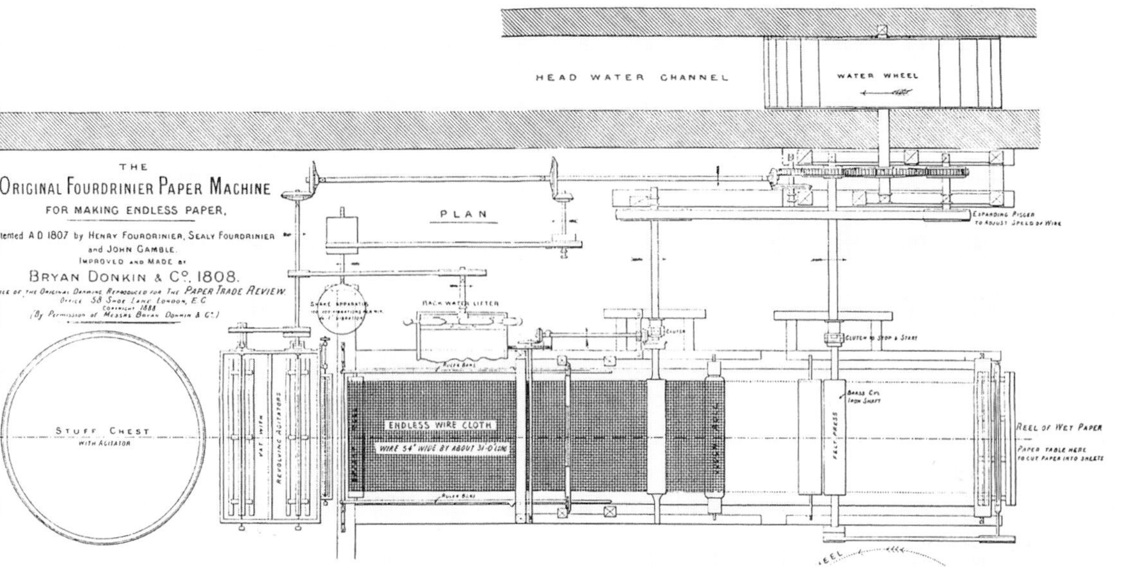

9 *Plan of* 1807 *paper machine, redrawn later.*

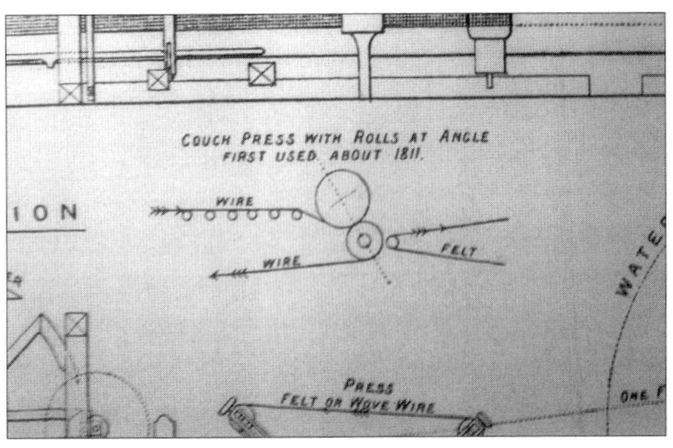

9b *Detail from* 1807 *paper machine drawing.*

water from the forming paper was a thorny problem. With Robert's system, the paper was still very wet and fragile when it left the machine. Donkin made many experiments over the years, and after altering the configuration of the machine, the difficulty was largely solved by introducing another set of rollers incorporating a moving wire between them (known as the 'wet press' or 'top wire'), which squeezed out a copious amount of water before it reached the couch.

Another improvement brought further versatility to the machine when Donkin incorporated adjustable deckle straps which could be set to make paper of different widths. Made from leather, these deckle straps ran on rollers and touched the top face of the wire, preventing spillage of the pulp, and for the first time, giving a good finish to the edge of the paper. Almost all the working parts were now made of metal. The wire was supported and kept level by a series of identical rollers made from brass tubes, each drawn to a precise size on Donkin's own tube-drawing machine. Cleverly designed friction wheels, machined with great skill each to the same precise measurement, kept the moving wire taut across its width. Equal precision was employed in machining the couch and press rollers that squeezed out the water. Now made from brass, each set of rollers had to be machined parallel and to exactly the same diameter to ensure the smooth passage of the paper. An improvement at the last roller (the 'dry press') made it possible to reel up the paper without fear of breakage. The full reel was then taken to the cutting tables, where it was carefully sliced with knives to its final sheet size before being taken to the lofts for drying. These were busy times for Donkin, so it was not until much later that the cutting process was mechanised.

It has to be borne in mind that Donkin had to design and build precision machine tools, which had the repeatable accuracy to bring this monumental feat of mechanical engineering to fruition. Also, in these opening years of the nineteenth century, he was drawing together and training a growing workforce of intelligent artisans, machine tool operators who were capable of absorbing the new skills of metal machining – turners, milling machinists, drillers and detail fitters – adaptable men, men he could rely on to read his drawings and transform them with their combined skills into the many different and highly accurate components needed to achieve the goal of building a successful paper-making machine.

Getting the paper machine to the level of sophistication of the 1807 patent had cost the Fourdriniers dearly, and they applied in that year for an extension for fifteen years.[20] The House of Commons approved the application, but it was challenged in the House of Lords and reduced to seven years, bringing the patent to an end in 1814. With more development work still to be done, this was very little time to claw back enough money to avoid bankruptcy. They were able to prove to the satisfaction of the House of Commons Committee, set up to examine the merits of the extension of the patent, that more than £60,000 was withdrawn from their wholesale stationery business to finance the invention. Bryan Donkin presented the only balance sheet scrutinised by the committee and offered to open his account books to them, proving that he had spent on behalf of the Fourdrinier brothers more than £31,000.[21] The sum included all the costs incurred in buying and renovating the mills, the cost of building and developing the paper machines, and all the running costs. When cross examined, he stated 'The whole expenditure since I took up the machine was £31,667, which passed through my hands'. This statement, together with the balance sheet, gives a valuable insight into Bryan Donkin's true position within the project.

As well as building and developing the paper machines, he was also trusted by the Fourdrinier brothers to buy and renovate the mills and to control the general day-to-day running costs of the entire enterprise. Donkin brought to bear the skills learnt as a land agent; not only was he a wise and prudent engineer, he now proved himself to be a excellent project manager. Neither Gamble nor Didot was examined by the committee, which is a pity, as Joseph Liddell, the Fourdriniers' chief clerk, revealed under strong questioning, that separate to the £31, 667 paid through Donkin's hands, a sum of £14,879 19s. 10d was paid to Didot, and 'to

Mr Gamble, as a salary for attending, for expense of patents, and for expense of going to France and back, £16,724 16s. 9d.' – together more than half the total cost of the development. These were huge sums for the time, and a drain on their sponsors' resources, especially in view of the fact that both Gamble and Didot had a vested interest in the success of the venture. In contrast, Donkin received a salary from Lady Day 1804 to June 1807, of £2,600 or £69 a month. Gamble, it seems, retained a financial interest in the machine until 1804 when, in spite of the money he had received, his own dwindling resources forced him to make over his share of the patent to the Fourdriniers. Up to that point, he had been supervising, under Donkin's direction, some of the trials at the Frogmore and Two Waters mills and demonstrating the machine to prospective customers. The Fourdriniers, recognising Gamble's valuable contribution in obtaining the first English patent and enabling them to pursue this business venture, signed over to him a part share of their new paper mill at St.Neots, which he managed until 1809. Their inborn sense of honour ultimately contributed to their downfall.

Didot on the other hand, was an entirely different kettle of fish.[22] Although he came from a long line of paper-makers, and had the confidence of the Fourdriniers, he in fact made very little contribution to the success of the venture. He also seems to have had little or no idea about mechanics or the finer points of machine paper-making, although he later laid false claim to the entire invention and improvements. He was a constant source of annoyance to Donkin and a great drain on the financial resources of the project. At a time when every effort should have been concentrated on getting the paper machine ready for the market, Didot had a different idea – an adaptation of the machine to produce sheets of paper with watermarks. Unable, as a foreigner, to patent his idea he persuaded Henry Fourdrinier to back it and apply for the patent: 'a machine for manufacturing paper of indefinite length, laid and wove, with separate moulds' (Patent No.2951). Known as the 'chain mould machine', its construction and development spanned the years between 1806 and 1817. The original patent was submitted without drawings, and although he never had faith in it, Donkin was saddled with the task of drawing up the elaborate plans and with the entire manufacture of this very complicated machine. Despite Donkin's best efforts, the chain mould machine was never a commercial success, but sealed the fate of Henry and Sealy Fourdriner as they descended into bankruptcy.

Léger Didot was a constant thorn in Bryan Donkin's side, often insisting on trying useless and costly experiments. We have no record of Didot's looks or true demeanour, but the exasperated Donkin paints a picture of a rather pompous, self-assured little man with no knowledge of engineering or physics but, when found wanting in these disciplines, given to outbursts of passionate rage. During the vital development period of 1806-9, Donkin confided his thoughts to his diary, providing an insight into this volatile Frenchman's character, and Donkin's slightly sardonic, 'told you so', attitude in dealing with him.

> Saturday, 19 April 1809
> Saw Mr Sealy Fourdrinier and Mr Didot at the warehouse, but notwithstanding anything I could say of the impropriety of laying the machine wire out of level, Mr Didot insisted it would be useful having an opportunity of doing so.
>
> Tuesday, 22 April 1809
> Mr Sealy and Mr Didot came down to the shop and ordered that the springs should be applied to the shaking bar … producing up and down motion in the wire … In my opinion most of the above alteration is absurd'.
>
> Monday, 28 April 1809
> Mr Didot proposes to make more alterations in the machine, but they are too ridiculous to describe.'

These alterations and trials instigated by Didot, executed by Donkin and Gamble and paid for by the Fourdrinier brothers, were soon abandoned, probably along with many more 'too ridiculous' even to be recorded. Alarmingly, the Fourdriniers allowed Didot to continue with his stupid ideas. At the same time that Donkin was using his every endeavour to hold down the costs, Didot was busily ordering extravagant experiments, some of which had nothing to do with paper-making. The most infamous of these was his obsession with perpetual motion. Donkin's caustic comment was:

> Tuesday, 27 June 1809
> Mr Didot came to the factory and examined his hydraulic pump (intended for perpetual motion) which we now had ready for an experiment. He enquired what I now thought of it, if I had not now a better opinion of it. I told him that being perfectly satisfied of the impossibility of a perpetual motion, I could never change my opinion. He said he was sorry for that 'but we will try'. Two men being put to work the pump, he desired them to 'turn more fast you can'. Of course they raised a considerable quantity of water, on which he exclaimed: 'It will do, it will do; very much waters'. I told him I was sorry to see him so deluded, and in order to convince him, I would, if he pleased, make out a calculation, in which I would plainly point out to him that the power expended must necessarily exceed the weight of water raised. 'No,' he said, 'me no like calculations, me will now put up a water wheel'.

He came again the next day, demanding that Donkin should make a wheel of fifteen feet in diameter, and the day after, countermanded this order, saying:

> Wednesday, 28 June 1809
> He would not have the wheel made yet, but would try many experiments, requesting at the same time that I would not quiz him, for, says he 'I will be mad for about two monts [sic]'.

About a month later, Didot wanted a second pump, which he thought would bring his quest for perpetual motion to fruition:

> Friday, 21 July 1809
> Mr Didot came to the factory and talked about putting up another large pump, so that the piston in one might be rising whilst the other was descending. I again expostulated on the absurdity of the scheme, but to no purpose. He told me he was mad, and the experiments he meant to try were for his own information, not mine, as he did not understand the calculation he could be only be satisfied by experiment.

Didot did not confine his ineptitude to paper-making or perpetual motion. Evidence of his almost obsessive silliness can be found in a specification (Patent No.3209), which he both prepared and patented in his own name. This describes a totally impractical design for an umbrella, which incorporated a gutter and drainpipe; its construction was such that it needed to be held perfectly level to avoid spilling from its gutter and drenching the unfortunate user. This bizarre contraption illustrates the true boundaries of Didot's inventive powers and engineering knowledge.

Despite Bryan Donkin's attempts to look at Didot's antics in a humorous way, the working relationship between the two men was rapidly deteriorating. This culminated in a showdown instigated by Didot; on Wednesday, 2 August 1809, a meeting was called by Didot, where the differences between himself and Donkin could be aired in front of the Fourdriniers. Donkin, unaware of Didot's intentions, was rather taken aback when the Frenchman laid claim to a number of inventions and improvements which were Donkin's own. When challenged, Didot flew into a rage, the ensuing argument lasting for more than ninety minutes. Donkin steadily destroyed Didot's arguments until the poor man, thoroughly beaten, tried to save face by pretending that he had 'meant a different thing'.

He had won the argument, but Donkin was now on his guard. He called a private meeting with the Fourdriniers at which he disclosed his planned improvements to the paper machine, by shortening the length of the continuous wire. He insisted that Didot should have 'no authority to interfere', and 'he ought not and should not, as far as I could prevent it, derive any advantage from this'. However, despite Donkin's protestations, Didot carried on with his interfering ways; but because of his involvement in the early stages, the Fourdriniers allowed him to continue to derive financial reward for each and every improvement.

Nevertheless, regardless of all adversities, real progress was being made. From early 1805, genuine commercial interest was shown. On March 1st, Donkin went to Two Waters and found Sealy Fourdrinier there with Mr Appleton from Manchester 'who was very much pleased with the machine and talks about having one'.[23] With the help of the prospectus that accompanied the patent of 1807 there was great enthusiasm among the leading paper-makers, who were quick to recognise its commercial value over paper-making by hand. Between 1807 and 1810, Donkin sold thirteen machines of up to thirty-three feet long, producing continuous paper of between 44½ and 56½ in. wide. Improvements continued to be made well into the second decade of the century. A clever rearrangement of the wire in 1809 gave rise to an increase in speed of from twenty feet per minute to thirty-four feet per minute.

During the entire development period of the paper machine, Donkin continued to widen the scope of his own professional interests. He became a sought-after valuer of property and machinery, and a respected appraiser – a profession practised under licence, which demanded annual renewal, with the sum of six shillings paid to the Commissioner of Stamps.[24] For a fee, Donkin also arbitrated in many industrial disputes. He was also the engineer employed to redesign and expand an ill-managed mill on the Thames at Greenwich.[25] Another large-scale business venture to consume his energies was his exciting food preservation enterprise.[26] Like his contemporaries, Maudslay and Bramah, he understood the necessity for diversification.

This deliberate independence stood Donkin in good stead, for in 1809, when the Fourdriniers began to find their finances difficult, they first persuaded Donkin to rent the engineering works and eventually in 1811 asked him to buy the factory. It was the pivotal moment in his career which would often, over the ensuing years, leave him short of cash, but Donkin readily grasped the nettle and on May 18th of the same year, took out a mortgage 'in security for £2000' from Matthew Stainton, a financier and relative of Mary Donkin.[27] The factory, its equipment and all the machine tools, which Donkin had built and acquired, now formed a permanent, secure base from which he could expand his own business, Bryan Donkin and Company, Engineers of Blue Anchor Road.

Despite this new-found independence, Donkin never shirked his first responsibility to the Fourdriniers and their investment, and was often at Two Waters overnight. On one of these visits, after a long day supervising trials, he was sitting in his room at the Bell Hotel, puzzling over the long-standing problem of paper 'breakages' (tearing) caused by insufficient water being squeezed out. Suddenly, after the years of working on the process, he had his Eureka moment. Like all good theories, Donkin's was an essentially simple one.[28]

> By placing the couch rolls at an angle, instead of vertically one over the other, so that the upper one should bear slightly onto the web before receiving the full pressure between the rolls, thus causing more water to pass from the sheet of paper through the wire, the effect would be that the sheet was stronger and less liable to break in passing the couch roll.

Didot was in residence at Two Waters but had already retired to bed. Anxious to try his new idea and not wanting Didot's presence, Donkin decided to work into the night to reconfigure the machine. In the early hours, after much exertion, the mill was started and the trial took place. As could be expected, the steady rumble of the water wheel and the clatter of the paper machine woke Didot, who appeared almost immediately. Donkin noted:

> This arrangement of the couch rolls proved perfectly successful, and, as fully expected, the individual referred to [Didot] tried to claim credit for this important invention, but in this, he was not successful.

The realigning of the couch rolls in 1811 is referred to as a stroke of genius and had several effects. The paper was drier, stronger, and far less liable to tear; also the top wire was now redundant. With this gone, the way was clear to introduce moveable deckles making it possible to produce paper of different widths on the one machine.

The machine made altogether better paper, and was simpler and more reliable; just as importantly to the trade, it could now be offered to the paper-makers at a cheaper rate. On the strength of this breakthrough in new technology, a new prospectus was drawn up, setting out the advantages of 'the improved machine'.[29]

> Instead of five men, formerly employed, three are fully sufficient for the management of the present machine, without requiring that degree of attention or skill, which before were indispensable.
>
> In 1806, the machine was capable of doing the work of six vats in twelve hours; it is, however, now capable of doing that quantity at one fourth of the expense.

Donkin could now sell the machines at a reduced rate, ranging from £715 for a 30 inch machine making three vats per day, to £1,040 for a 54 inch machine making twelve vats per day. On top of this, an annual royalty was levied on each machine by the Fourdriniers for the use of their patent. Sales increased a little and paper-makers paid cash on the nail for the machines, but once they were installed and working in their own mills, many of them took advantage of the Fourdriniers' bankruptcy and weak financial position and refused to pay their licence dues. The Fourdrinier brothers' enthusiasm for the paper-making machine project had blinded them to the dangers of over-committing their finance. They were declared bankrupt in November 1810, but continued to have an influence on the paper machine business, which was then run under the direction of assignees. Honourable businessmen that they were, Henry and Sealy stuck fast to the belief that one day success would come, enabling them to discharge their debts and reclaim their position in society. Writs were issued and court cases heard, but to little avail. The decades slipped by, and eventually Parliament was asked to recognise the great benefit that the machine had brought to the British economy.

As late as 1837, the select committee set up to look into compensating the Fourdrinier brothers recommended they be given £20,000 – this of course was whittled down by the Treasury and on 8 May 1840, a reluctant Chancellor awarded the Fourdriniers £7000, little more than their litigation costs. Let down by society the brothers died in much reduced circumstances.

4
Ebb and Flow

When Bryan Donkin first lived in Bermondsey, he and his little family occupied a terraced house in a row called Fort Place, in Grange Road. A cluster of houses – speculative building in this open space outside London – had sprung up at the meeting of three highways.[1] Turning right from his front door, he could walk to work across the T-junction where Grange Road turned sharply to the right and the road continued as Blue Anchor Road, where it was only a few minutes' walk to the factory, set back from the thoroughfare on the left. (Part of Grange Road still exists; the southern section is now Dunton Road. Blue Anchor Road has been renamed Southwark Park Road.) The route into London along Grange Road was a turnpike road; in the middle of the junction was the toll gate keeper's house where coachmen and drovers had to stop to pay their fees for passing through. In 1808, at the age of forty and with four children – two others had died young – Bryan Donkin's life as an engineer was beginning to flourish and, with his paper machines beginning to sell, he felt ready for a new enterprise. So he devised a new kind of pen.

It may seem strange now, but for at least 1300 years people in Britain wrote with pens made from birds' feathers. The entire instrument, handle and nib together, was made from a single wing feather, its tip cut with a sharp knife into a writing point with a slit to help the ink flow. There was no reservoir – one simply dipped the quill pen into the ink, wrote a few words and dipped again. If the nib wore down or split, it could be re-shaped with a pen knife, but new quill pens were readily available by the dozen from bookshops or stationers, and uncut quills could also be bought by do-it-yourself pen makers. Only a few feathers on each wing were suitable for pen-making, the rest being too soft or small. Goose feathers, the most widely used, had to be hardened by plunging them into hot sand before they could be successfully cut into pens. In the early nineteenth century, geese were specially bred for their feathers, and goose feathers were later imported by the million from Northern Europe and Russia.[2] Quills were also made from the feathers of swans and turkeys, and the tiniest were fashioned from the feathers of crows.

What we now know as a 'nib' was then simply called a 'pen' or a 'point'. Experiments were made with different materials for making 'pens', in a quest for a more hardwearing writing instrument. There are accounts of small numbers of

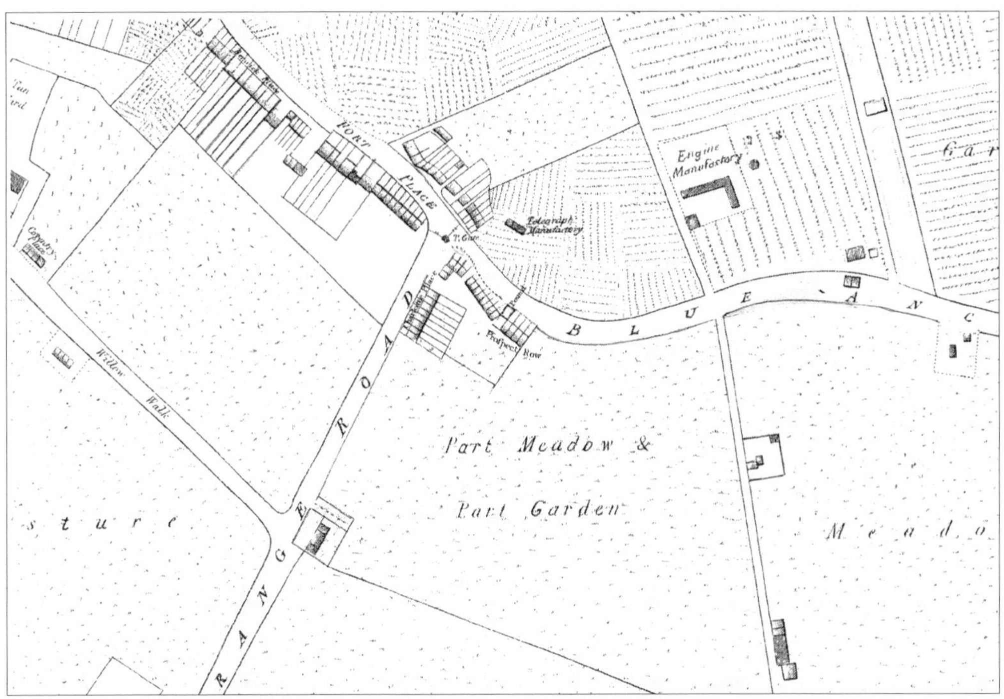

10 *Map of Bermondsey showing Donkin's engine manufactory,* 1813.

brass, copper or steel pens being used in Europe from as long ago as the fifteenth century.[3] In England, Samuel Harrison started manufacturing steel pens on a small scale in Birmingham in about 1780. His pens were made by hammering out a sheet of steel and bending it to form a tube, the join becoming the slit in the nib; he gave one to Dr Joseph Priestley, the philosopher and chemist.[4] Round about 1803, Jacob Wise of London made similar barrel pens, mounted in bone cases so that they were portable.[5] Daniel Fellows in Wolverhampton was another early pen-maker.[6] Clearly, interest in producing a more durable pen was growing, but these early pens were hand crafted in small numbers and therefore costly to produce, and were considered inflexible and rather impractical.

Bryan Donkin, unable to resist the challenge of a half-developed new idea, was the first to bring out a patent for a steel pen (Patent No.3118, March 1808). Neck and neck with him was a Baltimore jeweller, Peregrine Williamson, whose first attempts lacked flexibility; an additional slit each side of the main cut helped him towards his 1809 patent – the Americans claimed that 'the English' had borrowed his invention.[7] Donkin used greater precision in his manufacturing methods than before. Donkin's drawing in his published patent showed how the nib part of his pen was made from two lengths of shaped steel brazed together at an angle, most of the way down but leaving a slit at the shaped end to form the pointed nib. The pen could be partially retracted into a brass tube to tighten the gap in the nib,

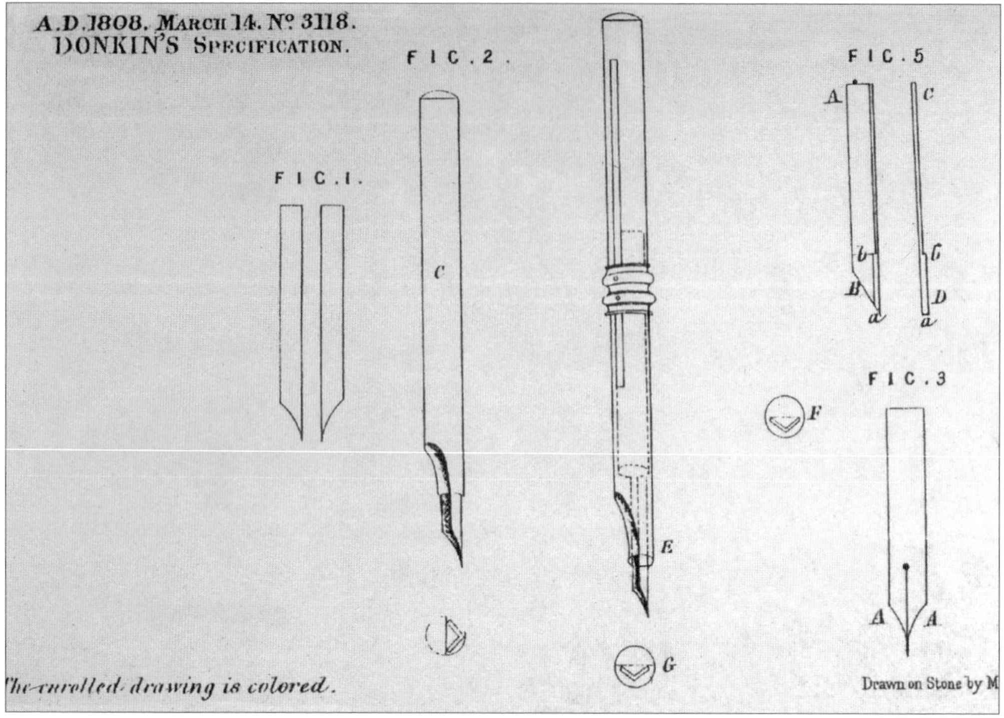

11 *Patent drawing for steel pen,* 1808.

thus reducing the flexibility. For a softer touch in writing, the nib could be pushed further out. Donkin's advertisement proclaimed:[8]

> The principle on which these pens are constructed combines at once the elasticity and freedom of the quill with the durability of a metal point.
> Mounted in gold, silver, metal etc. and fitted up in a variety of cases for the counting house or pocket: points of gold, platina, silver, steel or metal.

For carrying the pen in the pocket, the nib was removed, reversed and tucked away in the tubular case. A different casing was fashioned to hold a pen at one end and a pencil at the other, made with the best lead by Brookman and Langdon. Donkin's recommendation was to place a few sheets of paper under the writing sheet (to soften the writing surface), to use thin ink (to ease the flow) and to wipe the pen clean after use – and not leave it in the ink (inks at that time being corrosive).

The pens were made in a small factory in Charlotte Place, in Grange Road, which Donkin had acquired in 1809.[9] He sold the pens mainly through retailers but also from his manufactory, where the papermaking machines were made. The price for a complete wooden pen with a silver holder and steel nib was 3s.6d; a silver case with pen and pencil 6s, and with two pens, 6/3d. A steel nib alone cost a shilling.[10] There were variations on the theme: a silver telescopic case with one

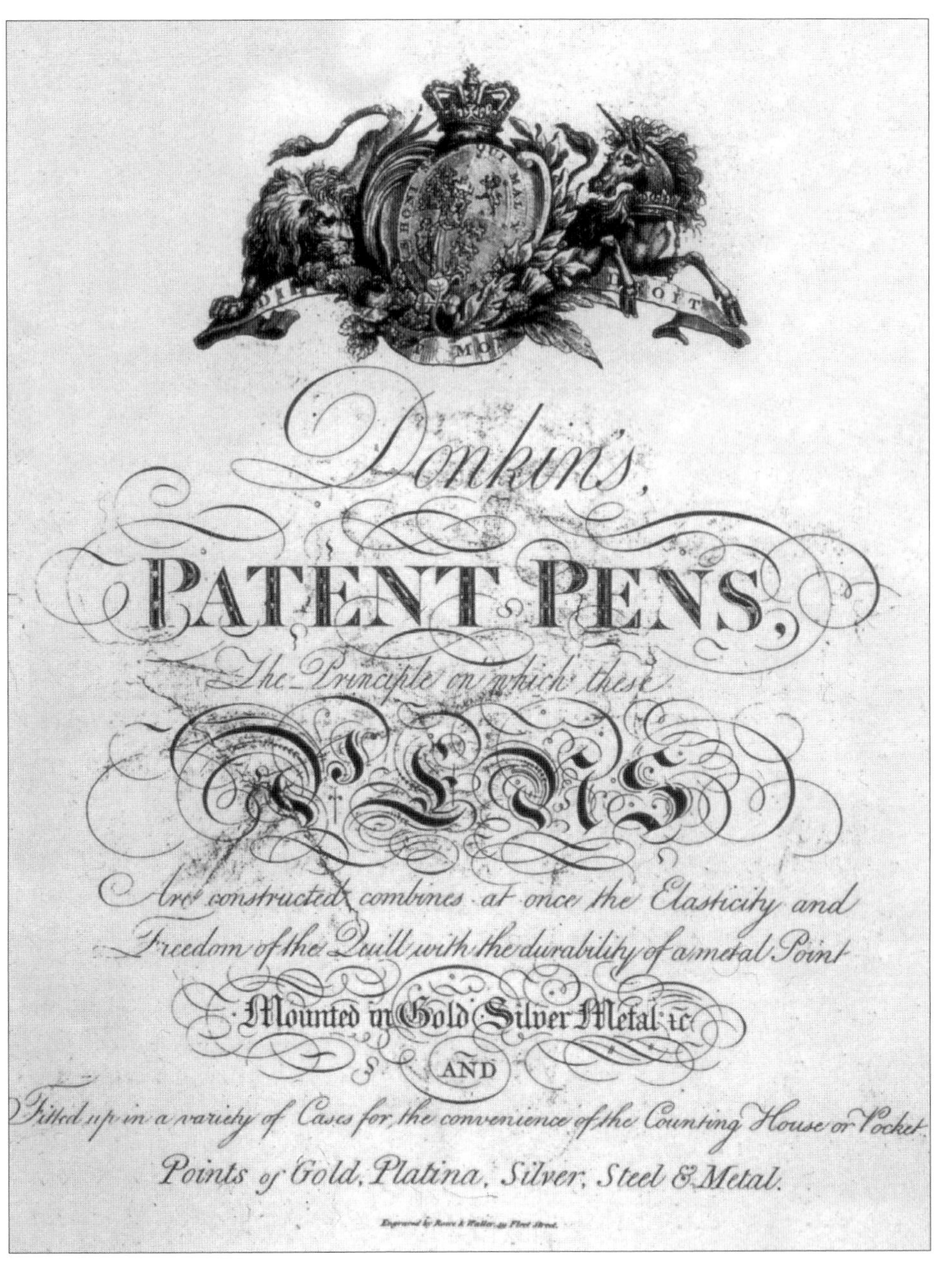

12 *Advertisement for patent pens,* c.1808.

or two parts and the same in brass; silver-mounted steel nibs, brass-mounted steel nibs, and pattern cards of pens and handles. One customer, Wilkinson, Rowlatt & Co, ordered a typical selection in May 1810, an order worth £2 4s. 6d.; Mr Oppenheim bought a dozen brass pens with black lead pencils at one end; and in 1815 Benjamin Whitrow wanted 'a dozen Donkin pens mounted in brass –

immediately'. In spite of a constant trickle of orders, though, Donkin was in need of funds, partly because he had just purchased the extensive premises and factory in Bermondsey, which had previously been rented to him by the Fourdriniers.

Perhaps realising that the time was not ripe for expensive pens of this quality, and knowing that better profits could be made in his other work, Donkin auctioned the rights to his patent three years later, when it still had eleven years to run before expiry. Making sure of finding the best buyer, Donkin paid nearly £22 to have the auction advertised in the newspapers in Birmingham, Bristol and Sheffield as well as 'in all the different London papers'.[11] Notice was given that the auction was to be held at the Auction Mart near the Bank of England, on Monday 5 August 1811 at noon; the rights to the patent would go under the hammer of Mr Munn, the auctioneer, and the stock in trade and tools were to be taken by the purchaser at a valuation.[12] In the same advertisement, Donkin announced that

> Mr Donkin avails himself of this opportunity to acquaint the public that he continues his Business of Civil Engineer, and that he has recently purchased the extensive premises and factory lately belonging to Messrs H. & S. Fourdrinier, where he will carry on the general Business of a Millwright.
>
> Fort Place S, Bermondsey, 12 July 1811.

Whether at the auction or not, the buyer was Joseph Bramah, an engineer of a similar innovative turn of mind to Donkin but older by twenty years.[13] Now known mainly for his locking mechanisms, he was a genius with hydraulics but also a prolific inventor in many fields. He had experimented with improvements in writing instruments for years and perfected the cutting of a goose quill into several short nibs, by chopping the barrel of the feather into lengths, each with a split nib at one end, to be pushed onto a tapered stick. Then he made short barrel 'pens' with a nib cut at both ends for economy; then, by splitting the quill up its length and cutting it into sections, he produced up to thirty 'slip' nibs, which needed a different type of holder (patented in 1809) to clamp the thin nib into place. Cutting by hand left little profit, so Bramah invented a cutting tool, mounted in a fly-press. Next he thought up the 'Perpetual or fountain pen', a device that stored ink in a metal tube or even in a quill pen. His idea for keeping the pens of office clerks constantly supplied with ink through flexible tubes from a common reservoir was not a great success. Bramah was willing to pay £350 for the rights to Donkin's patent pens, but does not seem to have made much use of the addition to his business. With the success of his own quill-cutting machine, he perhaps realised that it was unwise to confuse the public with two innovations at that time.[14] Meanwhile Donkin, although he no longer owned the patent, had an agreement with Bramah and continued to sell his pens for at least four years.[15]

It was a long time before quill pens were abandoned by the public – some continued to use them until the end of the nineteenth century – but steel pens gradually began to come into use in homes and offices. In 1815 Thomas Sheldon of Wolverhampton was producing nibs – still handmade – made from roughly shaped blanks stamped from thin steel, which were hardened, tempered and ground, and selling them for 18s a dozen.[16] From the early 1820s, Joseph Gillott, the Mitchell brothers and others used steam power to produce larger numbers in the back streets of Birmingham. Gillott, a Sheffield man and a pioneer in the steel pen industry, experimented over the years with different qualities of steel and with ways of preparing it to increase its elasticity.[17] His first efforts, it is said, were made with the aid of a frying pan. Ten years later, James Perry, finding the early nibs inflexible, made improvements to the design, and advertised widely to popularise his machine-made Patent Perryian Pens; his collaboration with Josiah Mason (whose enormous head was later analysed by Fowler, the phrenologist) kick-started the industry with their mass production methods. By 1838, the average cost of nibs had dropped to four pence a gross (144) and by the end of the century, pen nib making was a huge industry, the thirteen principal factories in Birmingham producing some 175 million nibs a year, in dozens of shapes and sizes.

Before Henry Stephens produced his 'durable and indelible ink' in 1834, most people made their own.[18] Simple carbon ink could be made from soot or lamp black, water and gum, but for a better consistency the most common ingredients were oak galls (parasitic growths on oak trees caused by wasps) and iron salts. These inks suited quill pens, but their corrosive properties were injurious to the new steel nibs. Bryan Donkin's personal recipe was typical:[19]

> *To make black ink*
> 3oz of galls, broken; 1oz of logwood; 1oz green vitriol; 1oz gum Arabic; 3 pints spring water.
> Put the above into a stone bottle and shake it now and then.

Logwood was the heartwood from a South American tree, imported as logs for use as a purple dye but, like vitriol, was readily available for purchase. Green vitriol is iron sulphate: it reacts with the tannin in the other ingredients, to turn the ink a good black.[20]

For business use, a different ink for copying letters and drawings was necessary, for utilising in conjunction with a copying press.[21] The technique was to write with special ink on normal paper, and press it between sheets of dampened transparent copying paper in a copying press: the ink was transferred to the copying sheet and could be kept to read later, through the reverse side of the paper because the pressed image was back to front. James Watt (of steam engine fame) was the first to patent a copying device of this sort in 1780 (Patent No.1244).[22] It was presented in two forms, one with a screw-down press and the other using rollers It is probable that Donkin used one of these clamped to a table in his office for reproducing drawings and plans – John Smeaton, the civil engineer, certainly did, and Donkin perhaps used a later, portable version to copy his on-site sketches and notes. At home he used a small press for keeping a record of letters he had written to business colleagues as well as to his family. A recipe for copying ink comes from his own notebook:[23]

> *To make ink for copying drawings*
> 1oz gum Arabic; 40 grains liquorice; 6oz water; 4½ oz ground lamp black
> The gum and the liquorice must be dissolved in the whole quantity of water and boiled for about 5 minutes; to this add as much water as may have evaporated. At successive operations grind well together upon a muller stone small proportions of the lamp black and the liquid. A spoonful of spirits added to this ink will preserve it.

Doubtless Donkin and his family were among the first to make the steel pen their writing instrument of choice but for the general public, quill pens did not lose their popularity until the steel pen trade was at its height in Birmingham, in the late nineteenth century.

Tied up though he was with the constant development of the paper mills and machinery, as well as the pen-making and retailing enterprise, Donkin leapt at the chance to take on a new project that was to continue for four years. In the midst of Didot's tantrums at Two Waters, Bryan Donkin turned his engineering and personal skills to a tumbledown corn mill on the River Thames at East Greenwich.

After the death of the owner, Mr Russell, the Dickensian executors Messrs. Sharp and Handasyde were handling the estate. They first approached Donkin at the end of June 1809, asking him to give his opinion on the state of the mill and any necessary repairs. Donkin went to examine the mill and found it in a dilapidated condition: the foundations were poor and it was sinking into the soft ground causing the walls to twist. Water had found its way under the building, diagonally across from the river side to the back corner. Practically all the wharves had collapsed. Donkin needed to know how it had been built before he could judge the extent of the repairs required. The best people to ask were the builder, John Lloyd, and his foreman, Dryden. Unfortunately neither was amenable; they were on bad terms with Sharp and Handasyde. Dryden flatly refused to have anything to do with it, and Lloyd declined to give any information until the executors had paid him £300 that they owed him. Donkin quickly wrote a report, realising that work needed to start 'this season'. The venture could prove expensive because to inspect the foundations properly a dam might have to be built, and the water pumped out – unless Lloyd would reveal how the mill had been built. With Donkin's intervention, the £300 debt was soon paid, and Lloyd cooperated willingly. He brought the original drawings to the site, and agreed (sheepishly, no doubt) that the front wall had been built resting on a piece of timber, supported by only a few wooden piles driven in afterwards and bolted to the plank. Similarly, the side walls were supported only by a 4½ inch thick plank laid on gravel. No wonder the tide mill was falling over.

Tide mills had been in existence at Greenwich since the eleventh century, to harness the power of the tidal movement on the Thames; they were not very common because of the expense of building and maintaining the structure.[24] The water from the rising tide was channelled into a reservoir and trapped there until the full height of the tide. When the tide turned, the water pouring out of the mill pond activated a water wheel and set the machinery turning. It worked pretty well; however, every time the water in the basin decreased, the machinery slowed down; there was also a tendency for sediment from the incoming water to build up in the basin, gradually reducing the depth of water and necessitating costly cleaning out.

One man thought he had a solution to the inadequacies of the traditional tide mill: at the end of December 1800, William Johnson wrote a column in *The Times* explaining his plan for a newly invented type of water mill.[25] His design theoretically doubled the efficiency of the milling process by using the energy of both the rising tide and the ebb tide. As the tide rose, the water would be channelled from the river into the mill pond or 'basin'. Passing through the wide channel, the rush of water activated a huge water wheel, which turned to set the mill machinery in motion. In addition, the wheel itself would be made to rise and fall, to keep in contact with the water. At ebb tide everything, including the wheel, operated in reverse as the water was released from the basin, thus producing power four times a day instead of twice. A smaller basin could be utilised and the whole mill would be more efficient. Johnson first built a model to demonstrate the principle, and then, in 1802, put his idea into action by constructing the Greenwich tide mill, with Lloyd as his builder.[26] Unfortunately he had overlooked the cumulative effect of the constant movement of the water and machinery, which shook the mill to pieces. The relentlessly rushing water caused wear and tear to the foundations, and washed away the gravel underneath; large quantities of mud were brought in, clogging the machinery. Johnson was evidently an inventor rather than an engineer or a designer. Under Johnson's orders, Lloyd was probably not asked for his opinion, and perhaps felt that it was not his place to criticise the deficiencies in the structure. In any case, Donkin was left to deal with the consequences of Johnson's mistakes.

Donkin and Lloyd worked amicably together on solutions; Donkin suggested that operating the wheel in only one direction (in the time-honoured way) with the water coming out of the basin, would reduce the strain on the building and the machinery. Lloyd thought that the 'breast work' or wall – over which the water runs out of the basin into the mill and over the wheel – could be raised to six feet above low water. Thus, the tide would have to rise six feet before any water went into the basin from the river, and the amount of mud that washed in would be reduced. The need for the second, small basin, which had held water to flush mud out at low tide, would be obviated, enabling the mill pond to be enlarged. After discussions with Lloyd, Donkin wrote a report – and was given the job; he was told to do whatever he thought necessary, and to employ the best tradesmen. He would have liked to work with John Lloyd, but Sharp and Handasyde objected because they had not been satisfied with his conduct. Donkin's second suggestion was to employ John Hall, which was readily agreed. Together the two friends drew up plans for Jones the bricklayer to take down and rebuild walls, and for piles to be driven deeply into the river bed to make firm supports for the tide mill. The wharfing would be renewed, and the basin reshaped. A week later, they had written permission from Mr Handasyde to go ahead, but not to spend too much money and to keep the executors informed of progress every eight to ten days, in writing. Donkin told Mr Sharp exactly what he planned to do: not just repairs but improvements to increase the power of the mill in the interests of the estate. Mr Sharp told Donkin that they left it entirely to him to do it as he would for himself, 'so as to render the mill as productive as possible hereafter'.

Work began in mid-August 1809. Brickies started taking down the front wall; Hall's men took out the old wooden wharves; Donkin and a surveyor measured the basin; Donkin procured an old piece of canvas to stop the rain beating in on the machinery. They got an estimate for digging out the basin and a valuation for the scrap iron that John Hall wanted to buy and take away. The tides started to impede progress and it was decided to drive in 12-foot piles to form a wall, in order to protect the labourers from the water. Hall acquired a barge to hold the piling engine in the river; permission had to be sought from the Commissioners of Sewers to change the drainage system round the mill. Donkin discovered, by taking out one of the old piles and poking down the hole with an iron rod, that there was firm gravel seventeen feet down, but the piles were not long enough to reach it: they had to be replaced with new, longer ones of fir rather than oak, for economy's sake. Donkin, ever mindful of efficiency, arranged for some of the fir to be made into planks to make it easier for the men to wheel barrows of soil up the slopes.

By November work at the tide mill was in full swing, though the tides and the large boulders in the earth hindered progress at times. At Donkin's instigation, Mr Cook was brought in as Clerk of Works to handle the accounts; he moved into the old mill house with John Hall's foreman and was given £10 in advance to buy a bed and other things, as well as a salary of two guineas a week. There was some pilfering: workmen were found to be taking wood chips and timber off the site and ordered not to. Excavation of the basin began and the good clay brought from the bottom was used to fill spaces between the mill walls and the piles.

It was in Bryan Donkin's nature to calculate weights and measures and to work out how long it took to carry out tasks – his notebooks were full of such reckonings. Donkin and Cook did time and motion studies, such as: 'Four men filled thirty-six barrows in eighteen minutes … .' He noted that a cubic yard of earth filled nine barrows and it required two men to wheel it every twenty yards, so that 'six men will fill and remove four cubic yards to the distance of twenty yards'. With a barrow of earth weighing about two hundredweight, it was no mean feat and the men worked hard. Cook proved to be an asset, but he claimed that two guineas a week was not enough to live on and he would have to leave: after a visit to Mr Sharp, who said 'do as well as you can with him', Donkin raised his salary to three guineas, with back pay.[27]

The work was time-consuming. A lot of loose, peaty earth was found under the foundations in the north corner and water had penetrated the soil. Clay was rammed in to stop the water. They were a good team. George Knight, the foreman, had developed an efficient way of driving the piles in – ram them half in, close together, and securely fix them side by side, then drive them in alternately without danger of their twisting out of place. George had averted the danger of a serious accident to the men working in the basin below the mill. He had found little fish stuck in the joints of the planking of the mill and realised that one of the main timbers had been badly put in, overlapping by only an inch and a half. It had given way, loosening the planks and allowing them to spring in. If it had broken completely, men would have lost their lives.

The Greenwich tide mill endeavour continued into 1812 with its attendant difficulties, though none were insurmountable. Mr Sharp, sitting in his office with candle and quill pen, complained that it was taking too long, but it was a complex job, and most of the delays were caused by high tides beyond anyone's control. Finally, two new sluice gates were constructed from oak and the water wheel repairs were finished. Doors in the sides of the mill were bricked up for strength and new doorways were made. Then Sharp went bankrupt.

Having been given carte blanche to carry out the renovations as he saw fit, it must have come as a surprise to Donkin when the money ran out. Gradually his unsatisfied claims for expenses from Sharp and Handasyde built up, and he was forced to tell them that if payment was not forthcoming, work could not proceed any further and the tide mill would be left in an insecure state. Money was needed to pay tradesmen's bills. Amazingly, Handasyde claimed that he had never had in his possession any money belonging to the estate! Donkin reminded him that his instructions had come from both the partners, and that Handasyde should consider the consequences of suspending operations at this critical juncture: Handasyde had better consult his solicitor.[28] For all their apparent caution and their insistence on receiving written reports on progress, the two executors had never been decisive and had clearly mishandled the finances. John Hall joined the fray with his bills to the estate, and summoned his solicitor, Mr Lee.

In the midst of the controversy, Donkin was called to inspect the West Ham and the East London Water Works, to examine the finances in a dispute between the water works managers and the suppliers of pumps and other machinery. With him went his fellow engineer Peter Keir, and Simpson from the Chelsea Water Works.[29]

The case of Hall v. Handasyde was heard on 29 April 1813, at the Guildhall, where Bryan Donkin gave evidence. Handasyde was proved liable for debt, as Sharp's co-executor. Five days later, Donkin was required to attend the Temple Coffee House to give evidence at the arbitration. That evening he had a celebratory dinner at the Cross Keys, with John Hall, Mr Lee and other friends, including Maudslay and Keir, his fellow engineers.

Perhaps Mrs Donkin thought Bryan needed some light relief after working six days a week for months and suggested a break; a couple of weeks after the case was settled, they had a long family weekend together. Mary's sister, Sarah, and her father, Peter Brames, went with Bryan to The Royal Academy exhibition at Somerset House on the Saturday. They climbed the spiral staircase to the main gallery. Rowlandson, the noted cartoonist of the time, had dubbed it the 'Stare Case' and depicted a cascade of ladies tumbling down the steps in disarray, revealing all their bare bottoms to the delighted audience below – apparently the gentlemen frequently lingered there to look up the ladies' skirts. In the Great Room, the paintings were crowded together on the walls. The annual exhibition had enormous popular appeal; Turner and Constable met for the first time at the Academy dinner that year.[30] Although they had great respect for each other's work, competition between the two of them was intense: it was said that some years later Turner upstaged Constable by titivating his paintings in situ at the last minute, while Constable went for impact, exhibiting his largest canvasses.[31] At a rival exhibition the same May, the British Institution in Pall Mall showed pictures by the late Sir Joshua Reynolds, who had founded the Royal Academy in the year of Bryan Donkin's birth. It happened that Jane Austen, on a quest for the perfect portraits of her Pride and Prejudice characters, visited both exhibitions the following month.[32]

The other diversion for that weekend was a visit to the Vauxhall Gardens – Donkin knew them by the name of 'Spring Gardens'. Here music, fireworks and jollity of all sorts took place.[33] All day and into the night the rich and famous mingled in the pleasure gardens with the more ordinary people of London, walking through the tree-lined avenues and enjoying the entertainments and refreshments that were presented in the pretty pavilions. The Donkins's entertainment for the day was a performance by the American calculating boy, the nine year old Zerah Colburn.[34] The child and his father had arrived in London the previous year and made their base in rooms at the Gardens, where Zerah, in his buttoned-up jacket and ruff collar, demonstrated his astonishing facility with arithmetic. His father had discovered that, even before he could read, Zerah could perform remarkable feats with numbers, and decided to exploit his son's talents by travelling to Europe. They were based in London for two years, except for six months in Scotland and Ireland. Among the notables who came to marvel at the boy's powers of calculating figures in his head were dukes, earls and bishops, as well as Sir Humphrey Davy, and Princess Charlotte, the daughter of the Prince Regent, who asked the boy to give the square of 4001 (answer: 16,008,001). Even Bryan Donkin might have needed a pencil and paper for that; on the other hand, his facility with algebra probably would have seen him through the problem. Zerah was taken to see William Wilberforce, the statesman, and was invited to dinner by Sir William Congreve. Later he went to school in Paris, where he met Dr Gall the phrenologist, who without any knowledge of his young visitor, examined his skull and immediately felt, at the sides of his eyebrows, lumps that indicated to him the faculty for computation. Colburn eventually returned to America, became a Methodist minister, married, and died at the age of thirty-four. While in London, he had been treated by Dr Carlisle: Zerah had been born with an extra finger on each hand and six toes on each foot – useful perhaps, but although he allowed Dr Carlisle to remove the fingers, he resisted the suggestion that his extra toes might inconvenience his dancing, and found them no trouble in later life.[35]

Mrs Mary Donkin did not accompany her husband on the outing to Spring Gardens. She was pregnant again and little Jane, her youngest, was only two. She had given birth to eight children, but unfortunately had lost two boys when they were very young. Her son Bryan was three, Sarah was five years old, William seven, John was approaching his eleventh birthday, and Mary Ann coming up to thirteen.

5
Strength to Strength

Although Donkin's main preoccupation was still with the development of the paper-making machine, he had interests outside his work and his family. A strong social conscience guided his life, and his ability to recognise the plight of the poor was one of his many strengths.

In Bermondsey a move was afoot to set up a school for poor boys, to provide education for youngsters between six and twelve years of age. At a meeting at the Bermondsey workhouse on 18 January 1812, nine men came together to discuss the foundation of a charity school; Bryan Donkin was one of them.[1] Following the tried and tested philosophy of Joseph Lancaster, whose methods in education were enthusiastically supported by the Royal family, the school would teach children through the medium of the Bible, but without enforcing any particular religion; in that way moral standards would be introduced without bias, and a healthy attitude towards other creeds and denominations would develop naturally while the children gained knowledge. About 2,000 children in the Bermondsey area were in desperate need of education. Such schools could accommodate up to 500 in one huge room, under the tight but reasonably humane discipline administered by one school master.

The actual teaching was done by several grades of monitors, who were drawn from the best of the older children.[2] The children benefitted from the opportunity to learn to read, starting in the 'sand class', where the youngest children learnt to form letters by drawing them in sand with their fingers, and were taught writing and arithmetic under a highly structured but effective regime. Samuel Bevington was in the chair at the meeting when Bryan Donkin and the other local business men agreed to approach likely supporters and collect subscriptions to finance the school. Bevington was the owner of a local leather-dressing factory; less than four years later, when interviewed by a House of Commons Committee as Treasurer to the Bermondsey and St. John's school, he spoke of the school as being run on the British and Foreign system (a development from the Lancasterian method).[3] Out of the 440 pupils that the school could hold, the average attendance had been 260 boys, but was increasing rapidly after a campaign to inform poor parents that their children were eligible to attend. Four boys under seven who, he said, had been in school for less than a year and a half, could 'read the Testament well enough for their parents to understand them, although they did not know their letters when they came in'. Many of these children, when they left school, would serve an apprenticeship at a local factory or workshop: Bryan Donkin would certainly have accepted boys from the school he supported, to give them further training and employment.

While the main work in Donkin's factory was the manufacturing of paper machines, smaller jobs cropped up from time to time and Donkin rarely turned down the chance to supplement his income with these quickly achieved commissions. He greatly pleased Mr Langdon, a renowned maker of black lead pencils, who had asked him to make rounded pieces of cedar to improve his product. So delighted was Langdon, that he asked Donkin to make a lathe and a set of tools so that he could round his pencils himself.[4] In May 1811 Mrs Guppy, wife of Samuel Guppy, a prominent Bristol merchant with interests in the copper trade, asked him to design a chain bridge; Donkin delivered the drawing himself to their London office.[5]

On the same day, Donkin was on an entirely different mission when he accompanied Marc Brunel to the veneer cutting works of Messrs Gabriel in Banner Street. Requests for help with patents frequently came Donkin's way; on this occasion he was asked by Brunel to arbitrate in a dispute between the Gabriel brothers and himself, over the use of his recently patented veneer cutting saw. Messrs Gabriel, who had been openly using circular saws for cutting wood veneers for six years, had been dismayed to find that Marc Brunel was thinking of taking them to court for breaching his patent. Their view, as small-time veneer-cutters, was that they were innocent of stealing any idea: they knew one person who had used saws like Brunel's for nine years. Gabriel had not kept the saw secret; the workmen and many others had seen it, but he would certainly not let everyone from the street see the saws. Gabriel was happy to talk to Brunel and come to an agreement if possible – because 'they were anxious to prevent too many from getting hold of it, or words to that effect' – if not, the Gabriels were ready to defend themselves in court. On a second visit several days later, both Donkin and Brunel talked to Mr Gabriel, who reiterated that he was prepared to prove that their saws had been in use before Brunel's patent; they had enough evidence to bring an action. The other Gabriel brother chimed in, adding that they would refer the matter to arbitration, if that would solve it; they were as anxious as Brunel that the difficulty should not be made public, and if a mutual agreement could be made, it would be understood by the public that they worked under Brunel's patent. There would be no problem with other people who had seen the saw at work; they were in different trades and would not be concerned. It seems that the difficulty was overcome without recourse to court action. Cordial arbitrations such as these were grist to Donkin's mill: it was important for him to remain on good terms with Marc Brunel and other influential friends who provided him with occasional pieces of work.

Soon after the negotiations with Gabriel and Brunel, on 18 May 1811, Donkin signed the mortgage deed for the purchase of the factory in Blue Anchor Road to Mr Matthew Stainton, in security for £2,000. He was now the owner of his expanding business. When he did his accounts at the end of June 1811 Donkin valued his assets at £7672 11s. 1½d.[6] His already established customers included several paper makers – Phipps, Buttanshaw, Martindale, Swann and other owners of paper-making machines. His steel pens were still selling, too. The mill and premises at Blue Anchor Road cost £21 a quarter to rent.

Donkin had also been working on another patent. With Joseph Taite (a 'gentleman', probably with money) and William Dixon, a practical millwright, Donkin was the perfect third partner for bringing the idea to fruition. It was 'a machine for finishing piece-goods [lengths of fabric] or other flexible articles of materials of the like description, by glazing, burnishing, graining or making impressions on the surface thereof' (Patent No.3455, 1811). The finished product may have been used as floor coverings, similar to the later linoleum.

With his growing reputation as a scientific engineer, Donkin was asked to set up an experiment for a grand plan that was to take years to achieve: the building of a tunnel across London's great river. The Thames Tunnel project would suffer numerous setbacks before coming to fruition, but Donkin played a decisive part in its progress. The notion of tunneling under the Thames was by no means new. In 1798, the civil engineer Ralph Dodd brought to the attention of the prosperous and influential burghers 'the want of a grand uninterrupted line of communication in the south-east part of the Kingdom, which could easily be obtained if the River Thames could be conveniently passed'.[7]

Britain's far flung colonies and expanding empire were providing an almost limitless source of raw materials to feed London's burgeoning factories, and a ready outlet for their finished products. Like Donkin's factory, many of these new workshops and businesses were thrown up in the newer districts to the south of the river where land was still cheap. However, London's new deep water docks, the conduit for most of this trade, were sited almost opposite on the north shore. They were within loud-hailer distance and separated by only a few hundred yards of river, but the passage of goods between the two banks involved a steady stream of horse-drawn traffic back and forth in a laborious journey up to the old London Bridge and down the other side. A fleet of swift ferries made hundreds of journeys each day carrying foot passengers and, of course, horses but the Thames was Britain's busiest and most dangerous highway, a vital artery for the country's trade, which could not be allowed to become further restricted by slow cargo barges or lighters crisscrossing the shipping lanes.

Ralph Dodd soon gathered support for a tunnel some sixteen feet in diameter and incorporating a roadway wide enough for horse traffic to pass, positioned further down river between Gravesend and Tilbury Fort. Tolls would be gathered from all forms of traffic using the tunnel, ensuring a handsome profit for its investors.[8] Unfortunately, the ill fated – and judged by some 'foolish' – Dodd did not obtain a full survey of the river bed but was under the impression that the chalk, on which most of London was built, extended under the full width of the Thames. Chalk would be easily excavated, but would be strong enough to support the weight of the river above. Had this been true his modest estimate of £15,995 might just have been sufficient to see the project through. A vertical shaft was begun and a steam engine erected to pump out the workings, but there was no chalk bed to be found. Even at 146 feet deep the earth was still soft and waterlogged. Without firm ground Dodd could not even begin his tunnel. The investors' money was spent and the workings abandoned but the publicity surrounding the venture ensured that more attempts would be made.

In 1805 the grandly titled Thames Archway Company was formed with the express intention of driving a tunnel under the Thames between Rotherhithe and Limehouse.[9] The Cornish engineer Robert Vazie (aptly nicknamed The Mole) was engaged to oversee the project but was considered not up to the task and was replaced in 1807 by a fellow Cornishman, the brilliant but headstrong Richard Trevithick, pioneer of the steam locomotive. Trevithick had been based in Rotherhithe for some time and was earning a decent living from royalties on his high pressure steam engines and also on his latest venture, a steam dredger on the Thames, but he saw the Thames Archway contract as easy money.[10] He would receive £1,000 for building a small pilot tunnel, a mere five feet high and three feet wide at its base, tapering to 2ft 6in. at its roof. £500 would be paid once he had passed the halfway mark and a further £500 on 'holing out' above the high water mark on the opposite bank. When completed this would act as a drainage and service channel for a much larger tunnel to be built above it.

Work started in late August 1807 and, using steam engines to supply fresh air to the miners and pump out the workings, Trevithick got off to a good start, reporting that they had driven twenty-two feet in the first week. By mid October they were advancing at almost twelve feet per day. Quicksands were encountered on several occasions and undulations in the river bed left them perilously close to inundation. At a distance of 930 feet under the river the almost inevitable happened.[11] Trevithick's men encountered a hole (or sump) above them in the bed of the Thames. Water rushed in, quickly flooding the workings and bringing with it all manner of filthy detritus including a piece of uncooked ship's beef. The hole was soon stopped with large quantities of clay dumped from above and, undeterred, the fearless

13 *Richard Trevithick (1771–1833).*

Cornish miners pushed forward at an average pace of more than six feet per day, close boarding the shaft to prevent further flooding as they went. On passing the low water mark, it looked as though they were literally home and dry, but once again disaster struck. The cause this time was not entirely due to the vagaries of Old Father Thames but more to the pride and obstinacy of one Richard Trevithick. The Archway Company surveyor reported that 'the tunnel had reached a length of more than 1,000 feet but was out of line by about a foot or so.'[12] On hearing this, the normally volatile Trevithick became incensed, seeing the statement as an insult to his engineering skills.

In a scheme of madness Trevithick bored a hole in the roof of the tunnel at low water and pushed up a series of jointed rods (rather like a chimney sweep's). The end of the rod was caught hold of by a man in a boat moored above and the position verified from the shore. He proved the surveyor to be wrong, but the delay in fitting the rods together allowed the water to increase the size of the hole to the point where it could no longer be plugged from below. Once again, water flooded in, rapidly undermining the river foreshore and exposing more quicksands beyond the mouth of the tunnel. Showing typical courage, Trevithick sent his men before him to make good their escape, but his great bulk hindered his own progress and by the time he reached the exit shaft the water was up to his neck. His limbs were skinned, he had lost both his shoes and his hat, and his shirt and breeches were torn. Miraculously no lives were lost. Undaunted, Trevithick plugged the gap and once more pumped out the tunnel. Within six days he was ready to continue the work, but the directors had lost faith in the red haired Cornishman and refused to believe he could overcome the problems with the quicksands and finish the tunnel. Trevithick received his first £500 but his contract was terminated. Through nothing but his own pigheaded pride he had snatched defeat from the jaws of victory.

The Archway Company then offered £500 for a new plan. Of the many schemes that were submitted, forty-nine were vetted by the arbiters Dr Charles Hutton, mathematician, and Mr William Jessop, civil engineer; of these, six proposals were found worthy of further scrutiny. The first and the cheapest was a design by Trevithick for a wooden tunnel sixteen feet in diameter, built in lengths of up to 200 feet. With the aid of a movable coffer dam (like a bottomless box), these pre-fabricated tubes would be lowered into a trench in the bed of the river. It was probably the most easily executed plan, but because it was put forward by Trevithick it was dismissed by the Archway Board.

Of the six, only one is known to have gained their sponsorship for further experiments.[13] It was proposed by Charles Wyatt, civil engineer, and John Isaac Hawkins, an eccentric but well rounded character, who besides being a self taught civil engineer was also credited with the invention of a portable piano and a multi-penned copying machine, and had a background in sugar refining. (His first thirty years were spent in America; in 1803, he presented to the Columbian Museum

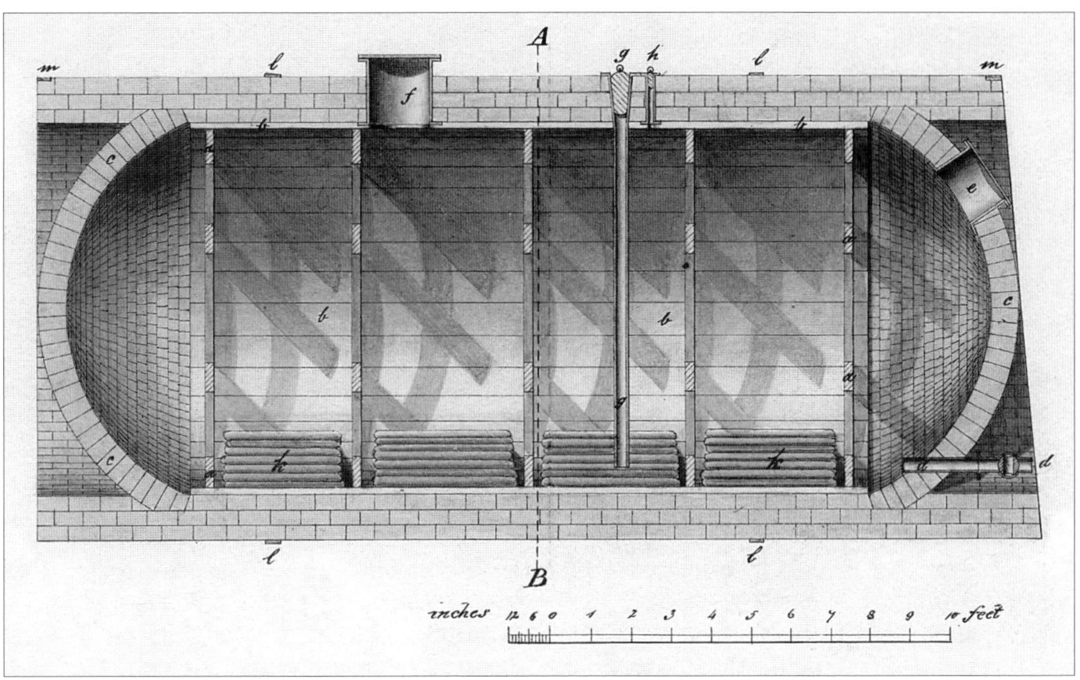

14 *Wyatt and Hawkins's cylinders for the Thames Archway Company,* 1811.

in Boston his newly-invented physiognotrace, a device for producing images of facial profiles.)[14] Their plan for the tunnel was indeed peculiar. They proposed to make a brick tunnel almost eleven feet in diameter with a wall thickness of 13½ inches.[15] Cylinders of brickwork some fifty feet in length and closed at each end, were to be built in a dry dock. When proved watertight they were to be floated into position above a trench already dredged in the river bed. Once the precise position had been established, sufficient water would be admitted to sink the cylinder to its exact location, where it would be weighted down by back filling the trench with the excavated mud and gravel.

Experiments with this new mode of tunnel building were started in October 1810 with the building of two half length brick cylinders each twenty-five feet long, which would be fitted together under the water. They were sealed at either end with a bulkhead containing a watertight cast iron door. When launched into the Thames they floated about two feet out of the water and were readily manoeuvred into position. A major reason for the trial was to demonstrate publicly the practicability and cheapness of the plan. For the vital final stages of the experiment, The Thames Archway Company needed the opinion of an independent, trusted and disinterested expert witness. Who better for Charles Wyatt to turn to than Bryan Donkin?

The procedure was complex, and involved lining up masts on the floating cylinders with poles on either shore. It took two attempts; but at high water on

25 May 1811 with the eyes of London watching, the second cylinder was sunk into position. At low water Donkin looked on and took his notes as Hawkins probed the joints between the bricks and concurred that the brickwork was tight shut at the top and the mismatch at the bottom was no more than an inch and a half. When pumped out and with the joints rammed with mud, the influx of water was less than eleven gallons a minute and would be easily stopped with the usual caulking techniques. But the trials were abandoned for want of cash to support the scheme and the plan was shelved, although it was acknowledged that it had been proved that the techniques tried out could well make it possible to build a tunnel under water in the future.[16]

With the openness of the London engineering fraternity and the publicity surrounding the sinking of the cylinders, there is little doubt that the Archway project would have been a significant topic of conversation when Marc Brunel and Donkin met over the Gabriel controversy the next day, and almost certainly influenced Brunel in his decision to include Bryan Donkin in his choice of engineers when forming the Board of the Thames Tunnel some twelve years later.

Donkin continued to manufacture items for Brunel, including (in 1813) a guillotine with two cutters, for cutting metal. Brunel sent his own beautifully executed drawings for Donkin to work from, annotated with precise instructions for him to carry out, with a note: 'Mr B wishes that cheapness may be attended to'.[17] At the time Marc Brunel, having established saw mills at Battersea and Woolwich, was working on a grand scheme for another at the Chatham dockyard, where he had devised an underground reservoir to enable logs to be floated from the dock to dry land, and sawn into planks and veneers by rows of up to three dozen mechanical saws, working together in a line.[18] At Leith in Scotland, Brunel built several saw mills powered by water;[19] for one of them, Donkin designed and constructed the water wheel.[20] A large bevel wheel and pinion that Donkin made in 1815 was probably for the same mill machinery.[21]

Henry Maudslay, too, consulted Donkin formally; on one occasion he wrote to ask the price of blocks that he needed for some of the driving gear in his factory. Donkin apologised for not being able to help, saying that he had no written record of what they had cost his firm, nor had they bored any out, 'at least none of any consequence'.[22] However, he had made six of different sizes recently and gave the cost 'without any allowance for common charges', of £31 1s. 3d. – quite precise enough to answer the question. The Master Millwrights had not fixed the price of such items since 1805, he wrote. Probably spurred by Maudslay's query, he said that he expected the matter to be considered 'next Tuesday', presumably at the next meeting of the Society of Master Millwrights (which Donkin had helped to form in 1805).

Donkin's visits to several paper mills in Buckinghamshire and Oxfordshire in four days in June 1811 were typical of his on-going work: he made adjustments to the paper machinery, measured up for new machines and sorted out problems with the flow of water to water wheels.[23] At Lunnon's mill at Woburn, he was asked to make drawings for new water wheels, spur gear and machinery, which later became a firm order. Joseph Wright, the proud owner of the new Marlow Mills (designed by Donkin), had ordered a paper machine, but decided that he would like a wider one: Donkin's reply was that he had no authority to alter the order without asking the Fourdriniers, but if it was agreed there would be no objection. As a trustworthy industrialist, Donkin was often invited to give evidence in disputes in his field of experience. One such case later in the year was that of Rutter v Barnard, concerning the regulation of water: John Rutter was the owner of a snuff mill at Ravensbury, near Mitcham in Surrey, where several mills competed for water on the river Wandle and arguments had arisen between the two owners as to the rights to usage.[24]

Keeping an eye on other people's engineering progress and evaluating new machinery together with other engineers was useful to Donkin, not only in broadening his practical knowledge, but also in cementing bonds with his fellow engineers by sharing opinions and learning each other's strengths. In July 1811 a group of eleven – mostly engineers, with a mathematical instrument maker and a miller – assembled to witness one of a series of experiments to determine how much wheat could be ground into flour by two pairs of French millstones of four feet in diameter, driven by Woolf's patent steam engine. Among the engineers were Bryan Donkin, Peter Keir, John Penn and Joshua Field.[25] The consensus was that in just over four hours, burning three bushels (252 lb.) of Newcastle coal, the pair of stones ground more than one and a half tonnes, a seemingly good result. Oddly, the measurements of coal and wheat were given using a mixture of capacity and weight; for example, the first pair of stones ground 'thirty-six bushels and forty-four pounds and a half', and the other 'twenty-four bushels and twenty-five pounds'. The difference in the result seemed to lie in the quality of the stones; had they both been in the same condition, seventy-three and a half bushels could have been achieved, so the experiment was deemed to have been worthwhile, particularly when analysed in hindsight in 1845, when the 'curious document' was quoted as still being of interest.[26] The *Star* newspaper report after the 1811 steam engine trials ended with a note: 'N.B. Engines on Mr Watt's principle may be altered so as to embrace Woolf's improvements, at a moderate expense'.

The demonstration of Woolf's engine was one of three in a series. Present at a previous experiment was the eccentric Richard Trevithick, who was well qualified to make such judgements, with years of engineering work under his belt, particularly in the field of steam engine development.[27] His steam locomotive was used as transport from the mines of the Merthyr Tydfil valley in 1804, some twenty five years before Stephenson's famous *Rocket* took to the rails. (When the much respected Trevithick ended his days in Dartford, carrying out experimental work for John Hall some twenty years later, he was borne to his grave by grieving mechanics from the factory; he was buried in a part of the graveyard reserved for the poor – John Hall probably paid for the funeral.)

1812 was as busy as ever. Donkin and John Gamble had had an entirely new idea and were embarking on experiments in preserving cooked food in canisters.[28] Difficulties with Didot were still rumbling on. Also, in the course of his work as a millwright, he had opened negotiations with Richard Mackenzie Bacon, for another unexpected venture.[29]

It came as a blow to Bryan Donkin when he heard of the death in April 1812 of James Davis, his old partner in the paper mould-making enterprise that had set him on the path to his own business.[30] What made it more distressing was that the old man seemed not to have made a will, and when Bryan went to Dartford to meet Davis's brother Jonathan, he was met with an overbearing attitude. Jonathan had decided to take arrangements into his own hands and was going through the old boy's chest of books and papers relating to the mould business, heedless of Donkin's interest in the articles of partnership and other important documents. Even worse, Donkin saw him pocketing bank notes and coins from a silver pot and challenged him to count the money, but the brother went off, saying he would do it at home. So Donkin took all the books and papers. The next day Donkin made sure that there was a solicitor and another man there with Mr Davis to make an inventory of the stock of the rest of the items. After attending the funeral, Donkin agreed to dispose of the mould business to Jonathan Davis and John Hall's son Edward, stipulating that they should pay him £300 for the good will and £25 for the tools and equipment, and should take the stock at valuation. The valuation took some days, but the agreement was settled without rancour. After a stressful fortnight, Bryan ordered himself a pair of patent boots and some shoes from a shop in Bow Street. By the following weekend Edward Hall, perhaps distrustful of Jonathan Davis, had persuaded him to relinquish his half share of the mould business in favour of two other interested parties, one of whom was John Marshall, who had worked with James Davis previously. These negotiations took place at Dartford, on Donkin's way to Canterbury in his own chaise; he was away from home for six days making a valuation of machinery. The round trip, in the first week of May1812, included a visit to a gunpowder mill that John Hall had built at Faversham, an overnight stay at the Mitre in Chatham, and lunch with Mrs Hall in Dartford on the way back. That same evening, he attended an important event at the Cross Keys; crucial to good relationships with his workforce in the future was his presence at this meeting of the Machinists Society. There, as a member of the committee, he took part in organising a petition to Mr Ryder, the Home Secretary, asking him to explain how journeymen were enabled to combine against their employers, a state of affairs that the Machinists planned to prevent.

Bryan Donkin's other work did not grind to a halt during this taxing time. In the same weeks of April and May, when he was trying to sort out James Davis's affairs, his mind was also on his experiments with tin cans – groundwork for his new venture – and finishing alterations to a cloth cutting machine for Messrs Norman of Cannon Street. As well, his fellow paper machine maker John Dickinson and his partner George Longman, who owned Apsley Mill (not far from Frogmore) were in dispute with the Grand Junction Canal Company. The canal ran alongside the river and caused problems for the water supply to the Longman and Dickinson mill. Donkin was called to give evidence. The arrangement was amicable; the two men, despite being rivals in the business of developing early paper-making machines, were on good terms.[31]

A few days later, Donkin heard the shocking account of the assassination of the Prime Minister, Spencer Perceval. A man named John Bellingham shot him through the heart in the lobby of the House of Commons: the assassin had a personal grudge, reckoning that the Government owed him money for his problems (of his own making) while working in Russia; but he gave himself up on the spot and was executed after a trial.[32]

Later in the month, Donkin was called to Westminster Hall on a Saturday, to give evidence at a case initiated by one of Joseph Bramah's men, who claimed that Bramah was employing a man who had not served a seven-year apprenticeship.[33] Industrial relations were not easy, but Donkin was always ready to lend support to his fellow engineering friends. The trial did not take place.

Business took Donkin away from London for a second time that May (1812), when he went to inspect the progress at two mills that he had set up with machines the year before, Howard and Lunnon's at Woburn, and Wright's in Marlow. Everything was going well: he made a few suggestions for controlling the water flow at Woburn (by driving in a row of wooden piles), and collected the balance of Mr Wright's account at Marlow. He then visited Frederick Spicer's Glory Mill and advised him on the size of the machine house for a new paper machine – it needed to be at least fifty feet long. He stayed the night at Mr Howard's. Two days later he visited Fawley Court Farm, owned by Mr Freeman, to see his steam engine. In the area, there was a small colony of Northumbrians. The farm next door was inhabited by Harbottles, relatives of a family well known to Bryan from his life in Sandoe. Freeman had engaged a Mr Forster from Northumberland (probably also related to the family of that name in Sandoe) as his steward and bailiff, who had invited Donkin to see the copper jacket that Donkin's man had put on the engine, which answered the purpose well and had made a great saving in coal. Forster was clearly efficient. He had adopted the system of agriculture, initiated in East Anglia by 'Turnip' Townsend and already adopted in Northumberland, whereby wheat, barley, clover and turnips were rotated in a four-year cycle, and he enforced the practice by means of leases among the tenants. The two men must have had plenty to talk about over dinner, and Donkin stayed the night at Forster's house before returning home. These visits were somehow fitted into his varied life; he was a good organiser.

In November, Donkin toured Buckinghamshire again, taking with him his nephew John (his brother John's son, who was a millwright). Visiting Fawley Court Farm again, his account was settled and he advised that a broken shaft

15 *William Herschel's 40-foot telescope, built* 1786.

should be sent to London for repair. He combined his mission with another visit to Howard and Lunnon's mill: the new water wheel was working well. He also examined the faulty engine spindles at the mill, where previously he had made several recommendations for strengthening the foundations. The two Donkins went on to Chesham where Bryan advised 'old Mr Pegg' on buying a paper machine for wove paper, rather than laid, before proceeding to Amersham for the night. Next morning, Donkin visited the paper mill belonging to Mr Pegg's son in law Mr Allnutt, at Chesham and found that it was under-performing badly: the water supply needed to be diverted, and a new, smaller paper-making machine installed in a different place. They stayed the night with Mr Allnutt; Donkin's easy relationships with his clients often earned him bed and breakfast. On their travels back, John and his uncle called at Slough, where the venerable astronomer William Herschel lived, to see his forty-foot telescope.[34] Built by Herschel in the garden of his observatory in 1786 with a grant from the King, it was the biggest telescope in the world.[35] On the Saturday they returned home, and Donkin had an informal Sunday meeting where he discussed the possibility of making the River Cam navigable. Then he returned to work on the canning business, cooking meat and negotiating with solicitors about the finances. It was a typically busy and varied fortnight for Bryan Donkin.

6
Honourable Mention

Keeping food fresh, whether at home in a mansion or a small town house was a problem in the early nineteenth century. Many houses had cold, damp cellars or pantries with stone slabs as a defence against hot weather, but they could not ward off attacks by rats, mice, silverfish, or ants. Unwrapped, unprotected meat was vulnerable to infection from nasty blow-flies that laid their eggs in it – and there were few cures for diseases spread by a lack of hygiene. Certain ways of storing food for future consumption were practised - drying it in the sun or using artificial heat, salting or pickling it, or preserving it in butter, sugar or ice - but all these methods had disadvantages.[1]

Home pickling was popular, though. Bryan Donkin recorded a recipe for preserving cucumbers, a long process involving covering them with salt water, letting them stand, heating them up, and changing the water several times; then heating sugar and ginger to make a syrup, putting the cucumbers in when cool, and boiling the whole concoction every two or three days for three weeks.[2] Pickled onions were easier: 'Take the onions as they come from the garden in their coats' and boil them up in cold salted water. 'Take off two or three coats', and put them in a jar with a mixture of vinegar and spice that had boiled and cooled; tie them down. Donkin added: 'You must not boil any of them in tin', an interesting observation in the light of subsequent events. In the Donkin household, Bryan found and recorded the recipes and probably enjoyed the science of making the gooseberry wine, the currant wine and the preserved foods himself.

As naval exploration of the world increased, more food was on the move; provisions for sailors in those precarious voyages had to be carried on the boats. Much of the meat was salted, but live animals were sometimes transported and slaughtered when needed, a system fraught with difficulties, as space had to be provided for the animals and their fodder, and there was always the risk of disease and injury to the poor creatures. Salted and dried foods were unpalatable and unhealthy for the sailors, and illness on board spelt misery and loss of manpower. There must be a better way!

In France, during the last decade of the eighteenth century, Nicolas Appert turned his mind to a solution. Born the son of an innkeeper in the north of France in 1749, he grew up learning the trade, brewing beer, pickling food, and bottling Champagne wines.[3] His onion soup was praised by Stanislaw, the King of Poland,

16 *Nicolas Appert (1749–1841).*

who sampled it on his way through Appert's home village of Châlons-en-Champagne, on a journey to Versailles. Later, he gained a wide range of skills in the art of preserving provisions by working 'in the pantries, the breweries, storehouses and cellars of Champagne, as well as in shops, manufactories and warehouses of confectioners, distillers and grocers'. At the age of twenty three, he took up the post of assistant chef at the court of Christian IV at the palace at Zweibrűcken in Germany and, when Christian died, he moved with the family to Forbach, back in France.

1784 found Nicolas Appert in Paris as the proprietor of a confectionery shop and a year later, at the age of thirty five, he married. France was experiencing a time of economic difficulty, revolt and civil disorder at this time; Louis XVI was King, and protests at the harsh regime and the unfair privileges given to the nobility caused rebellion in Grenoble and uprisings in Brittany, with demands that local parliaments should be restored and the monarchy overthrown. In May 1789 a National Assembly was formed by ordinary people. Appert spent the night before his fourth wedding anniversary patrolling the streets of his local area of Paris; as a signed-up member of the local militia, he had become an active member and supporter of the Lombard Assembly, carrying out guard duties. Next day, the Parisian mob stormed the Bastille prison, the symbol of the repressive power of the monarchy, where they believed they would find arms and ammunition. Their act signalled the beginning of the French Revolution. Peasants in the countryside joined the revolution, a new Declaration of Rights ('liberté, fraternité, égalité ...') was put forward, and the Royal family was forced by the people to leave Versailles and live under house arrest in the run-down Tuileries Palace. In 1791, the king tried to flee the country, but he was captured and forced to agree to a new constitution. The people were warned that insurrection would be punished severely. Somehow, Appert managed to keep his trade going throughout the fear and anger in the capital. The following year, National Guards arrived from Marseilles, singing 'Alons enfants ...' and ready to overthrow the king; more patriots arrived to join the movement against Louis. Eventually the king was tried and executed: Nicolas Appert was present at the event. The nation descended into chaos.

It was not a happy time to be living in Paris. Daily executions by guillotine of thousands of unfortunates became an entertainment for the crowds in Paris; the Reign of Terror lasted for a year. During this time Appert, in spite of being a staunch patriot, was accused of being an enemy of the state; his house was searched, and although no evidence of wrong-doing was found, he was nevertheless imprisoned for four months. The Terror ended with the beheading of the hard-line left-wing politician Robespierre at the end of June 1794. Then, like many other political prisoners, Appert was released from prison and was able to return to his relatively normal life as a merchant.

Throughout these turbulent times, Nicolas Appert had experimented with the preservation of meat and other foodstuffs. Since 1790 (when Bryan Donkin was working at Knole) Appert's knowledge had grown. He knew that fruit and vegetables could be dried, and meat could be smoked and fish salted, and appreciated that adding the necessary amount of sugar was costly, and that desiccation changed the flavour.[4] At his new home at Ivry, just south of Paris (where he quickly became absorbed into local politics), he bought bottles for his preserving process. Through experiments with meat and other foodstuffs, Appert worked out that to prevent food from decomposing, heat needed to be applied and air excluded. By putting food in glass jars, sealing it carefully with a cork, and boiling it in water for the right length of time, he had considerable success in preserving food and milk products. By the end of the 1790s, his breakthrough had happened and he was able to sell his bottled food both locally and to more distant markets. On the other side of the Channel at this time, Bryan Donkin was about to begin his experimental work on the French paper machine and in 1802 was first employed by the Fourdriniers to continue to develop it. That November, Appert bought an estate with two houses in Massy, to set up a home for his wife and five children, and a factory. He cultivated the surrounding land, growing vegetables to bottle in the factory, which was well equipped for producing preserved milk, cream and whey, broth and gravy, as well as other foodstuffs, such as meat, poultry, fish and fruit. He ensured that the glass bottles were of an appropriate size and fully sealed, using iron wire to fasten down the good quality corks. When he cooked them in the water-bath, he watched until the water boiled, turned off the heat and drew off the water after fifteen minutes.

Meanwhile, France was in the midst of the Napoleonic Wars, a series of conflicts with Great Britain and several other European nations, which lasted from 1799 until 1815. The English side was having some success with a new weapon of war, William Congreve's military rocket, introduced in 1805. It rapidly propelled its explosive head for up to two miles.[5] About three hundred rockets, fired from eighteen specially-designed ships at the battle of Boulogne, devastated the French fleet in 1806, and a year later Congreve's weapons caused huge fires at Copenhagen. Unfortunately they had a tendency to behave erratically, and could change direction like a squib, sometimes causing more mayhem in the British ranks than to the enemy.

Appert tried to interest the French Navy in his preserved foods, but without success, and in the winter of 1806 toured France to visit his contacts and advertise his wares. But times were still hard: in February, Nicolas Appert filed for bankruptcy and was forced to rent out part of his property and sell some of his equipment. Nevertheless, the great Exposition de l'Industrie Française, held in Paris that autumn, provided Appert with an opportunity to exhibit thirty-two bottles of his various foods and gave him much-needed publicity, although alas, little improvement in trade. Help came from a celebrated gourmet and food critic, Grimod de la Reynière, who became a keen champion of Appert's ideas over the next few years, taking him out of the doldrums towards commercial success. Meanwhile, the French Navy had turned to Appert's products for their long voyages and he received several letters of praise from the naval commanders for the freshness and quality of his bottled preserves. In January 1809 Nicolas Appert boldly presented samples of his food to a special committee of La Société d'Encouragement pour l'Industrie Nationale, who found the preserved stew, green vegetables, fruits and milk products to be excellent in every respect, even though the food had been preserved for up to fifteen months. The upshot was that Appert was asked to write a book on the art of preserving food substances. Happy to share his knowledge and make public the details of his invention, Appert complied, choosing not to patent the process, but instead to take the nobler option and serve the wider community. Government Commissioners travelled to the factory at Massy to see it for themselves and, in exchange for a reward of 12,000 francs from the French Government, Nicolas Appert presented them with 200 copies of the book, entitled *L'Art de Conserver, pendant Plusieurs Annés, Substances Animales et Végétales'*. The book was published in France and translated into English: Appert's secrets of 'Appertising' were out.[6]

Events moved quickly. It seems that a Frenchman by the name of Philippe de Girard brought Appert's ideas to England.[7] He too was an inventor, and an unfortunate one – his new ideas for a flax-spinning machine were stolen in 1810 while he was in a debtors' prison and later successfully patented in England under a British name.[8] Girard claimed the invention of the food preservation process.[9] He was a friend of Peter Durand, a London broker, and persuaded him to patent Appert's invention in England, which he did in that same year; it was granted in 1811. Sir Humphrey Davy, himself a great and wide-ranging scientist, gave Appert's method praise and publicity in England in a lecture at the Royal Institution.[10] Durand openly declared that the idea had been communicated to him by 'a person residing abroad'.[11] Previously, in 1807, the Society of Arts had awarded a premium of five guineas to one Thomas Saddington, who had presented to the Society his method of bottling fruit without sugar, using a process of heating and sealing glass bottles very like Appert's.[12] The question of the validity of Durand's patent had arisen: Saddington had travelled to France and may have picked up his ideas from Appert; it was thought that the patent was not for a new idea. Oddly enough, Augustus de Heine, who also lived in London, was a few months ahead of Durand with *his* very similar patent – both were for a method of preserving 'animal food, vegetable food and other perishable articles a long time from perishing or becoming useless'.[13]

Appert had used only glass jars, with wired-in corks, sealed with a mixture of cheese and powdered limestone, but they were difficult to seal quickly, and ran the risk of breakage during the process. Durand's patent specified that vessels of practically any material could be used, including 'tin', meaning tin-coated iron sheet. Appert himself had toyed with the idea of making canisters from tin, but recognised that French tin was not of a sufficiently high quality for the purpose. In his own experiments, Durand had substituted tin for glass, with great success. He had opened some of the finished preserves for Sir Joseph Banks, one of the greatest scientists of the day, and the food had been perfect. Durand had shown it to gentlemen of the Royal Society and the Royal Institution, who found that two tin 'cases' that had spent four months at sea were still in good condition.[14] Whether Durand did not have the resources to go into production himself, or whether he lost interest is not known, but he sold his patent almost as soon as it was granted, finding a willing buyer in John Hall, who paid £1,000. Hall quickly decided to enlist the help of Bryan Donkin.

Donkin, fascinated as always with new technology and committed to perfection, recognised another challenge; encouraged by Hall and John Gamble, he spent many hours experimenting in a spare room in the factory to find the ultimate solution to the preservation of food.[15] Sometimes working with Gamble, he tried out a variety of foodstuffs, cooking them in different containers, then sealing them up, leaving them for a time, and tasting and examining the results. In April 1812 they opened a tin 'bottle' of milk ten days old and found it perfectly good and almost the right colour; a glass bottle of milk that had not been previously boiled tasted sweet but was more highly coloured. Milk in two stone bottles was good, but in a third, it curdled when put into tea. Cream tasted peculiar and easily turned to butter. The next day, Donkin made soup, and left it, partly covered, in the boiler house overnight, but in the morning it was sour, and unfit for preserving. More was made and quickly cooled outside, and after being left in the counting-house until the next day, when the soup had turned into a perfect jelly that had to be warmed so that it could be poured into the preserving bottles. Mr Gamble procured a patent brewing machine to make the soup in.

The method of preserving beef was to fill the container, whether glass, stone or tin, put the lid on loosely, and heat it in a steaming apparatus for an hour and a half, by which time the meat would be half cooked. It was then cooled, and the lid, with a tiny hole in it, was sealed on. After another two and a half hours in the steamer, the hole was sealed quickly with 'cement' to stop air entering while the meat cooled, the container was removed from the steamer, and more cement applied to seal the lid securely. (Donkin collected various recipes for cement used for different purposes e.g. 'iron cement'.)[16] The metal cans proved to be the best containers, and it was using these that brought the process to perfection. In fact, the canisters were not made of tin, but of iron, coated on both sides with a thin layer of tin to prevent rusting and to act as an inert barrier to protect the food inside. Each can was hand-made by bending a sheet of iron into a cylinder and folding the ends together, soldering it to form a good seal, applying circular pieces to the top and base in a similar way. Donkin had his own recipe for tinning iron:

> *To Tin Iron*
> Throw your work into Spirit of Vitriol, dilute with 8 times its quantity of water, and scower [sic] it clean with sand wet with it; when clean wet it well with solution of Salamoniac in water, then throw it into powdered resin and dip it into your Tin.

(Whereas modern usage has adopted the words 'tin' or 'can' for the container, it was known as a 'case' or 'canister' in Donkin's day.) When filled and cooked, the can had concave ends, caused by the contraction of the contents as they cooled, indicating that the can was completely sealed. A typical can containing four pounds of meat was 195 mm tall and 170 mm in diameter (approx 7⅝ x 6¾ in.).

By September 1812, Donkin, Hall and Gamble were confident that their business would be a success. Hall had acquired and renovated a house in Finch Lane and they agreed to set up an office there, where Hall's gunpowder (part of his Dartford business) and the canned provisions could be sold; they appointed a clerk at £200 per annum to live in the house and take care of both concerns. Plans were also in hand to build another building at Bermondsey, for preparing the provisions for sale. Then John Hall suddenly decided to opt out for financial reasons; in spite of owning a long-established and respected business, he felt he could not afford to put more money into developing the new partnership, and wanted to relinquish his share and reclaim the amount of money he had paid for the patent. Within days, Bryan Donkin persuaded him to stay in the firm, with a slightly smaller share – he gave John Hall some preserved beef to try, and it tasted so good that Hall's opinion was swayed. A Mr Brandon was appointed as an agent, to earn a

17 *One of Donkin & Gamble's tin cans.*

four per cent commission on the first £22,000 gained from sales and only slightly less after that.

The enterprise flourished. In the late spring of 1813, the names of the partners – Donkin, Hall and Gamble – were engraved on a new trade card, and they decided to deposit stocks of the preserved food in the major sea ports in the south, and to appoint agents to sell it to outbound ships. Mr Brandon, agent and publicity officer, was instructed to advertise the provisions in the newspapers. In spite of having other things to do (attending arbitration meetings, visiting mills, making ironwork for Brunel, and ferrying Mrs Donkin around) Donkin took an active part in publicising the products that summer, travelling to the ports carrying samples of the meat. John Hall explored the possibilities at Dover, and at Gravesend, Messrs A. and T. Payne, after trying the meat and finding it excellent, agreed to be agents. At the port of Deal it turned out that the outward bound ships rarely took in stores, so Donkin, with Hall, gave up the idea of appointing an agent there. At Portsmouth, milk, soup and meat were tasted with approval by officers and gentlemen – and another agent, Mr Hammond, was appointed, agreeing on a 10 per cent commission. (Later, an agent in Liverpool, William Fosbery, was appointed to deal with shipment from that port too.) With Gamble and Brandon, Donkin opened two cases of meat at the Old London Tavern for the benefit of directors of the East India Company, who expressed themselves highly pleased with it and promised to recommend the products.

Commercially, they were on a winning streak. Sales to seafarers took off, as explorers and traders sailed the oceans. The price of the good quality boned meat, at 2s. 3d. a pound, compared very favourably with the cost of keeping livestock on board ship, which Donkin calculated to be up to twice as much, or more for a long voyage. One of the first expeditions to benefit from the canned food was led by Rear-Admiral Viscount Torrington, who sailed in 1813 in the *Warrior* to the West Indies, taking with him a considerable quantity of preserved meat.[17] Two cases of veal opened eight years later were as fresh as when they had been canned: 'Indeed it had a preference to many dishes served up with it at my table', wrote Torrington. A similar accolade was accorded to Donkin, Hall and Gamble when meat canned in 1814 was opened by Sir Gilbert Blane, Physician to the King, in 1822 and found to be 'not only free from any sort of decay, but possessed of the perfect flavour of the soundest and richest provision in its most recent state'.

Donkin, Hall and Gamble announced improvements to the process of canning in 1813.[18] Because, in the very early days, they had had no means of testing for defective canisters, the contents of a few – a very few – had turned out to be bad. Donkin had received very favourable reports from captains of ships of the East India Company who sailed with provisions, but occasionally noting that one or two of the tins had turned out to be defective. In May 1813, the new building was completed, with a special 'proving room' that put paid to the previous difficulties. The sealed and finished canisters were kept in the testing room at a temperature between 90 and 110 degrees Fahrenheit, simulating the highest temperatures likely to be encountered on tropical explorations. If the seal were to be breached in any way, the contents would swell the cans, so that any defective ones would be easily detected. Since building the proving room, there had been little or no trouble, and congratulatory reports had come from the Admiralty, the Commissioners for Victualling the Navy, the Directors of the East India Company and many high-ranking officers, as well as eminent medical and scientific gentlemen, stating that the newly 'proved' provisions, shipped after May 1813, were perfectly fresh and in every other respect excellent. In the Prospectus advertising the proving process, Donkin, Hall and Gamble named thirty or more rear admirals and captains who had been delighted with the preserved stores that had travelled with them to the West Indies, India, Brazil, the Cape of Good Hope and beyond. The meat was described as 'in the most perfect state of preservation' and 'delicious'; the vegetables 'retained all their original flavour, colour and freshness'; the milk was 'very sweet and good'; and the 'soup and bouilli was capital, far beyond my expectations'. Everyone was full of praise.

Word spread. On 29 June 1813, Donkin and Gamble had the great honour to be invited to present some of their preserved meat to the Duke of Kent, brother of the Prince Regent, at Kensington Palace; Prince Edward tasted them and was greatly impressed by the discovery. He asked for a sample of every kind of food that the partners produced. Two days later, a letter arrived from Kensington Palace, asking for written details of the products. The beef had been served to the Queen, the Prince Regent and several other distinguished people who had dined with the Duke of York (another son of George III); it had been highly praised. His Majesty and many others had expressed the wish to have 'an opportunity of further proving the merits of the thing for general adoption'.[19] Donkin, Hall and Gamble were recognised by the highest authority.

Nicolas Appert, anxious for recognition as the inventor of the process, but with no hard feelings towards Donkin, arrived in England in June 1814, bearing samples of his food.[20] A committee of six eminent scientists, including Sir Joseph Banks and William Hyde Wollaston, welcomed him and tasted the foodstuffs, writing afterwards that the milk was perfectly smooth and not sour, but with a slightly different flavour from fresh milk; the other food was perfectly preserved and had not lost any taste. While in London, Appert also visited the Donkin factory, and realised the superiority of tin cans, resolving to set up his own means of manufacturing the tin. This he did, but not until fourteen years later.[21] (In spite of many setbacks, Appert single-mindedly pursued his method into old age, selling his produce to the French Navy, achieving success in canning his preserved food, and from another invention, a steam pressure cooker or 'autoclave'. Unfortunately, in spite of winning many prizes and accolades, Appert remained a poor man and was buried in a pauper's grave.)[22]

Praise for Donkin and Gamble knew no bounds. In 1815, *The Times* announced that a canister of boiled beef had been opened at Lloyd's Coffee House in the presence of 'a numerous body' of captains, ship owners and other interested parties, and had been found to be perfectly preserved, with a good taste, although it had been in the can for twenty-one months.[23] The renowned scientist, Sir Joseph Banks, also stated that he had eaten beef that had been kept for two and a half years, and it was in a perfect state of preservation.[24] He said that it was 'one of the most important discoveries of the age we live in' and asked for some concentrated consommé to be sent for his own use, as 'I consider it better soup than I generally meet with either at home or abroad'. Such acclaim put the undoubted seal of approval on the tin can, coming as it did from Banks, the explorer and naturalist who had circumnavigated the globe with Captain Cook in the year of Donkin's birth, and who had been the President of the Royal Society since 1778.

Otto von Kotzebue, a Russian, set out to explore the South Seas in 1815, having equipped his boat *Rurick* in England with Donkin's cans of meat and vegetables.[25] Nearing the Tropic of Cancer on 29 May 1816, he opened some mutton and found it 'so delicious that an epicure might have feasted upon it'. His Russian stock of dried meat and 'sour crout' [sic] was mouldy and spoilt. Kruzenstern, who wrote the introduction to Kotzebue's book of his experiences, considered the discovery of the preserving method of great importance to navigators: the meat was better than fresh meat because the thick gravy in the tin boxes penetrated the meat. It was highly recommended for long voyages; no fodder was needed to keep animals on board (which in itself was a hazard – the *Queen Charlotte* had been gutted in 1805 when hay caught fire); the cans required little space; the sailors were protected from scurvy; the lives of the sick could be saved by the soup, when medicine failed. The editor of the *Literary Gazette*, where Kotzebue's journal was published, was interested enough in the report to write to Donkin, who called at the *Gazette*'s office with an extract of Donkin, Hall & Gamble's order book for 12 September 1815, showing that Captain Kotzebue had paid £75 17s 0d for sixty-nine canisters of boiled beef, thirty-three of boiled mutton, twenty-eight of boiled veal, including four with vegetables. Kotzebue also mentioned that Donkin's meat was supplied by the Admiralty to hospitals in the West Indies, and that a large supply was also sent to Admiral Cochrane's fleet on the coast of America.

Captain Basil Hall, who had already explored Chile, Peru and Mexico, set off to the East in 1816 in the sloop *Lyra*, taking with him a great number of cases of preserved food, worth £88. In a testimonial to Donkin and Gamble three years later, he commended the meat, soup and milk that he carried with him to China and the East Indies: all were excellent, and not one of the tin cases had suffered from the vicissitudes of varied temperatures.[26] The food could be eaten hot or cold and it was far better than taking accident-prone live animals on board. On one of his voyages he discovered a new talent in his steward, Henry Capewell.[27] At sea in stormy weather, the stock of crockery soon became depleted and the sailors were hard put to find anything to drink their cocoa from, or a bowl for their food. The resourceful Capewell, known for his kindness and ingenuity, neatly stacked his storage shelves with the empty tin cases left from Donkin's preserved provisions and, with the help of the ship's armourer, transformed them into useful, unbreakable bowls for the men's food and drink, much to his Captain's amazement.

Mr Brandon, the London agent, did his job well, and often advertised the partners' products in *The Times*, sometimes with testimonials from satisfied customers. New developments were announced: the gravy soup was offered in a highly concentrated form, so that a quarter of a pint could be watered down to make a quart of strong soup. More water could be added to make a thin bouillon soup suitable for invalids, giving nourishment in a palatable form. Donkin, Hall and Gamble even sold, from 1818, an invention by Mr A.S.Burkitt – the first home brew – a preparation of concentrated malt and hops.[28] A barrel-load would make twenty barrels of ale or porter when yeast and water was added. In the 1820s, canned meat cost between 1s. 3d. and 3s. a pound; milk was 15s. for a dozen pints and cans of soup cost 30s–60s for a dozen.[29]

England was then at peace with France; the ships' captains and their craft were free from wartime duties. Attention returned in earnest to the discovery of new territory, and in particular to exploring the Arctic regions. For three centuries, Europeans had searched for a seaway through the frozen wastes between Greenland and the north of Canada. The North West Passage would link the Atlantic and Pacific Oceans, providing a faster trade route to the lands of eastern Asia and Australasia. So important was the quest for the North West Passage that, following an Act of Parliament in 1775, the Government offered a prize of £20,000 to the first person to discover a way through.[30] The Admiralty sent the veteran Captain Cook on the search, without success, and a subsequent voyage by Captain Vancouver also failed to find a route through the ice, although the regions charted by both expeditions added to the knowledge of that desolate area. As a result of the explorers' testimonies, the firm – by then Donkin and Gamble – gained a contract from the Navy in 1818, and held the monopoly for many years.

So it was that in April 1818, John Ross set forth in the *Isabella* with Lieutenant William Parry commanding the ship *Alexander*, laden with Donkin and Gamble's preserved food. Unfortunately, although they reached the ice-bound regions, the expedition turned back amid some controversy, because Ross imagined that he saw mountains blocking the way.[31] A year later, William Parry, together with ninety-four sailors in two ships and hundreds of tins of canned meat and vegetables, sailed to the Arctic again and spent a long winter ice-bound before returning, having discovered Lancaster Sound and several new islands, but not the North West Passage.[32] Being stuck in the ice for so long, the men appreciated the home comforts of real meat and vegetables as an alternative to the rock-hard biscuits and

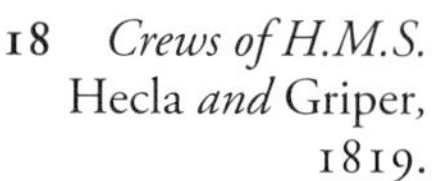

18 *Crews of H.M.S.* Hecla *and* Griper, 1819.

tough salted beef that had formerly been the staple fare of sailors. Parry believed, too, that the healthier diet prevented scurvy, and allowed much longer voyages than before.[33] After his second journey to the Arctic, commanding the amusingly-named ships *Fury*, *Hecla* and *Griper*, William Parry found it impossible to speak too highly of the preserved meats prepared by Messrs Donkin and Gamble.[34] Not a man to give up the search for the North West route through the Arctic, Parry tried again in 1824, but was forced to abandon the *Fury* in the ice, and returned in the *Hecla*, leaving canisters of untouched food frozen in the Arctic wasteland. Five years later John Ross, following the same track, came across the abandoned *Fury* and found the stores left behind by her captain.[35] The canisters were piled up in two heaps, and had survived wind and weather for four years without suffering 'in the slightest degree'. The secure joints had prevented the bears from smelling the contents; the cans were not frozen, and the food tasted fresh. Ross and his crew were themselves stranded in the icy wastes for four years and celebrated the first Christmas and New Year with preserved meat pie and extra rations of grog. Back home in October 1833, they persuaded their contemporaries of the value and possibilities of British exploration into the Arctic regions, and stressed the great advantages of preserved food in helping to achieve the goal of discovering the way through the icy north to link the Atlantic and the Pacific Oceans.

An accolade of a more permanent nature was awarded by Captain Robert Fitzroy, commander of the *Beagle* on her voyage round the southern shores of South America in the 1820s.[36] After adventures on land and sea, encountering savages and terrible weather, the crew weighed anchor in a sheltered channel one night in May 1829 on the coast of Chile 'at a place we named Donkin Cove, as a mark of respect to the preserver of meat, to whom we had been so often thankful'. They had eked out the meat by mixing a little with wild fowl and wild celery, and had found the preserved meat useful when away from the ship on boat service; being already cooked, it was 'fit for dinner without the aid of fire'.

In ordinary life, too, the process was appreciated. The writer of the epic satirical poem *The Age of Intellect* applauded

> … another important invention
> As justly deserves the most hon'rable mention.
> 'Tis Donkin's I mean, by whose art we are able
> To keep a supply of fresh meat on the table:
> His method is chemical, - lately found out;
> It prevents all the maggots from breeding, no doubt!
> For a turkey or goose he would cook at Guildhall,
> And convey it thence, perfectly sweet, to Bengal!

A note was added:

> The cook-maid may now put the meat in her cupboard without dreading the blow-fly; - and the master of the house may keep his larder constantly stored, even in the warmest weather, without feeling any apprehension that it will cause the least unpleasant sensation to the olfactory nerves.[37]

Thus, the canning business was firmly established and would continue, thanks to Bryan Donkin's inventiveness, drive and high principles. However, with other pressing work to deal with, he opted out of the partnership in November 1821 (amicably, as had John Hall previously) allowing Gamble to take over the patent and continue to run the successful business under the name Gamble & Co., setting up his food-processing factory in Cork. He had the habit of keeping old canisters of food and proudly opening them to prove that the contents were still good. [38] Among his collection in the 1860s were some from Parry's 1824 expedition, which his fellow explorer John Ross had found to be tasty in 1833, and James Ross had enjoyed in 1849. By then the repertoire of foodstuffs had increased to include pheasants, partridges, calipash and calipee (delicacies from under the shells of tortoises), ham, salmon and several other sorts of fish, custard, mushrooms and many types of vegetables and soups.

But because Bryan Donkin's name, together with Gamble's, was the byword for good tinned food, his reputation was in jeopardy when decades later, the canning process was hijacked by a good-for-nothing imposter, and ignorant reporters associated Donkin with the dire consequences.

The explorer John Franklin had also undertaken long voyages in the quest for the North West Passage. For his third expedition in 1845 his ships *Erebus* and *Terror* were well equipped with every comfort and luxury for the men, including a library, an organ for entertainment, writing equipment, tobacco and liquor.[39] The Admiralty, in its wisdom, had thrown open the contract for canned provisions to tender the year before and John Gamble had lost it to a candle maker by the name of Stephan Goldner, who put in a bid with much lower costs. So the tinned food for Franklin's voyage was provided not by Gamble but by Goldner.

Candles in the nineteenth century were made from tallow, which is produced by rendering beef or mutton fat. The fat is procured by simply cutting it from fresh meat. Thus lean meat was a bi-product of candle-making.[40] As a candle maker, Goldner saw how to turn this to his advantage, capitalising by putting the meat into sealed containers and cooking it for human consumption, rather than throwing it away. Hungarian by birth, he owned an establishment in Houndsditch, London, and another factory on the Danube at Galatz in Eastern Romania. Goldner patented a process similar to Donkin's for preserving meat, but – to say the least – failed to produce goods of the same quality. The 'meat' was disgusting: some of it contained revolting pieces of heart, roots of tongues, throat ligaments and 'indescribable garbage'.[41] The big orders from the Admiralty stretched his resources, and he hurriedly prepared over-large cans of preserved food, neglecting to cook them properly, with the result that the already inferior contents went bad. Taking Goldner's food as provisions on his expedition was a catastrophe for John Franklin and his men. Stranded in the Arctic ice, they all perished, dying of what seemed at the time to be an unknown illness: it is now known that they succumbed to a combination of botulism and lead poisoning. Evidence from subsequent expeditions, where the remains of Franklin's men were found, and particularly the research of Dr Owen Beattie in the 1980s, seems to leave no doubt that Goldner's cans, with their suspect contents and their joints soldered with lead, were a contributory cause of the death of Franklin and his entire crew.[42] A later theory lays the blame for the poisoning on the ships' newly-installed, unique water system, which would have left lead residue from the pipes and in the bread and biscuits baked on board.[43] Either way, the effect would have been lingering; lead poisoning causes erratic behaviour and paranoia, which accounts for the fact that the men abandoned the relative safety of their ships, leaving food behind, and fled in panic, crazily carrying with them writing desks and other extraneous belongings that were found years later, scattered around with their bones.

Such a disaster had never happened in the all the years during which Donkin and Gamble had supplied the Navy with provisions. After all, Donkin had a great knowledge of chemistry and physics, and a skill with metals; he never would have used raw lead in a food container, and probably soldered the inside joints of his cans with a mixture that was more like pewter, with much more tin in the mixture than the deadly lead.

Another incident of widespread mortality took place among European troops stationed in Hong Kong in 1849, when 130 men died in a single regiment.[44] They had apparently all been previously poisoned during the passage to the East, by the putrid preserved meat supplied by the Admiralty. Spurred into action by numerous complaints about Goldner's dreadful canned meats, the Government ordered an enquiry, and hundreds of Goldner's cans of food were seized. The unfortunate inspectors had to examine the horrible contents over a period of four days.[45] Of the 643 tins opened on the first day, they found that 573 were unfit for consumption; in all, out of the 2,707 canisters examined, 2,510 were condemned. They found further horrors during the inspection – lumps of tallow, coagulated blood, and intestines. At times, the Board of Examiners were so overcome by the sight of the loathsome mess and the ghastly stench that they had to stop and recover. The revolting stuff was thrown into the sea. The Navy cancelled and then renewed its agreement with the despicable Stephan Goldner, but the contract was finally terminated in 1851.[46] Goldner was a ruined man.[47]

Donkin was an old man by then, and probably gave a wry smile at the twists and turns of fate since his first experiments with boiling milk and soup in the early days of the amazing development of his method of preserving food. He was secure in the knowledge that, once again, his perfecting of an incomplete French invention had benefitted the lives of his contemporaries, and would continue to flourish in the future.

7
Making Impressions

By the time Bryan Donkin had reached his half century, he had claimed a 'first' in patenting the steel pen, and was responsible for major contributions to two important aspects of social and commercial life: the mechanisation of paper-making, and the successful preservation of food in cans.

Everything happened at once in the second decade of the century. The canning business was flourishing and Donkin continued to carry out developments to the paper machine. His work increased as his reputation grew. Small jobs supplemented his earnings when the cash flow from the larger projects slowed down. As a certified appraiser, Donkin was often called on to give valuations of stock or property when a mill went bankrupt or machinery had to be sold for other reasons. As well as assessing property and inventions, Donkin was also regarded as a reliable expert witness who gave sound judgements in court cases and Government enquiries. In spite of his various business interests, there were times when money was short, and paying off the mortgage on the factory at five per cent added to his outgoings. The next few years were not easy.

Meanwhile, the world around him was grappling with the new technology of the industrial age and the engineering initiatives that proliferated. How could Donkin resist the excitement of taking the plunge into yet another major enterprise?

So his involvement with the printing industry began. Since Gutenberg and Caxton, books and pamphlets had been printed in the time-honoured way, by hand, using wooden printing presses.[1] With the expansion of education and the growth of trade in the early nineteenth century, and now the easier availability of paper, the printing industry looked towards new methods in order to satisfy the increasing readership of books, magazines and newspapers. First came Earl Stanhope's magnificent iron press; it speeded up the process and enabled larger sheets to be printed, but still relied on the traditional unmechanised methods.[2] The printers usually worked in pairs: the single letters of typescript were assembled in a frame, or 'forme', and inked all over with 'dabbers' (known as printers' balls) before the paper was laid over them by hand, then squeezed under the heavy weight of the press to take the impression, for a poster, visiting card or local newspaper. In the first decade of the century, the newer machines introduced cylinders to produce the impression, and a different way of applying the ink, with a roller. In these leaps forward, William Nicholson was the leader in theory, although the machine he actually produced was deemed to be defective.[3]

It was left to others to perfect the application of the new principles, and to use steam power to mechanise the printing press. The first to use a steam engine to drive a printing machine was Friedrich König, although as Thomas Hansard (himself a printer) said: 'Whether he was indebted to Mr Nicholson for his elementary principles, or whether the same ideas spontaneously occurred to each individual, is a question that can only be satisfactorily solved by the former'.[4] It is not unusual for individuals to produce inventions at the same time, when the need is felt. Usually it is the inventor with money and influence who takes the credit for the leap in progress.

Naturally, these developments in printing methods did not pass Bryan Donkin by. He watched and noted current events in all fields of engineering, and had already seen that König had invented a new metal for forming printing type, made of tin, zinc and bismuth.[5] Although he was busy with his other large projects and the smaller jobs that constantly came his way, he could not pass up the chance to take on the challenge of developing a new printing machine. The general economic climate was bleak, and Donkin saw insolvency strike in unexpected areas. As a consulting engineer he was paid fees for individual jobs and was therefore cushioned from major financial loss, but he was willing to diversify to enhance his business and guard against a downturn of trade in any one area of work. So, while König was gearing up to bring his steam-driven machine into the public domain, Donkin was working on an ingenious new press as well. Unfortunately, he made a mistake in the choice of a partner in the venture.

Richard Mackenzie Bacon was, like his father before him, the proprietor and editor of the *Norwich Mercury*, regarded as one of the leading provincial organs of liberal opinion.[6] He had printing ink in his veins, having become the manager of the printing department of the *Mercury* at the tender age of eighteen. Later, through that paper, he published his opinions on social issues and many other topics, and was well respected for his liberal views and as a champion of workers' rights. He was a fine musician, and a classicist. Alas, as with many armchair social reformers, his public moralising was not always matched by his own actions in private life. He was a flamboyant and confident man, a part-time major in the Norfolk Rifle Volunteers, who liked to cut a dash, and enjoyed the social high life, frequenting London's theatres and gaming clubs. New technology fascinated him and rumours of Bryan Donkin's paper-making machine excited him.[7] Enthusiastically, he applied for a licence for a Fourdrinier in 1807, and took over a paper mill at Taverham, near Norwich, where he supplied the *Norwich Mercury* and *The Times* with paper. To the public (and to the writers of the present-day Dictionary of National Biography) he seemed a respectable and respected man of the world, but as Donkin was to find out, he had an unscrupulous and sneaky side. Donkin, usually a good judge of character, did not see through him until it was too late.

Donkin first encountered Richard Bacon when he was called to survey Taverham Mill at the beginning of October 1809, in preparation for installing a paper machine. Donkin went to Taverham to survey the site and examine the water levels, which had changed due to the accumulation of weeds.[8] There he met Bacon, who told Donkin that he had invented a machine for printing, and asked for Donkin's help in perfecting it: in return Donkin would have a share in the eventual profits. The next day, a model of the machine (made for Bacon) convinced Donkin there was potential in the scheme, and he resolved to make a better model himself as soon as he returned home. When Bacon visited Two Waters to see a paper-making machine in action, they discussed the printing machine again, and two days later, Donkin went to his solicitor's office and 'entered a caveat against any invention for printing'.[9]

For the next four years the paper mills and the restorations at the tide mill at Greenwich took up most of Donkin's time, but he did indeed perfect the printing machine. Bacon's design was feasible, but it was through Donkin's skill that the

19 *Donkin & Bacon printing machine,* 1813.

printing machine was modified, adjusted and adapted to bring it to completion. It was a small but perfectly formed and ingenious press of unusual design.[10] It promised mechanical precision, increased speed, and the saving of skill, labour and expense.[11] Activated by turning the handle on a large wheel at the side, the mechanism consisted of horizontal cylinders at the top, which inked a square roller: the inking mechanism rose and fell to accommodate the corners of the block as it turned. The type was clamped on to each of the four sides; underneath, the sheet of paper was placed on a flat, padded board that passed under the revolving block of type to receive each impression. Two dozen sheets could be printed in one minute, it was claimed, which was four times faster than any other press. The prospectus for the machine was actually printed on the Bacon and Donkin press, four pages to the sheet; the whole sheet of paper measured 17½ x 10½ in. (approx. 440 x 270 mm.). Everything was finely tuned, and adjustable – and it worked. Being much lighter than previous machines that could be injurious to the workmen, it could be easily and safely controlled by one boy operator, an advantage when 'one eminent surgeon in the metropolis has had four thousand ruptured pressmen under his care during his practice'.[12] Donkin's meticulous engineering skills and attention to detail had turned Bacon's basic design into a beautifully crafted little machine.

The patent was granted to Bacon and Donkin in November 1813 (Patent No.3757). The University of Cambridge was the first to show an interest: they had a contract with the British and Foreign Bible Society, and the new machine seemed ideal for producing the small-sized Bible. The Society for the Propagation of Christian Knowledge had also made enquiries.[13] In February the next year, Donkin and Bacon sent the machine to the Cambridge University Press, followed it to supervise its setting up, and demonstrated it to principal members of the University.[14] It was approved after three days of examination and printing trials by the University's Syndicate.[15] This was a high point for Donkin, seeing his creation successfully come to fruition. The printing machine was highly praised, and not only by the flamboyant Bacon himself.[16] Rees's popular *Cyclopaedia* 'found it to display so much mechanical ingenuity, and to produce such beautiful specimens of printing, with rapidity unequalled by any other means, that we have made a drawing of it'.[17] It was said that Donkin's friend and rival, König, burst into tears when he saw it, crying 'I'm a ruined man!' The machine also took up half the usual space and could be operated by a twelve year old boy, whose job was simply to lay on and take off the paper.[18] Hansard saw it demonstrated at Donkin's Bermondsey factory and praised it as a most beautiful piece of workmanship, ideal for printing books.[19] The little machine would stand on an ordinary writing table but, Hansard thought, was impracticable. He criticised the machine for the limited size of the pages it could produce, and reckoned that London printers would not be likely to buy it.

The day after the machine had been dispatched to Cambridge, Donkin had a long conversation with Bacon, and it was decided to draw up a written contract defining their respective shares in the agreement – not before time, perhaps.[20] The terms of agreement were that Bacon would defray all the expenses as they arose, and that if the machine proved unsuccessful, Bacon would stand the loss.[21] If successful, or if any profit should accrue from sales, Bacon would be reimbursed for his expenses and the remainder, if any, would be shared between the two of them. Bryan Donkin had volunteered to claim only the basic expenses of parts made by his firm, provided that Bacon paid in cash. But although Donkin had regarded Bacon as a friend, their relationship took a downward turn. Donkin played fair, but Bacon turned out to be a cheat who, under the guise of friendship, hoodwinked Donkin and nearly bankrupted him.

Negotiations had already started as early as 1813, between Bacon and the British and Foreign Bible Society, who hoped to have bibles printed in French by the machine.[22] Bacon promised a 30 per cent reduction on the cost of printing; he would make the paper himself. 20,000 copies were needed for the captive readership of French prisoners of war in England.[23]

With the paper mill at Taverham failing because of a previous partnership, Bacon had persuaded a friend, Simon Wilkin, to go into partnership with him, knowing that Wilkin had considerable wealth – a sum of nearly £40,000. Between them, over the next four years, Bacon and Wilkin managed to get into debt with both the mill and the development of the printing machine. Wilkin, fourteen years younger than Bacon, seems to have been under the older man's spell, and was sucked into the mire that Bacon created. Together with Donkin's contributions, the hapless Wilkin's fortune disappeared into the black hole caused by Bacon's mismanagement and his guile. Donkin knew nothing of Bacon's worsening financial difficulties until well after the machine was brought to completion; by that time, he had committed a considerable sum to the scheme, and had borne all the costs of development.[24]

The London contract with the British and Foreign Bible Society faltered. The board of directors had trusted Bacon as a 'person of unquestionable responsibility' and had ordered the 20,000 bargain-price copies of the French Bible, printed by the machine.[25] Suspicious directors, who attended a meeting because they had been warned (without justification) that the patent might be an infringement of Nicholson's, were silenced by Bacon's salesmanship and charm. But things went downhill fast as Bacon over-reached himself. He asked for more orders, larger orders, and wanted his name on the title pages; there was a problem with damaged printing plates, which had to be repaired by Donkin. Bacon could not fulfil his commitments to the BFBS, and when he was declared bankrupt in 1816, he owed them £202 16s 0d., and dozens of half-finished books had to be recycled. The paper had come from Taverham Mill, supplied by Bacon and Wilkin. At twenty-four shillings a ream, it earned them the grand sum of £5,438 15s. 11½d.

between April and September of 1816. A large percentage of the left-over paper was found to be rotten.

Some sympathy must be conceded to Richard Mackenzie Bacon, though; many paper-makers were struggling with problems of over-production. The demands of the market were not sufficient to warrant the amount of paper that was produced by the efficient new paper-making machines, resulting in a glut for paper-makers such as Bacon, who were reluctant to lay off their workers.[26]

However, by this time, the Cambridge University Press machine had been in operation for some time. Disappointingly, when Donkin visited in August 1816, the printer, Mr Matthews, reported that time was being lost because fitting fresh printing plates, which needed a lot of packing underneath, meant that the overall speed of the machine was less than anticipated.[27] Nevertheless, five of the machines were in use, including Bacon's own in Norwich and Donkin's, which was being used by the Bermondsey Deaf and Dumb Institution. The sixth was bought by Agustin de Betancourt, a talented and experienced Spanish engineer ten years older than Donkin, whose work on buildings and machines in France, Spain and Russia had brought him acclaim.[28] Visiting England in 1788, he had asked to see Watt's steam engine; Watt had been rather secretive about his newly invented double-action machine, but Betancourt had managed to have a good look at the one in action at the Albion corn mill in London. Although he declared that he had not seen its inside workings, he made a working model of an identical one himself; he was reported to have 'made a kind of secondary claim to the invention of the double engine' as a result of this blatant act of industrial espionage. During Betancourt's subsequent visits to England, Donkin would have met him through their mutual connections with Marc Brunel and Henry Maudslay, and their common interests. When Betancourt fled to Russia to escape the Spanish Inquisition, he organised several high-level engineering developments in St Petersburg including, from 1816 to 1818, the setting up of the steam driven Government printing works where bank notes were printed.[29] It was at this time that Betancourt purchased one of Donkin and Bacon's printing machines.

Financially, the whole partnership with Bacon was a near-disastrous venture for Bryan Donkin. In spite of high-profile sales, the financial side of their business went from bad to worse, and deeply affected Bryan.[30] It became clear that Bacon was not prepared to keep his side of the contract. Simon Wilkin did not have the sense to detach himself from Richard Bacon, and they continued to act as a partnership until their debts overwhelmed them. In the final year of the dispute they had the nerve to accuse Donkin's firm of supplying inferior wires for their Fourdrinier paper machine, although they had already put them to use and ordered more: Donkin politely informed them that they should have sent them back before putting them on the machine.

As the disagreements about finance came to a head, Wilkin became the go-between in the ensuing dispute between Donkin and Bacon – a seemingly invidious position, but it turned out that he was acting as deceitfully as Bacon. Incidents that Donkin generously called 'misunderstandings' occurred; money that Bacon claimed to have sent did not arrive, and a draft for £78 came without a signature. Donkin had to borrow money; Matthew Stainton stepped in again to help. In letters written throughout 1816, Donkin's distress and anger was barely disguised. His exasperation showed through in one letter he sent to Wilkin: 'All that I have to say to Bacon is that he is ruining me; if such a communication will be gratifying to him, you may tell him so'.[31] Bacon dallied when it came to valuing his mill in order to sell it to pay his creditors, and put off a meeting. Donkin wrote: 'It appears to me to be not only trifling with our feelings, but imposing upon our judgement'. Donkin soon realised that there was little chance of getting his money back – Bacon kept asking for more time to get monetary support from his friends, and it became obvious that the sale of the mill would not result in enough cash to pay off the debts. Writing to Maria Dobson in Isleworth, Bryan openly regretted not only his 'almost ruinous loss', but also the fact that he had encouraged his friend Maudslay to build a steam engine for Wilkin worth £900, letting him in for a huge loss of earnings, too.[32] Donkin was appalled that Wilkin, who had been brought up by a Christian minister, had lied to him, making 'sacred promises and assurances of security' only months before the crash, and had swindled Donkin out of £300. 'To aggravate the calamity to me, they have under the semblance of the most sincere friendship, treated me in the most shameful and villainous manner.' Bacon failed to turn up at another meeting of the creditors, sending his brother-in-law to negotiate the amount of the debt that could actually be paid: 12s. 6d in the pound was suggested, but there was no agreement.

When the situation reached this impasse, Donkin took himself off to Margate by steam boat. While on the boat, he took the opportunity of a good snoop round, making copious notes with details of the engine, the pumps and the paddle wheels, and said afterwards that he had gained information that would materially assist him in his forthcoming task of constructing steam boats for the Caledonian Canal.[33] He seems to have had the knack of pacing himself, combining work with pleasure even in difficult times, maintaining the 'work/life balance' to hold stress at bay. (He bemoaned his situation in several letters to his family, writing in one that under such circumstances he could only pray for health and strength of mind to extricate himself from his difficulties; but there was a homely P.S: 'I have paid for the wines' ...!)[34] The trip to Margate was a pleasant journey of about ten hours, with good accommodation and plenty of amusement, and he enjoyed the three-day break. He had not swum in the sea for years but bravely took a dip, which made him feel 'greatly improved and invigorated'. In early September the water must have been freezing: 'I went rather into deepish water head foremost, but before I got myself fairly upright again, I was in a little bit of a flustration (can find no word half so good to express the sensation produced by plunging into cold water!')

It took a couple of hours longer to get home from Margate, because the boat got lost in the fog, but next day, he was back in the thick of the argument. He thought Wilkin's conduct was 'something worse than absurd ... contemptible'. The haggling continued. Bacon and Wilkin owed £700 as paper-makers and upwards of £800 on the printing machine; Wilkin owed £80 for Donkin's expenses, as well as the £300 which had been a 'temporary' loan. Wilkin had written to Maudslay with further accusations against Donkin. Bryan Donkin felt 'abused on all sides', but there was little he could do at the time. A day or two later, he sailed to Scotland, a long-planned trip to meet Thomas Telford to advise on the machinery for the Caledonian Canal, and was away for several weeks.[35] He had to miss a meeting of the creditors, but when he returned home from his travels just before Christmas, he found that the situation was still unresolved. On Boxing Day, he travelled to Norwich to find that Bacon and Wilkin had still not presented proper accounts. (He 'took charge' of Miss Maudslay on the way to Norwich, and delivered her next day by poste chaise, to stay at her friend's house about six miles away.) However, the assignees, appointed to deal with the bankruptcy, were allowing him scope for redress in the matter of the printing machine. Because he was not yet sure that Cambridge University was going to keep the machine, Donkin was undecided about taking up the offer by the assignees to buy from them the half of the patent that would be theirs by right, so that it would become solely his property to develop as he could. The University did indeed use the machine for several years, but the development of speedy mechanised machinery, pioneered by König, gradually rendered Bacon and Donkin's delicate little press redundant, and in 1846, after it had stood unused for many years, a member of the University Syndicate was authorised to dispose of it.[36]

One good thing to come out of the Bacon and Donkin debacle was a long-lasting side-product of the printing press: the inking method. Whereas the previous rollers had evolved from the printers' balls, which were made of padded leather, Donkin invented a method of casting cylindrical rollers from a mixture of treacle and glue that was poured into tin moulds.[37] There is some controversy over the originator of the idea, but Donkin was given the credit and certainly built them into his printing machine.[38] The rollers were soon introduced into general use: König was one of the first to fit them to his machines. However, the rollers tended to become hard and dry in time; the suggestion by Mr Tyrrel, an accomplished engraver, that adding carbonate of soda to the mixture would aid its elasticity, was taken up by Donkin and with his permission, printers continued to use his roller for many years.[39]

As soon as the unpleasantness with Bacon and Wilkin was settled, the indomitable Donkin pressed on with another venture. Undeterred by his bad experience with Bacon and Wilkin, he entered into a new agreement to develop a different printing machine, with a new partner. Again, he was approached by somebody with an idea; this was Charles Brightley, an experienced printer and publisher. Originally a schoolmaster, he had relinquished his profession in favour of the 'typographic art', and ran a business for years in Bungay, Suffolk.[40]. A good deal of his work came from booksellers in London, where the printing trade was suffering a depression. He was able to print and publish books and maps more cheaply, partly because most of his workers were women. In 1809, Brightley – his name is often spelt 'Brightly' – published his booklet 'An Account of the Method of Casting Stereotype' in which he gave details of his own way of making stereotype printing plates. This process involved converting a passage of text composed from individually-made letters and punctuation into a single block. Stanhope, who had made innovations to the design of the printing press, had also had ideas about stereotyping, but Brightley's were slightly different and greatly simplified; he used his own recipe for the plaster to take an impression from the set type.

When Hansard saw the finished Donkin and Brightley machine, he described it as 'a beautiful piece of finished mechanism', but with many defects in its operation.[41] Nevertheless, it was patented in January 1818 (Patent No.4202), as an 'improved machine or printing press for printing from types, plates or blocks'. Inking the paper was done by cylinders, coming into contact with the paper laid on top of the formes, which rose and fell, and passed over and under each other. Still experimenting in July 1818 – it was quite usual for a patent to be applied for before the work was completed – Donkin had had difficulty in making all the adjustments and alterations to make the forms work 'pleasantly'; but he had solved the problems and was happy with the ease with which it worked, and had hopes that one worker would be able to operate it singlehandedly.[42] The pressing and inking rollers were still to be tried out, and the patent had been criticised: in desperation, Donkin suggested that a working model should be made, big enough to print an octavo page according to the patent specification, to prove that it could be done. He was worried, though, that there might be a flaw in the design, and was anxious to rectify it. Two months later, there were more difficulties with the feeding mechanism for the paper but, ever optimistic, Donkin saw no reason to doubt that the obstacles would be overcome. He wrote to Brightley, who was standing in the sidelines complaining about the delay, pointing out that it was he (Donkin) who was spending the time and energy on the work and bearing the financial loss, and that instead of moaning, Brightley should concentrate on the business side, which was being neglected.[43] In the end, it seems that only one machine was ever made. Quite why it should have been a failure, with the combined expertise of Donkin and Brightley, is a mystery, although there was certainly a clash between Donkin's meticulous engineering and Brightley's expectations.

Brightley died in 1821. On April 6th he was at the Crown Inn at Stamford, buying a ticket for a journey to Leicester by coach.[44] A bystander noticed that he was a fine, robust-looking man of about sixty, seemingly in perfect health. Charles

Brightley paid his fare and had just reached the gateway of the inn, when he fell down and died instantly, without uttering a word or a groan.

Now in the forefront of the development of printing machines, Donkin was called upon to work on his third, this time at the behest of Sir William Congreve. His brief was to build a printing machine of an entirely new design, and to make the machinery to produce the complicated printing plates for printing bank notes in two colours, in one movement.[45] The aim was to combat the forgery of bank notes, by making designs that were impossible to copy.

Congreve was versatile and influential, and an entrepreneur. He had studied law as a young man, and in 1810 became a much-favoured equerry to the Prince of Wales. Two years later, he was the Member of Parliament for Plymouth. As an inventor, he became best known for the invention of a military rocket, a device so inefficient that it succeeded only by causing terror among the enemy with its noise and novelty.[46] He was full of ideas and wealthy enough to put them into practice, and his arrogant nature allowed to him to bluster his way through any criticism. He was unpopular. Many accused him of copying other people's inventions and claiming them as his own.

Congreve's idea for a printing method was a case in point. The need for banknotes had increased because of the war with France, and forgery was rife. In the race to find a method of printing that would deter bank note counterfeiters, Congreve was accused of abusing his position as Commissioner for the Enquiry into the Protection of Bank Notes, by copying his plan from proposals submitted to the committee. One of several accusers was Thomas Bewick, Donkin's fellow Northumbrian, that wayward boy with a flair for drawing, who had lived not far from Sandoe as a truanting school child, and matured into a brilliant engraver. By 1820, Thomas Bewick was well established, and had published hundreds of his tiny characterful engravings and books on quadrupeds and birds. More recently he had turned his hand to engraving copper plates for the printing of bank notes. Hand-engraved bank notes had been notoriously easy to copy, but Bewick set about creating a densely drawn design for the Carlisle Bank, which was eventually shown to Sir Joseph Banks, President of the Royal Society. Later, he experimented further with anti-forgery designs, combining etching and engraving, and printing the notes in blue and red, a difficult process which demanded high quality ink and the right kind of paper. When the Parliamentary Commission was set up, Bewick made the suggestion that paper with highly decorated anti-forgery borders should be supplied to the provincial banks. The idea was not deemed suitable. In 1816 the Grand Duke Nicholas visited his workshop and looked at Bewick's samples; Sir William Congreve happened to be in the entourage. When compound-plate printing was put forward as a solution to the problem of counterfeiting, Bewick was convinced that Congreve had stolen his idea; but he felt that he could not compete in a battle of words with a man like Congreve, and so gave up.

There were wrangles between Congreve and others apart from Bewick, who had similar ideas. Printing in two interlocking colours had been attempted as far back as the fifteenth century; Congreve had seen a copy of a large initial B in red and blue, from a Psalter of 1457, and had been convinced that it was printed by one impression; this may have inspired his patent for two-colour printing. John Holt Ibbetson, among others, put forward a series of ideas for security printing by means of patterned and coloured wooden blocks, and he too believed that Congreve had seen and copied his idea when it was presented to the Commission of Enquiry.

Whoever it was who really invented compound-plate printing, Congreve's patent described a very ingenious process for printing complex patterns in two colours, and Bryan Donkin certainly had the knowledge and skill to perfect it (Patent No.4404). For the printing plates, two metal slabs were made, and cut with holes in one and raised shapes in the other, so that they fitted exactly into each other. The parts were cast in sand, and fettled to make a perfect fit. (Later, a pantograph milling machine was built at the Donkin works to shape the basic parts.) Donkin's partner, John Wilks, also played a part in the construction of the printing machine and plates. Congreve issued instructions, but had not worked out the details of manufacture. Donkin constructed a geometric lathe, a beautiful machine made of iron and shining bronze, with the mechanism of cogs, belts and turning parts, mounted on a solid mahogany table, six foot long. Its purpose was to engrave the combined surface of the printing plates with complicated symmetrical patterns of whirls in circles, oval and straight lines; this was done with a steel engraving tool fixed on the lathe and set to revolve and change direction. The lathe was also known as a 'rose engine' because the simpler patterns, such as circles formed by wavy lines, could be engraved by setting a follower against the edge of a 'rose', a vertical bronze disc with an undulating edge. One man could operate the lathe, making the various adjustments to the settings, before turning the handle to start the engraving. (Later in the century, it was mechanised by steam, and then by electricity.) Donkin's lathe was unique and required a specialist to operate it, someone who knew the intricacies of the settings, who could keep them secret, but reproduce them exactly when required.

To print the pattern, the plate was fitted to the purpose-built printing machine, which separated the two parts, taking the bottom section below the fixed top part.[47] Then rollers, charged with two different colours of ink, rolled simultaneously across the two separated parts of the printing plate; the machine brought the two parts together again, and when a sheet of paper was rolled onto the combined surface it produced a lovely two-colour pattern, with the white lines from the engraving showing up crisply against the bi-coloured design. Bryan Donkin and John Wilks constructed the complex printing press that performed these actions, working from Sir William Congreve's ideas, and brought it to perfection; Donkin probably wrote the patent specification too.

It seemed the perfect answer to the problem of counterfeiting. At least, Sir William Congreve thought so. He had a worthy protagonist, though, in the shape of Jacob Perkins, who had arrived from America in 1819, just too late to put forward his method for combating forgery when the Government threw the problem open to competition. A bitter debate took place between the two of them; the wrangling was conducted in public through the pages of the monthly magazines, as well as in private letters. Congreve wrote at length about his process, comparing it favourably with Perkins's siderographic anti-forgery method. 'Siderography' was a lengthy but effective procedure which entailed first engraving a master plate in soft steel, which was then hardened. A soft steel cylinder, or roller, was passed over the plate under great pressure, creating a mirror image of the original on its surface. This roller was then itself hardened, and by rolling it over the final printing plate, an exact copy of the first engraving was made. Many impressions could be struck from the one roller, but if this failed, another could be made from the master plate. The printing plate might be as small as a postage stamp or the size of a banknote, and even as large as a share certificate. For the engraving, he used the skills of both a hand-engraver and a geometric lathe, to produce intricate patterns. Perkins's own lathe had been brought from America and patented on his arrival in England. Donkin would have seen the patent (Patent No.4400). Congreve induced the master engraver, Robert Branston, to prove that Perkins's work could be imitated: his copy was damned as a failure by Perkins and others. Ibbetson, piqued by the rejection of his ideas by the commission, and wishing he had approached the Bank of England directly, pitched in with the Perkins camp. The battle of insults raged on.[48]

The Bank of England made the final decision about which method should be adopted for printing on banknotes. The directors gave consideration to compound-plate printing for its notes, but the upshot was that the Bank's engraver, William Bawtree, submitted the designs to his ultimate test and managed to produce excellent copies. Instead, an expensive five-colour process by Applegath and Cowper was given the Bank's support for development, until Bawtree scuppered that too, creating a perfect multicoloured copy. So the design of the Bank of England's notes remained unprotected from forgery, relying on the same black-on white design that had evolved from the first handwritten bank notes, and which lasted throughout the century.

The part played by Bryan Donkin in these controversies was important, but he managed to remain on the side-lines. On the one hand, he was employed by Congreve to build the compound-plate machines, and to make and engrave the unusual two-part printing plates that were an essential part of the production of the printed images. Although the principle of geometric lathes was understood, and several were in use, Donkin's rose engine was made expressly to his own design for the purpose of engraving bank note printing plates under Congreve's patent. On the other hand, he knew Jacob Perkins quite well and had much in common with him. In April 1819, he agreed to build Perkins's newly-invented fire engine at the Bermondsey factory. As well, they must have discussed the design of engraving machines; but Donkin kept his cards close to his chest, and Perkins was not allowed to see Donkin's rose engine, in spite of asking Congreve, and Robert Branston the engraver, on four separate occasions. Donkin was well aware of the rival process. Some aspects may even have inspired the design of his own machine, although the two geometric lathes were rather different.

Moreover, Donkin had given his endorsement to Jacob Perkins's use of siderography as a means of security printing for bank notes. Gentlemen of the Society of Arts were invited to examine the merits of bank notes designed to prevent forgery. They singled out Perkins's finely engraved designs, which were compilations of the work by hand and machine by some of the best engravers, as the best for the purpose. Bryan Donkin was among the signatories, who also included George Rennie, Marc Brunel, Henry Maudslay and Timothy Bramah. They presented a report.[49] The group agreed that the method of reproducing the engravings was accurate and easily multiplied. The same engravings could be used in different configurations; it was an advantage to have the work of several engravers on one plate, and that the only way of counterfeiting it would be by employing the same engravers and processes as for the original plate. Once the plates were made, there was little extra cost. They recommended it to the Bank, who rejected it. Ultimately, siderography was adopted by many of the country banks, as was compound-plate printing. Donkin was not injured in the game of piggy-in-the-middle.

Compound-plate printing was the most successful and long-lived printing enterprise that Bryan Donkin undertook. The red and black designs were used as duty stamps, printed on the back of provincial bank notes in the 1820s and 30s to protect the notes from forgery, and some of the country banks used the beautiful patterns for the front of their £1 and £5 notes. A handful of skilful forgers did make attempts (ranging from the ludicrous to the laudable) to copy the front and the back of the notes, but the complicated pattern of lines combined with the two colours was a strong deterrent. Packets of paper were also subject to taxation, and large, attractive paper duty labels were printed on the compound-plate machine; medicines, too, were labelled with a strip of paper round the bottle or packet, denoting that the government tax had been paid by the manufacturer – these were also printed with the distinctive red and black patterns, a practice that continued for over a century, from 1823 until as late as 1941. When the Government, seeking a design for a postage stamp for the new Penny Post, announced the Treasury Competition in 1839, compound-plate printing was a strong contender, but the process was considered too expensive, and the Penny Black, produced by Perkins, won the day.

The printing plates were mostly designed by the up-market London printers, Whiting and Branston. Robert Branston was an acclaimed wood engraver, but

20 *Compound printing plate, for Whiting's trade card,* c.1840.

he adapted his methods to working with the bronze plates, and embellished the lathe's formal patterns with florid hand-engraved flowers and leaves. His son, also Robert, later took over his father's work. Whitings' skills (both father James and son Charles) were with inks and machinery, and the firm produced beautiful, crisp work. Official printing, for tax stamps, was carried out in the Excise Office at Somerset House, but Whiting also had one of Donkin's compound-plate printing machines in his establishment off the Strand, and developed the technique for less serious printing, making attractive labels for merchants who wanted an eye-catching feature for their products, which would also protect them from unscrupulous rivals who might try to sell counterfeit goods. Throughout the early decades after its invention, the general public saw the red and black compound-plate printed duty labels in everyday life. As well, many people would have bought goods adorned with the prettily coloured, highly decorative labels – ink, wine, jam and other everyday products. Eye-catching advertisements for the national lotteries in the 1820s were produced in a variety of sumptuous designs and lovely combinations of colours. Later, Stephens Ink bottles bore the highly patterned, bi-coloured labels, printed on the compound-plate printing machine until well into the twentieth century.

In the early 1820s, Donkin was also heavily involved with the building and maintenance of compound-plate printing machines. The most heavily used compound-plate machine was in the Excise Office at Somerset House.[50] A steam

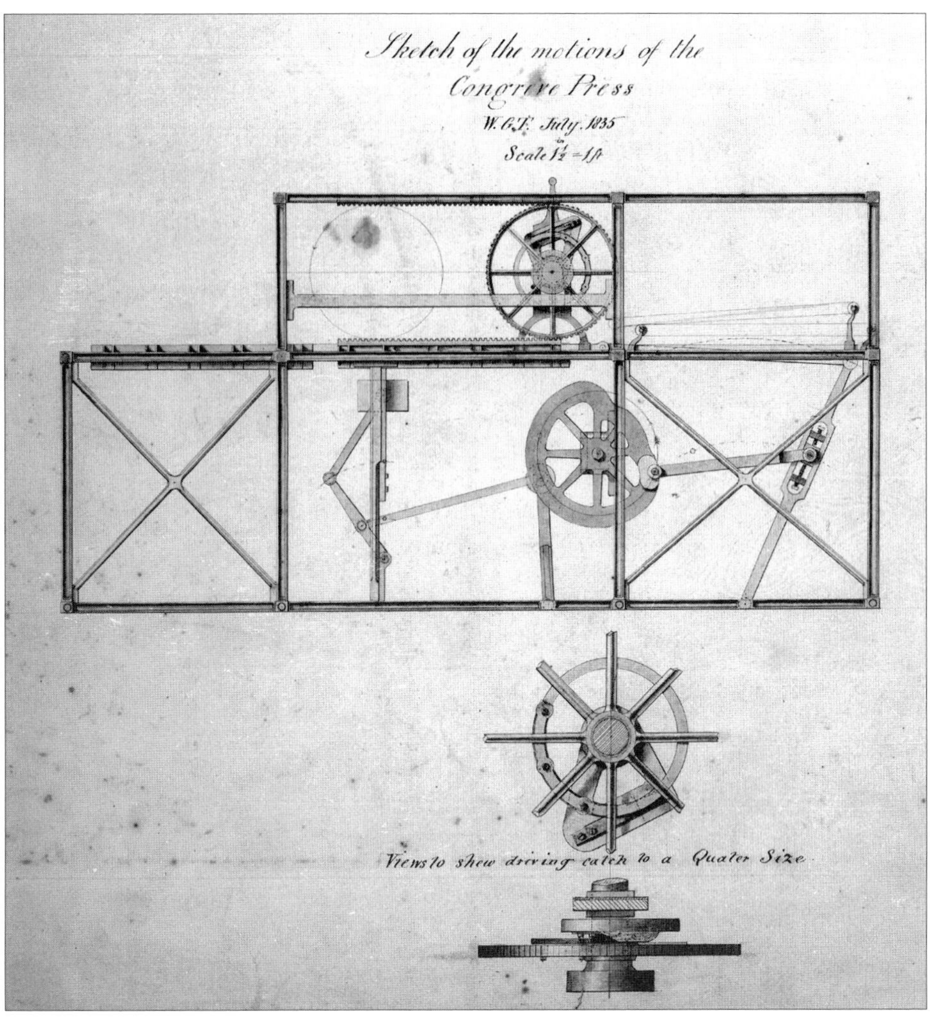

21 Charles Whiting's compound-plate printing machine, 1835.

engine built by Henry Maudslay's firm was set up to drive the press, at a cost of £205 3s.10d. Because of the precision and complexity of the compound-plate presses, trained men from Bryan Donkin's works had to install them, and if anything went wrong, Donkin would send a team to repair it. A great deal of work was done for the Commissioners of Excise in London between 1826 and 1828; during those and subsequent years, the Company provided continuing maintenance of all the different sorts of printing machines at the Excise Office, such as repairing the label- and permit-printing machines, altering and flattening a paper duty label plate, mending the steam engine, making casts for new rollers, and providing and fitting numerous parts. The compound-plate printing machines were in constant use, and there were frequent orders for new rollers or renewal of the composition coating on the old ones. At the same time, specialists working in secret at the

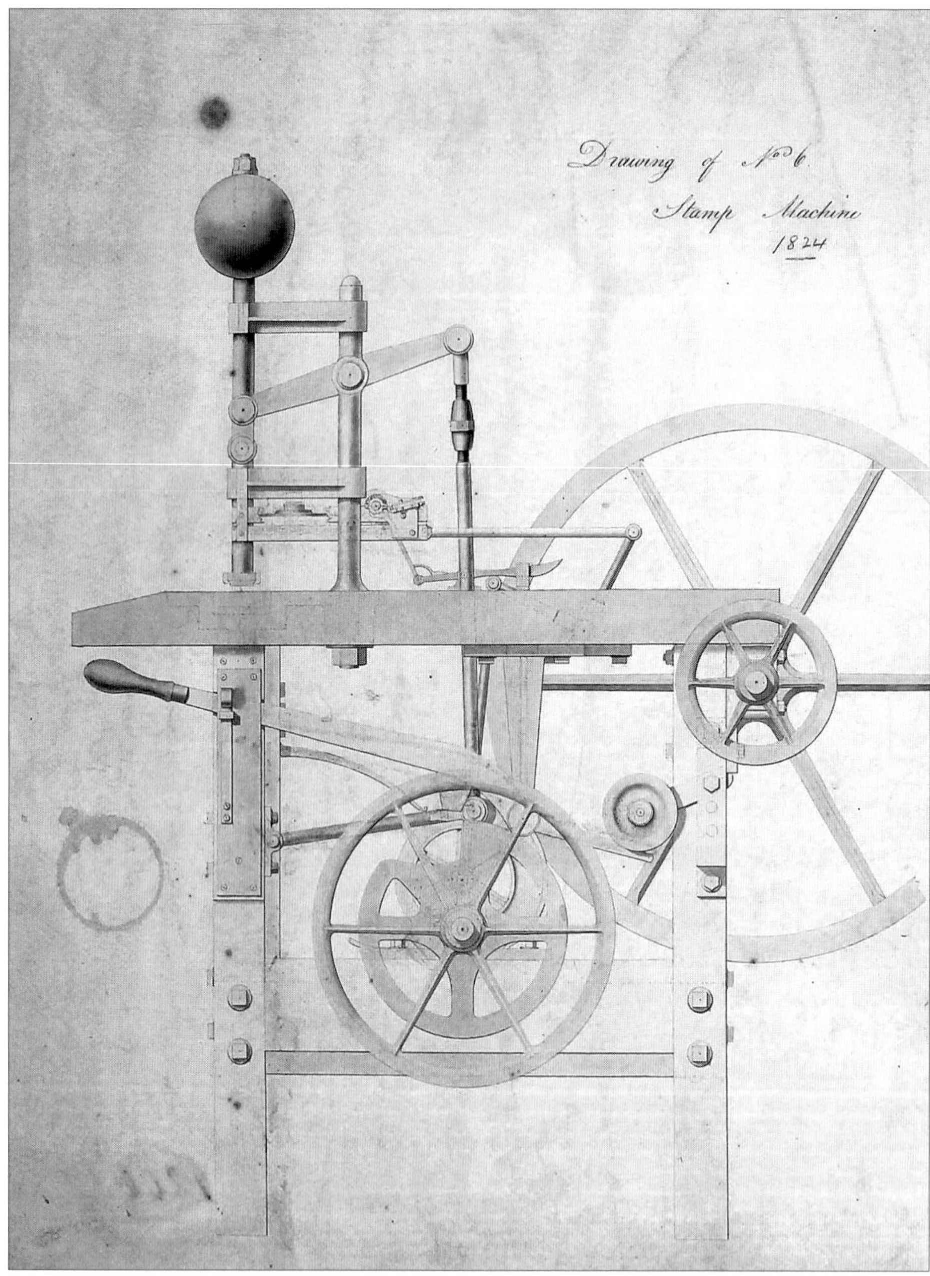

22 *Embossing and printing press for Dublin Stamp Office,* 1823.

Donkin firm were making the gun metal printing plates for paper duty labels, to be sent to the Government office.

James Whiting's compound-plate printing machine needed repairs sometimes, and Donkin's men also repaired the embossing press that he used for his beautiful commercial work in conjunction with the two-colour printing machine.[51] When his son Charles took over, he bought a new compound-plate printing machine;[52] and four pairs of compound dies were re-cut and hardened at the Bermondsey factory for him. Throughout the decade, and into the 1830s and beyond, the Donkin company had sole rights in the provision and maintenance on compound-plate printing machines, including those sent to India for printing tax stamps.

News of compound-plate printing reached Eduard Haenel of Magdeburg, Germany, who set up his own business by buying a compound-plate printing machine from Donkin in December 1827, together with an apparatus for stopping and starting the machine, seven extra printing rollers, and an iron mould twenty-two inches long, for casting the composition rollers in; Haenel already had a Donkin paper-making machine.[53] A man was sent to Magdeburg early the following year to set up the machine, at the cost of nearly £100 – clearly worth the price for Haenel, who had the monopoly in Germany. His bi-coloured labels were printed from plates bought from Whiting in England, and adapted for his own wording.

Sir William Congreve had his hand in another enterprise, which arouses suspicions about his motives. In 1823, the Dublin Stamp Office heard of his expertise with anti-forgery printing, and sought his assistance in foiling expert counterfeiters who were successfully producing fake duty stamps.[54] Representatives from the Board had, by invitation, watched a forger at work on authentic-looking dies and, although the man had generously put forward suggestions as to how forgeries could be prevented, none of his ideas satisfied the official group. Instead they commissioned from Congreve a machine for embossing and printing paper at one stroke. Bryan Donkin was asked to make a wooden demonstration model and a press.[55] After months of official letters between the Board, the Treasury and Congreve, Sir William conned them into ordering another five machines, at the cost of over £2,000, which entailed heavy annual expenses in salaries, repairs and running costs. In fact it was discovered, too late, that one machine would have sufficed; the others were 'a mere incumbrance in the Stamping Room.'[56]

8
Body and Mind

Until the early nineteenth century, medical care was provided by men who were not qualified physicians, but who had served apprenticeships and passed exams as apothecaries or surgeons.[1] The situation improved gradually, and from 1815 qualifications became more meaningful. In 1826 The Association of General Medical and Surgical Practitioners was formed, thus creating the 'general practitioner' who attended to the medical and surgical needs of families. During Bryan Donkin's lifetime, great strides were made in all aspects of medicine.

In these decades before the discovery of anaesthetics and antibiotics, doctors relied on time-honoured methods in an attempt to cure, or at least alleviate, the sufferings of their patients. Pneumonia, meningitis, and tuberculosis were often fatal: treatment for these diseases was as yet unknown.[2] The first pandemic of cholera hit England in 1831 and returned in force in the 1850s, and no cure was known; childbirth was risky, and death from typhoid fever was common.[3] Scarlet fever was a killer: in March 1847, a little girl in Sandoe contracted the disease, and was dead within four days.[4]

23 *Bloodletting.*

Ignorant of the causes of such illnesses, and with no known cures, doctors fell back on the medieval theory that the body must be flushed out to get rid of the malady. Some clung to the eighteenth-century belief that a fever, a symptom of most infections, should be sweated out by piling blankets on to the already feverish patient.[5] However, the most common treatment during the nineteenth century was bloodletting, or phlebotomy.[6] This horrific procedure entailed cutting lengthways into a vein with a lancet (a small sharp knife) and releasing blood into a small bowl, supposedly taking the infection with it. Alternatively, a multi-bladed device, a 'scarificator' could be used to pierce the skin.[7] Even Mrs Beeton, writing in 1861 in her *Book of Household Management*, gave instructions for bleeding at home in an emergency, by placing a tourniquet in the upper arm and finding a vein in the forearm to dig into with the lancet.[8] She advised that the patient should be bled standing up or sitting down, so that if he fainted, he could be laid on the floor to recover; if he were already lying down, he could not be placed any lower, 'except, as is most likely to be the case, under the ground'. Bryan Donkin's sister Mary, who lived in Sandoe all her life, kept a diary of events that were important to her between 1819 and 1847, and records in 1830 that her neighbour, Mr Gibson, 'had 80 ounces of blood taken from him' and then another 88 ounces three days later.[9] Perhaps village gossip exaggerated the poor man's plight, but if he really had five pints extracted, and then five and a half more, he was lucky to survive. The Duke of Kent did not. In January 1820, in his fifty-second year, the strong and fit brother of the Prince Regent went out for a long walk and returned with wet feet; he did not change his stockings, preferring to play with his smiling little daughter, the Princess Victoria.[10] By evening he was cold and hoarse, but refused a medicinal draught, and in the morning he was feverish. 120 ounces of blood was taken from his arms, and he died – which is hardly surprising.

An ancient and less drastic form of bloodletting was the use of leeches; the small bloodsucking worm would cling to the patient's skin and painlessly extract 'impure' blood from the affected part.[11] There was method in this madness: the saliva of a leech contains an anaesthetic substance and an anti-coagulant. (Even now, in the twenty-first century, the advantages of the leech as a medical aid have been recognised again, and there has been a resurgence in the use of leeches for plastic surgery and reconstructive surgery, as well as for treating black eyes.) Mary Donkin noted that in February 1824, she had an inflammation of the throat and 'had six leeches applied which relieved it'.[12] Some years later, as her brother William approached the age of eighty, he had eleven leeches placed on his arm for an unspecified complaint, and, just before Christmas 1842, Mary herself had twelve leeches to treat what must have been another bad sore throat.[13]

When Bryan Donkin worked at Knole, he was given a purge – another common weapon in the doctor's armoury; this method of relieving constipation and other bowel disorders was relentlessly administered in the form of enemas, or 'clysters'.[14]

Laxatives could be made from senna, aloes or other vegetable ingredients mixed into water, and were often given to alleviate fever as well as to open the bowels. The stronger purgatives usually contained sinister substances including metallic chemicals, and opium, which afforded some relief as a painkiller.[15] Another favoured means of ridding the body of toxicity was to induce vomiting by means of an emetic, perhaps a draught containing ipecacuanha, or simply soap and water, or diluted mustard, or any mixture nasty enough to make the patient sick. In a whole section of Mrs Beeton's book, she advocated all manner of horrible mixtures as an antidote to noxious substances inadvertently swallowed by the patient; among them was a mixture of the whites of a dozen eggs in water, given by the glassful every three of four minutes.[16] Almost as unpleasant was a poultice or 'plaster' made from milk, bread, herbs, vegetables or even cow manure, placed on the chest of a sufferer from wheezing or chest pain, or to draw out the infection from a sore or wound. Medical treatment at that time was basic.

The situation was aptly summed up by a satirist of the day, William Hone, whose tongue-in-cheek set of poems, 'The Age of Intellect', poked fun at the social and political scene in 1819.[17]

Dr Lancet seeks applause
By exploring different laws;
He resolves to bleed and blister,
Purge and scarify and clyster,
Well convinced that all disorders
Must obey doctorial orders,
And that Madam Fate would even
Yield to doses he has given.

There were 'doctors', too, with their own theories of health care. Mary, Bryan Donkin's sister, wrote to him while he was still working at Knole, relating details of a demonstration and lecture she had been to in Hexham.[18] Her father and her brother William had been greatly entertained the previous evening and Mary, at the age of twenty, was given leave to go with Nanny. Dr Graham was celebrated by some in his day but described by others as 'notorious'.[19] He was an advocate of natural cures and condemned 'all physicians, apothecaries, chymists and their damnable drugs'; instead he believed in fresh air at all times of the day or season, and the drinking of fresh, icy cold water. Patients were advised never to drink wine or beer, and spirits were banned as 'the devil's liquid flames'. That afternoon in Hexham, he was speaking from inside his 'earth bath'. The idea was to sit up to the neck in the earth for three to eight hours at a stretch, sometimes munching a bit of plantain leaf, and often generating quite a lot of heat. When the perspiring patient emerged, the cold air hit him (or her) and the skin went crinkly as if he had been in water for a long time – but after a good wash in cold water and something to eat, the skin regained its natural plumpness and the cure began to take effect. Dr Graham showed off a young girl who had 'bathed' five times and been almost cured of scurvy. Another young woman, with consumption (tuberculosis) had experienced the 'bath' for three hours, two days running, but had to get out because of cramp in her legs, both times; nevertheless she felt so much better that she intended to continue the treatment. (Sir Walter Scott had tried the treatment, but it was unsuccessful: he later described Graham as 'the great quack of that olden day'.)[20] In the evening lecture, Dr Graham propounded his views on a healthy diet and the need for good air, light and water. Sensible Mary enjoyed the proceedings more as amusement than education, and wished Bryan had been there to enjoy the entertainment. Dr Graham's cures became even more bizarre and dubious: he claimed that a night spent on his 'celestial bed' would guarantee conception, and a population of super-humans would be bred.[21]

In spa towns such as Bath, Cheltenham and Harrogate, the fashionable elite socialised, sipped the often evil-tasting waters, and bathed, ostensibly as a cure for minor ailments. The long-established vogue for spa holidays spread in the nineteenth century to many small towns and villages, wherever there were enough facilities to attract the tourists. Not far from Hexham, was Gilsland, visited by Mary several times in her later life. [22]

> Here, from the restless bed of lingering pain
> The languid sufferer seeks the tepid wave
> And feels returning health and hope again
> Disperse the gathering shadows of the grave.

Praised by many as a fashionable place to drink the sulphurous and ferruginous waters, Gilsland was set in picturesque scenery on the River Irthing, and attracted hundreds of tourists.[23] It was well known for its connection with Walter Scott, who found a wife there and described the place in his novel *Guy Mannering*. Gilsland was immortalised by the legend of the gypsy Meg Merrilees, and commemorated in a poem by Keats.[24] To some, though, the resort was overrated: there were no medical facilities for the invalids, and people of the lower and middle classes frequented the place. Soon after sunrise, the local 'common people' would join some of 'the better class of summer visitors … who are not too idle to leave their bed at so early an hour' to drink the water from small cups; others preferred to have the water delivered to their bed-side in bottles and cans.[25] Wind and rain frequently swept the area, and the local population was sickly, pale-faced, and liable to consumption.[26] Nevertheless, Mary must have enjoyed the scenery and the holiday atmosphere, and sometimes spent several days there.

Family health in the early nineteenth century was largely the responsibility of the individuals concerned: for minor ailments at least, self-medication was the order of the day.[27] Attendance from a doctor came at a cost, and the ingredients for medicines for home treatment were readily available from local chemists and druggists, who began to take over the retail side of the apothecary's job, while apothecaries themselves were licensed to write and make up prescriptions.

Recipes for homemade remedies were exchanged between friends, and copied from newspapers and periodicals, and Bryan Donkin was among those who recorded recommended cures for his family's use in times of illness. In Mrs Beeton's book, the young authoress included a whole chapter on medical matters, giving tried and tested traditional recipes for home cures. Although written forty years after Bryan Donkin's own notes, many are remarkably similar.[28] The recipes were usually concocted from a mixture of herbs and chemicals; many included such exotic ingredients as ipecacuanha, sarsparilla, and sassafras, taken from the roots or bark of trees and plants from the Americas. Donkin's recipe book, written between 1797 and 1820, records potential cures for rheumatism, whooping cough and ringworm as well as other common complaints. Some sound innocuous – pills made from garlic and gum ammoniacum, a plant resin; or aromatic vinegar painted on to parts of the head with a camel hair brush where ringworm occurred; or for inflammation following blistering, finely powdered chalk was applied. For the 'gravel' or kidney stones, half a pint of an infusion of wild carrot in water, taken on two consecutive days would 'give certain relief and sometimes effect a cure for that dreadful complaint'. Some were more dangerous:

> *Reducing the hard and enlarged bellies of children*
> 1 grain calomel rubbed up with 3 grains prepared soda and 5 grains of prepared chalk or oyster shells to be given every night at bedtime, for 8 to 10 days.

and again,

> *Billious [sic] sickness*
> 3 grains calomel; 1 grain ipecacuana; 3 grains extract of poppy; made into a pill to be taken at bedtime.
>
> *For dysentery*
> 3 grains calomel; 1 grain opium; made into a pill to be taken at bedtime.

The ingredient 'calomel' sounds a benign substance, but is actually a mercurous chloride, a hazardous mercury-based compound that can be absorbed through the skin, and can be fatal if swallowed in too large a dose. Yet the deadly poison was given, albeit in tiny quantities, to weak patients, for all kinds of ills. Even the clear-thinking Bryan Donkin, with the best interests of his children at heart, probably mixed and dispensed these risky medicines, having no alternative remedy. His friend Joseph Bramah, another man of intelligence, recommended a recipe for an 'alterative pill', which combined half a grain of calomel with ipecacuanha and cayenne pepper, to be taken first thing every morning to purify a child's blood. Rheumatism could supposedly be cured with a course of five pills, each containing a potent mix of three ingredients: one whole grain each of calomel, opium and antimonial powder. (The last ingredient was a combination of oxide of antimony and phosphate of chloride, known as James's powder after the physician, Dr Robert James, who had first prepared it a century before, to combat the fever; it was itself a common ingredient in more complex prescriptions.) Fortunately, the advice given was: 'Allow an interval of a few days before the pills are repeated', or the consequences might have been worse than the rheumatism. As The Age of Intellect said:

> Calomel for each disorder
> As a panacea order. [29]

Calomel was not the only danger: acid abounded in recipes, too. One of Donkin's recipes suggested treating a child's ringworm with nitric acid, and another advocated a soothing remedy for a child's cough – a pleasant drink made of honey, almond oil and yolk of a new laid egg, but laced not only with rum, but also oil of vitriol, otherwise known as concentrated sulphuric acid.

Like Dr James's cure, there were other ready-made concoctions on the market, some prepared by authentic physicians who had experimented with their remedies before going into production, and others by quack doctors who peddled their wares in the street, claiming miracle cures. It was difficult for the ordinary person to know what was likely to be effective and what was just a useless phial of unidentifiable powder. The *Observer* of 5 January 1800 gives a flavour of the pills and potions on offer: disorders of the bowels could be cured by Appleby's Vegetable Tea; for winter colds, 'often the forerunners of asthma, consumption and death', the Pectoral Lozenges of Honey were 'superior to every other remedy ever known'. Children cutting their teeth, who had been 'at the brink of the grave' with fits and convulsions, could wear 'the true original Anodine Necklace' for one night and be saved. A member of the Royal College of Surgeons, Dr John Mather, endorsed the use of Dr Perkins's Metal Tractors (two small rods), patented as a remedy for all tropical diseases in humans, and horses; other doctors soon debunked Perkins's theory. Radcliffe's Antarthritic Tincture was meant to cure sprains, bruises, lumbago and gout – there was no end to the claims, and advertisements like these appeared throughout the century. Morison's Vegetable Pills and Dr Steer's Opodeldoc, a liniment for gout and chilblains, were among the most popular remedies.

The Donkin family seem to have been healthy on the whole. Bryan occasionally suffered from colds, headaches and minor illnesses, like everyone else. At the beginning of May 1806, on his return from several days away, he found that his three children all had measles at once: John, aged nearly four, was recovering, Sarah, only nine months old was showing signs of the disease, but William, not yet three at that time, was very ill, and was suffering from inflammation on his lungs. Mary, Bryan's sister in Sandoe, lived to a ripe old age, weathering influenza in the winter of 1836-7, alongside her 77-year-old brother William, who suffered for several weeks.

Perhaps something more serious afflicted Donkin's son William as a teenager: in Bryan's recipe book he noted Mr Abernethy's prescription for William, written in Latin and containing magnesium sulphate and senna, an indication of a digestive complaint. Mr John Abernethy was a very eminent surgeon, a professor who founded St Bartholemew's Hospital Medical School: a consultation with him would not have been requested without good reason. He believed strongly that the body and mind were irrevocably linked, one influencing the other: 'Whenever, also, the nervous energy and general powers of the constitution have been weakened and disordered by any violent disease such as fever, small pox, measles, hooping [sic] cough, etc., the digestive organs are frequently affected in consequence and such affection becomes … the cause of many secondary diseases'.[30] William's earlier bout of measles had been severe. The disease can lead to encephalitis, and permanent brain disorders; it is possible that William's childhood illness may have led to consequences that shaped his later life.

As teenagers, Bryan Donkin's daughters Jane and Maria were vaccinated against smallpox.[31] It is probable that the whole family were aware of the dangerous disease and took the precaution of being vaccinated; certainly Mary Ann, at the age of sixteen, took time off school 'for the commencement of vaccination'.[32] Long before that, when Bryan was working at Knole, some of the servants were inoculated, and he, too, probably accepted a dose of vaccine, even though the treatment had not been officially recognised. Like most discoveries, the development of a vaccine was not a sudden event by one person. The doughty Lady Mary Wortley Montague, whose husband was British Ambassador in Constantinople, studied the age-old method of 'variolation' while in Turkey in 1718: this was a practice whereby the individual was inoculated with infected matter from a smallpox patient and suffered a mild version of the disease, thereafter becoming immune.[33] Once back in England she bravely had her children inoculated and introduced the practice to the aristocracy. Another unsung hero was Benjamin Jesty, a farmer in rural Dorset, who in 1774 had noticed that exposure to cowpox gave immunity to the deadly disease of smallpox; he injected his family with pus from an infected cow and his wife became very ill, but she and her children survived and never contracted smallpox.[34] He had no medical connections or money, and was not credited with the discovery, but evidently word spread round the country; certainly it was only seven years later that the Duke of Dorset supported the inoculation of his staff at Knole. Dr Edward Jenner carried out experiments along the same lines as Jesty, receiving funds from the Government for his research, which led to his being credited with the discovery of the smallpox vaccine in 1796.

Donkin was certainly interested in the causes and cures of illness, and later became involved in promoting a cure for a rupture.[35] For some reason, one of his customers, James Swann of Eynsham in Oxfordshire, asked Donkin for advice, and the response was detailed. Mr Fletcher, surgeon to the Gloucester General Infirmary, recognised as an expert on hernias, had recently developed a promising treatment.[36] The recommended method was to rub oil on the affected part, and then spread Fletcher's 'plaster' onto it, applying the mixture with a piece of soft leather. Mr Fletcher would come and examine Swann to see how it was getting on, if his coach fare were paid, and he would like to receive a written certificate confirming the cure from a medical person, as he was anxious to obtain as many authentic testimonials as possible to the success of his preparation. The outcome is not known, but Donkin and Swann remained friends for years.

Writing a history of medicine in 1856, Dr P.V.Renouard surveyed the previous half-century and pinpointed orthopaedics (the correction of exterior deformities) as one of the two outstanding developments of that era – the other was phrenology.[37]

Even today, many people recall that phrenology is something to do with bumps on the head. Reproductions of porcelain heads, marked out in labelled sections, are still available as mementoes of the 'science' that made a connection between the shape of an individual's skull, the characteristics of its owner, and the functions of the grey matter inside his head. It has left its mark as an amusing but outmoded notion. Yet its claims cannot be dismissed out of hand: in the beliefs of the adherents to phrenology lay the germ of modern understanding of the workings of the brain, something that fascinated Bryan Donkin.

The idea that different parts of the brain were responsible for distinct faculties and attributes came from Dr Franz Joseph Gall, an Austrian doctor.[38] His studies in the 1790s led him to the conclusion that a large brain had a greater mental capacity than a small one, and that if one section of the brain was noticeably bigger than others, the faculty or attribute associated with that section would be more highly developed. He went further: he maintained that the skull was moulded on the brain, so that where part of the brain was larger, there would be a protuberance on the skull. Therefore, by feeling the bumps on a person's head, it would be possible to discover whether a person was friendly, secretive, good with words, or had criminal tendencies – as well as twenty-two other attributes. His ideas, he claimed, were supported by his research; he examined the skulls of people who had died with known mental conditions or particular attributes. In his lectures, Gall carried out dissections of brains to demonstrate his knowledge of its anatomy. In the absence of evidence

24 *Phrenological head, London,* 1821.

25 *Dr Johann Spurzheim (1776-1833).*

to the contrary, the belief in phrenology came to be accepted in medical circles as well as by enthusiastic laymen.

Gall's assistant and disciple was Johann Spurzheim, who collaborated with him from 1805, writing, travelling and lecturing in Europe until 1813.[39] Once disengaged from Gall, Spurzheim developed his own ideas, re-classifying the attributes into thirty-five types of feelings and intellectual faculties. He embarked on a series of lectures in Edinburgh in the summer of 1816: it was here that Bryan Donkin met him.

Although in the midst of his own business worries and money troubles, Donkin found the time to involve himself with the new ideas. Full of curiosity and keen to enrich his own knowledge and pass it to others, he obtained plaster casts of skulls from Spurzheim, studied them, and had them duplicated, so that fellow collectors could share the knowledge. For four years from 1817 the plaster casts were made for Donkin by an experienced mould-maker, James de Ville.[40] This man, uneducated but skilful, had been apprenticed to a plaster of Paris moulder as a boy and built up a trade as a lamp-maker, casting in metal. Through working for Donkin, he became fascinated by phrenology, learnt to 'read' heads, and later became a lecturer on the subject. Donkin sent casts of skulls to his friend Mr W. Stark in Norwich – one of 'a peculiar shape from St Thomas's Hospital,' and a girl and boy, 'both idiots'. Others listed included a cast of the head of Bellingham, (the assassin who shot the Prime Minister), and Raphael and Voltaire.[41] They could easily be replaced if they were broken in transit: Donkin had moulds of them, and 'as we are collectors, we can mutually assist each other'. In any case, they were good personal friends. Stark was keen to arrange a course on phrenology in Norwich, led by Spurzheim, and Donkin became a go-between, suggesting costings and viable numbers for tickets. After visiting a paper mill near Birmingham the following January, Donkin sent the owner some wires for his machine, and along with them, packed up a 'marked head' to assist Mr Gold with his new study of phrenology.[42]

Having been to hear several of Dr Spurzheim's lectures, and after hours spent in private conversation with him, Bryan Donkin was convinced of the truth of his theories and even carried out his own research, visiting the Bethlehem lunatic asylum (Bedlam) to examine the heads of sufferers from mental disorders. He wrote of Spurzheim: 'The more I know and hear from this great man, the more I love and admire him. His knowledge of human nature is astonishing and to many must appear almost supernatural. His zeal for increasing it and communicating it is unabated'.[43] High praise indeed from a level-headed man who did not readily express his emotions. While Donkin was travelling to and from work on the Caledonian Canal, he sometimes stayed with Mrs Hutchinson, his cousin in Leith. On one occasion, in October, Dr Spurzheim dined with them there: he soon became a personal friend, although Donkin's awe of him perhaps prevented a really close relationship. Johann Spurzheim was younger than Bryan Donkin by eight years; he was a well-built chap, with an open face and a jaunty haircut.[44].

At the end of January 1817 the Donkins issued an invitation to Sunday lunch. Through their common interest in printing, Donkin had forged a personal relationship with Friedrich König, who came from Germany in 1804 and lived in London for almost twenty years. He was the first to invent a power-driven cylindrical printing press, which in 1814 produced the first issue of *The Times* ever to be printed by a steam-driven printing machine.[45] (Yet it was he who allegedly burst into tears of admiration when he saw Donkin's pretty little printing press!) Mr and Mrs Donkin invited Mr König and his colleague Mr Bauer (or 'Bower' as Bryan spelt his name) to spend Sunday with them at their home in Grange Road.[46]. The Donkins had recently moved to a house in the same street, in the middle, standing back from the line of the other houses. They usually dined at about two o'clock but hoped that their guests would come a little earlier. Bryan was looking forward to renewing their friendship, particularly as König was soon to return to Germany. They must have discussed Dr Spurzheim's forthcoming visit to London, and less than two weeks later, Donkin wrote to tell König that he had taken the liberty of inviting the phrenologist to König's house! [47] He was not certain that Spurzheim would be able to go, as he might have to 'wait upon the Austrian Ambassador on that day'. He stressed that the Doctor would be an easy guest, being neither an epicure nor a glutton, who liked simplicity and hated ceremony. Anxious to do the best he could for his friends, Donkin wrote to John Barton, the 'Comptroller No 3' at the Mint, to arrange a private visit for König and Bauer, their printer partner Thomas Bensley and one of Bryan's brothers, 'in town from the country'.[48] Donkin had discussed the visit with Maudslay, who had suggested that Saturday would be a good day to go.

Phrenology was not without its critics. The writer of *The Age of Intellect* gently mocked Dr Gall:

Dr Gall is vastly kind
Curing each disorder'd mind
When the cerebellum flows
Through the pate in verse or prose
Probing reason's spent domains
He extracts superfluous brains![49]

More seriously, the phrenological meetings in Edinburgh were infiltrated by a Dr Gordon and his followers, who were fiercely opposed to Spurzheim's

26 *Cartoon: 'Dr Spurzheim in his Consulting Room', aquatint by J.Kennerly, after R.Cocking,* 1816.

philosophy and his demonstrations.[50] Gordon – Donkin refused to dignify him with a medical title – heckled and argued, but Donkin reported that the audiences were certainly on Spurzheim's side and rewarded him with frequent expressions of applause and approbation. Gordon also wrote a pamphlet slating the doctrine of phrenology, and a war of words ensued; but Dr Gordon was largely discredited because he produced no evidence as a counter-argument, and lost credibility through his aggressive attacks. Certainly Donkin and many others were totally convinced that particular parts of the brain were responsible for specific functions, an idea that, after moving away from the supposed connection with the shape of the head, has been shown to be true today.

On a personal level, Johann Spurzheim was a good friend to Donkin. Bryan Donkin's son William was fourteen in 1817 and ready, it seemed to his father, to learn French. To achieve this end, William was sent to school in Paris in July, together with two of Mr Gamble's sons. Spurzheim lived in Paris, and Donkin rather diffidently asked him to keep an eye on William and to attend him on a professional basis, as a doctor, should William's health require it.[51] By November, it had become clear that William had not settled happily and was proving to be a handful for his eminent supervisor.[52] His father suspected that William had plagued Dr Spurzheim with visits; he was not applying himself to the school work; he was lacking in confidence, and easily discouraged – 'a look of dissatisfaction from one he loves or respects makes him miserable'; William was complaining that the Gamble boys were treating him badly. Moreover, he was being taught Latin, which was not Donkin's intention, as William was not destined for any of the learned professions, and had shown little aptitude as a linguist. Altogether, it seemed that the best course of action was to remove the boy to another school, and Donkin enlisted Spurzheim's assistance. All this happened at a time when Donkin was feeling particularly gloomy about the future in general, so he was grateful for his friend's advice and practical help. By New Year, Donkin had sent him £20 to cover the expenses of installing William in a different school, and to pay for new clothes for him.[53] Spurzheim was asked to ensure that William would be allowed to send and receive letters without them being inspected; Donkin believed that such restrictions only encouraged boys to deceive their masters and deliberately do things they were not supposed to do.

The letters written by Donkin throw light not only on the trust and respect that he had for Spurzheim, but also on his role as a father to William. He recognised his son's academic deficiencies and his sensitive and perhaps wayward nature, and dealt with the situation in the best way possible, arranging the solution swiftly and with sympathy for his son's plight. Letters that Donkin wrote to 'My dearest William' at the time are a touching testimony to his love for his son.[54] Even when he was deeply occupied with business matters, Donkin always had time and concern for his family.

Another disciple who had attended the Edinburgh lectures was George Combe, who took up the study of phrenology and became Britain's foremost proponent of the subject, writing *Essays on Phrenology* in 1819 and *Elements of Phrenology* five years later. Sales of his influential book *The Constitution of Man in Relation to External Objects,* published in 1828, became a best seller, rivalling the popularity of Darwin's *Origin of Species* – an indication of the popular esteem of the science of the brain at that time. Meanwhile, in 1820, he founded the Edinburgh Phrenological Society, the first association of its kind; another was formed in Philadelphia two years later. Combe actually enlisted Donkin's help in diagnosing the characteristics of two men's heads – he wanted a second, more objective, opinion because the people concerned were personal friends.[55] Of all the phrenologists he must have known during his career, he turned to Bryan Donkin. He also introduced Donkin to a leading member of the Edinburgh Phrenological Society who wanted to meet 'the friends of the system' in London.

Dr Gall briefly lectured in London in 1823, and in the same year, Bryan Donkin and two others founded the London Phrenology Society; evidently he was still a devotee to the cause, seeing it as a branch of science like any other, to be investigated in order to find the truth.

For the next two or three decades, the popularity of phrenology flourished. Bryan's sister Mary went to hear Combe give a lecture in October 1835.[56] New phrenological groups were formed all over the country. Queen Victoria employed a phrenologist to feel the knobs on her children's heads; Bismarck, Marx, Balzac and the Bronte sisters all showed enthusiasm for the subject.[57] Dr Gall and Dr Spurzheim did not live to see their theories discredited – Gall died in 1828, and Spurzheim four years later, while on a lecture tour in Boston, Massachusetts. He was fifty-six, and died of typhus. They would have been pleased to learn that in 1861, Paul Pierre Broca, a brilliant young Professor of Pathology, was able to identify, without doubt, the area of the brain responsible for the powers of speech.[58] Broca had attended a man with speech failure (nicknamed Tan, because he was only able to say 'tan-tan') and when Tan died, had found a badly damaged area of the brain. Subsequent dissections of brains from twenty-five such patients proved the connection between loss of speech and damage to that particular area. It was the same part, on the left side of the frontal lobe, that had been identified by Gall and Spurzheim, as pertaining to speech.[59] Had Donkin still been alive at that time, he too would have relished and espoused the new knowledge. His interest, and his membership of the Phrenological Association, remained until at least the early 1840s, when he was still on the committee, with George Combe as its President.[60] Both his sons John and Bryan, who gave their addresses as The Paragon, Old Kent Road, became members in 1840.[61]

Interest in phrenology had begun to wane by then, although a short-lived revival happened in the 1860s, instigated by the American brothers, Lorenzo and Orson Fowler, who travelled Britain, giving lectures, writing a self-help manual and founding more Societies.[62] One of their articles was reprinted in the monthly *Phrenological Magazine* of October 1880: it was a detailed 'phrenological delineation' of Sir Josiah Mason, a prosperous entrepreneur and philanthropist who had made his fortune as a steel pen manufacturer in Birmingham and who built and endowed the science college that became the city's university. The description of the features of his head indicated (according to Fowler) that he was not only forceful and energetic, with versatility of knowledge and ability, but also prudent, perseverant and spiritual. Moreover, between the first examination in 1862, when Fowler described Mason's head as 'of unusual size' at 23½ inches, and 1880, he observed that his subject's head had actually increased in size by more than an inch, and had changed shape, reflecting the developing characteristics of a more easy-going and benevolent old man.

A few apostles persisted with their beliefs into the twentieth century, and it was not until 1967 that the British Phrenological Society finally closed its doors.[63]

9
Connections

Other things were exercising Donkin's mind while he grappled with the intricacies of the printing machines and the diverse personalities of his business partners. In his mid forties, he was still actively engaged in the development of the paper-making machine, the canning business and the Greenwich tide mill, but he managed to interweave his on-going interests with the new challenges that arose.

Donkin was not alone in his role as a leading industrialist, and took strength from his fellow engineers, many of whom became personal friends. Inventors and men with ideas formed alliances, as had the Lunar men in Birmingham in the 1760s. In the fields of science and technology, as well as in the arts, small groups of men met together to discuss matters of common interest. Before the Industrial Revolution, 'science' – still a relatively new term – had yet to find a place in the lives of ordinary people and their education, being the domain of the rich amateur, the military and those concerned with navigation, and a few in the narrow world of academia. It was gifted individuals such as Donkin who drove the Industrial Revolution forward, using their innate intelligence and the skills in science and technology that stemmed from their respective trades and crafts. In the late eighteenth and early nineteenth centuries, friendships between these individuals formed as they met in coffee houses and taverns to share and discuss the latest ideas. As with literary, artistic and philosophical groups, these gradually developed into learned societies.

The first and longest surviving of these learned societies had begun with a group of natural scientists, who started meeting in the mid seventeenth century to share opinions on the philosophical and scientific ideas of Francis Bacon.[1] Their discussions led to the formation in 1662 of the Royal Society, a body dedicated to experiment and discussion in the field of 'natural philosophy'. Science was very much in its infancy in the seventeenth century, hardly out of the realms of witchcraft, myth and alchemy. The emphasis of the Royal Society changed over the years and, being the first of its kind, it was often subjected to scrutiny and criticism.

The subject matter of the Society's publications in its first decades was the target of one such critic, Dr John Hill; this eccentric London physician, botanist and prolific author on natural medicine, was bright, and although he was not a member of the Royal Society, he had a group of friends who were, so he knew what was going on.[2] Writing in 1751, he first of all acknowledged a grudge against the President of the Society, Martin Folkes. He agreed that innovation and improvement of the useful arts was a worthy aim, but questioned the seriousness of the research that was promoted by the Society. He ridiculed the authors of articles on silly subjects such as 'A Way to kill Lions' (train a porcupine to shoot out its quills at the King of Beasts), accounts of a mer-man and an 'animal plant'. Best of all was 'A Way to catch Wild Ducks' – find an earthenware pot big enough to fit over the head; make two holes to look through; fix it on using bandages round the neck; take off the clothes and get into the river above the ducks; 'skulk' down with just the head above the water; creep downstream behind the ducks and get among them; grab the legs of the first and pull it down; then kill the others in the same way – hardly seemly behaviour for a Royal Society. Throughout the following centuries, criticism was levelled at the various presidents and the ethos of the Society, but it was indeed a hotbed of serious innovation by eminent men of science, and developed into the most illustrious and respected scientific society of all, as it still is today. The highest honour in the scientific world was to become a Fellow of the Royal Society, one that Bryan Donkin himself achieved later in his life.

In 1754, a group that began with meetings in a coffee house in Covent Garden evolved into another society with wide-ranging ideals: the Society for the Encouragement of Arts, Manufactures and Commerce, known as the Society of Arts. Among its objectives were ' to embolden enterprise, enlarge science, refine art, improve our manufacture, and extend our commerce'; it also intended to be a force for social progress, alleviating poverty and securing full employment – worthy sentiments indeed. Scientific experiments were now acceptable, and the practical application of scientific knowledge was one of the issues of the Society of Arts.[3] It has survived as the Royal Society of Arts, still dedicated to many of those principles. Back in 1804, when Donkin was in the early stages of work on the paper-making machine, he became a member of the Society of Arts, paying two guineas as his annual subscription.[4] Seven years later, he achieved their highest accolade, the Gold Medal, awarded for his invention of a mercury tachometer, a gadget that measured the speed of machines. (The tachometer worked thus: the rotating motion of the machine affected a cup of mercury attached to it, causing the level of the mercury to sink in the centre and rise at the rim. The lower end of a glass tube of spirit was placed in the mercury and the rise and fall of the column of fluid indicated the variations of level in the mercury, enabling the speed of the machine to be measured.) For this, Donkin was presented with his medal in May 1810. Later he was to gain another Gold Medal, and to take on prestigious positions within the Society.

Three years after Bryan Donkin's birth, John Smeaton – that great civil engineer who built so many grand edifices, including the ill-fated Hexham Bridge – formed a society of his own: the Society of Civil Engineers (not to be confused with the later 'Institution'). Its name alone was historic, for it was Smeaton himself who had designated the profession of 'civil engineering'. He believed that the country needed to recognise the work of practising engineers. It was a dining club, meeting after work on Friday evenings at the Queen's Head tavern, Holborn. Smeaton saw it as a club where engineers 'might shake hands together and be personally known to each other – that thus the sharp edges of their minds might be rubbed off, as it were, by a closer communication of ideas, nowise naturally hostile'.[5] The Society grew rapidly in its first twenty years, so that by that time there were over sixty members. Amongst them were William Jessop and Robert Whitworth (both canal experts), Robert Mylne, the Scottish surveyor and engineer, as well as Boulton, Watt, Rennie and several other distinguished civil engineers. In May 1792, there were some 'untoward circumstances': one of the members upset Smeaton, and although the good-natured Smeaton accepted the other's apology, the damage was done, and the Society disintegrated. The idea was to reinstate it in an improved form; John Smeaton agreed to be a member, but alas! – he died before the first meeting was held. The new Society of Civil Engineers began afresh, with Jessop, Milne, Rennie and Whitworth at the helm, and three grades of membership. The First Class were real, practising engineers. The Second Class, as honorary members, were men of science and gentlemen of rank and fortune, people like Sir Joseph Banks, the President of the Royal Society and a great naturalist; Matthew Boulton the industrialist; and Joseph Priestley, the elderly philosopher and scientist. In the Third Class were other honorary members, notable people whose professions were connected with civil engineering; these included the instrument makers, Jesse Ramsden and John Troughton and in the first instance, a printer, a geographer, and a millwright, as well as an engine-maker and a land-surveyor. Oddly, it was not until 1835 that Donkin was elected a member, probably because he had chosen to join other societies first; he became President of the renamed Smeatonian Society in 1843, and several members of his family subsequently joined the Society.[6] The term 'civil engineer' had a broader meaning than it does today, covering a range of engineering skills, including mechanics and fine instrument making as well as bridge and tunnel building. Donkin, with his many talents, was always known as a civil engineer.

During Bryan Donkin's adult life the Royal Institution was formed; it was founded in 1799 to introduce new technology. The aims of this institution were more outgoing than the other learned societies, seeking to teach science to the general public through lectures.[7] Michael Faraday was a guiding light and one of the first members to give a Christmas lecture, on Chemistry in 1827. The tradition of a lecture series at Christmas has continued to this day, diversifying from the strict disciplines of physics, chemistry and zoology of the early days, to 'How Animals Move' in 1951, 'the Language of Animals' by David Attenborough in 1973 and Kevin Warwick's 'Rise of the Robots' in 2000.

It was through friends in these groups, as well as through colleagues and customers, that Donkin's reputation flourished. Because of his multifarious achievements in engineering, he was recognised as conscientious, reliable and knowledgeable, and was frequently asked to give his opinion on the work of other engineers. Through his many contacts, word spread that he was the man to try out a new idea or to help with a tricky job. For example, he was approached by Mr Reid, an instrument maker from Aberdeen, to draw up the patent specification for what Donkin called a 'trigonometer', and Reid later patented this measuring device.[8]

Bryan's diary for 1813 records his many activities for the year.[9] One day in May, Marc Brunel, the talented father of Isambard, invited fellow engineers to see his new saw mill in Woolwich. He was experienced in building machinery to saw massive logs of ash and elm, and the oak used by the British Navy for building their ships. Donkin travelled in his friend Henry Maudslay's chaise to witness the process, along with Mr Ellicombe (Brunel's resident engineer at the Chatham Dockyard) and two officials from the Admiralty. Unfortunately there was a hitch, and the steam engine refused to perform. Nevertheless, Donkin was impressed. Brunel's saws seemed superior to any that he had seen, and were easy to get in and out of the frames that held them; they could saw wood at up to eighty strokes a minute. Some weeks later, Donkin went to have a look at Brunel's shoemaking machines in Chelsea. This unlikely-sounding venture had arisen from the wartime need for boots and shoes for soldiers, and for a time Brunel produced shoes in nine sizes, priced from 9s 6d a pair for everyday ones, to £1 for Wellington boots.[10]

The disabled soldiers who were employed at the factory produced four hundred pairs a day. A few weeks before Donkin's visit, the young Prince of Orange had commended Brunel for forming his shoe-making establishment, but when the war ended abruptly, the Government lost interest and left Brunel with a huge stock of shoes and in financial difficulty.

In spite of having been in competition with John Dickinson in completing the first workable paper machine, Donkin and this fellow machine manufacturer were on good terms and, with interests in neighbouring paper mills in Hertfordshire, they co-operated when it came to keeping the local water supply in good order. Donkin spent two days with Dickinson, examining the state of the four locks near Two Waters on the Grand Union Canal, as well as two others higher up in the Chilterns at the Tring Summit, an important canal junction completed only sixteen years earlier; already the canal was losing water through its banks. While in the area, he also took the chance to see how the Two Waters machine making laid paper, was performing with canvas-based stuff, and found that it made very good paper.

Back home, Donkin heard from two of his customers, Mr Abbot and Mr Smith, that they had been offered paper machines at a reduced price, by a man named Lewis Aubrey, who was Donkin's mechanic for the paper-making machines at

Two Waters Mill. Three years earlier, the Society of Arts had awarded Aubrey thirty guineas for inventing a gadget to cut leather straps of the sort used to support the deckles on the paper machine; the contraption was noteworthy for the evenness of the straps it produced, and was highly praised by several users, including an old friend of Donkin's, the owner of Ensham Mill, James Swann.[11] He and others bought the straps from Donkin's factory. Clearly there was no bad feeling between Aubrey and Donkin – who both lived in Fort Place, Bermondsey – since Donkin was supplying Aubrey's straps, but Aubrey was evidently trying to undercut Donkin's prices. The patent on the paper machine had run out, and there was little that Donkin could do but make sure his own prices were fair. No doubt he was confident in the quality of his machines, the level of service he provided, and the good relationships he had with his clients. Indeed, Mr Abbott, one of the mill owners who had been approached by Aubrey, affirmed later that he had not given his consent to anyone but Donkin to make the machines; Mr Smith was not so sure.

Disputes between mill owners continued; Donkin was called to arbitrate between two mill owners near Dover, to recommend a remedy in their arguments over the flow of water to their mills, and after supervising experiments with the water level, he suggested that they both cleaned out their stretch of the river. Requests for this sort of advice often came Donkin's way: he was known for his skill in understanding the flow of water and practical ways of remedying difficulties. More river inspections were called for in December 1813. Donkin took an early morning coach to Liverpool, arriving at the Saracen's Head the next evening; he then took a post chaise to meet his brother Thomas at Speke Hall, the home of Richard Watt. This Mr Watt (unconnected with James) had recently married and was undertaking renovations to the estate that he had inherited. He wanted advice on the jetties he had started to build on the shore of the river Mersey to protect his land, a project complicated by his neighbour, who was afraid that Mr Watt's breakwaters would adversely affect access to his salt works on the river. Thomas knew Richard Watt because Speke Hall was not his only residence; he was also the owner of the estate at Bishop Burton in Yorkshire, where Thomas was the land agent. The Donkin family ties were not only strong on a personal level, but useful professionally.

In January1814, Donkin was back in Liverpool, where he showed printed specimens from the Donkin and Bacon printing machine to Mr Harris, a printer. He spent the next day at the inn with a bad headache, before embarking on a tour to Bolton (to receive an order for a paper machine), to Manchester, and to Birmingham, where he discussed the possibility of making paper from tarred ropes – a practice that may have given rise to the saying 'money for old rope!' The following day, he walked to the Soho Manufactory, the factory set up by Matthew Boulton and James Watt to make their renowned steam engines; there he was shown round the iron works by Mr Murdoch. A skilled engineer himself, William

Murdoch had started his career at the factory in Birmingham in his early twenties, and later spent sixteen years as Boulton and Watt's resident engineer at Redruth in Cornwall, where he worked with their steam engines, making improvements to them so that they operated effectively in pumping water from the Cornish mines.[12] While living in the South West, he had invented the process of lighting by gas, and continued to develop his invention when he returned to Boulton and Watt's factory in 1798 as manager of the Soho business. It was an honour for Donkin to be conducted round the works by this eminent man.

Tuesday, 21 January 1814 was an exciting day. Donkin had breakfast with young Mr Watt, son of the great James Watt, and Sir Isaac Coffin, a naval officer who had been invited because it was thought that he might be of some help in the canning business. Old Mr James Watt, now eighty four, had requested that Donkin should visit him, so Murdoch accompanied Donkin to the grand Heathfield House, built by Watt as his home in 1790. Bryan Donkin was 'received very kindly', and they conversed for some time, on several subjects. Murdoch then took him to the Soho works to see nails being made – Donkin counted 144 small nails being produced every minute, while Murdoch explained the technicalities of preparing the metal. Next day, at the iron foundry, Murdoch showed him an experiment he was carrying out with plaster of Paris, and made him a gift of a nest of heatproof crucibles and some of Wedgwood's thermometers – graded clay pieces for measuring the heat in kilns. Donkin must have been thrilled and inspired by these encounters. On the Sunday, the sermon at the New Chapel in Birmingham was excellent, and perhaps apt: 'The Lord is greatly to be feared in the assembly of his saints and to be had in reverence of those that are about Him'.

From Birmingham, after agreeing a bill with a client, Donkin made for Alcester in a severe frost and snow drifts, but the next day eventually arrived at Mr Phillips's Littleton Mill, safely in the tracks of previous wagons. Despite the freezing weather, he managed to measure up for a building to house a new paper machine. Another mill visit followed, with another potential order for a machine. On Saturday, January 29th the weather was so awful that the innkeeper refused to send for a chaise because the roads were too dangerous: a thaw had begun and it was extremely wet, but there was still a lot of snow. The following day, Mr Phillips bravely came from his mill to pick him up, and took him by chaise to Evesham.[13] From Evesham Donkin took a post chaise to Moreton in Marsh, and onwards the next day to Oxford. From there, he made it back home to London. What a miserable, long journey it must have been, in a cold, horse-drawn carriage, with the thin wheels and the horse's hooves slipping in the icy tracks! However, all the roads were open on the way, with men continually digging out the snow, and Tuesday's diary entry reads 'Got home by coach in the evening and thank God found all my family well' – a relief all round.

In London the Thames had frozen hard. The previous week, the frozen upper reaches had melted a bit, and huge chunks of ice had floated downstream and

27 *Frost Fair on the Thames,* 1814.

lodged between Blackfriars and London Bridge. There the snow-covered ice had frozen again, right across the river, so that by 30 January 1814, people were walking on it.[14] Tradesman and shopkeepers lost no time in setting up booths and tents with flags and bunting, and in the first days of February, the Frost Fair was in full swing, alive with book stalls, music and dancing, skittle games and frying sausages. A sheep was roasted and the 'Lapland mutton' sold for a shilling a slice. Printing presses recorded the event, and souvenir poems were sold. On February 5th, the ice started to crack. Soon the empty booths floated off downstream, and it was all over.

Bryan Donkin did not describe the event; perhaps he was having a well-earned rest after his own taxing travels, and looking ahead to the next task. It was an optimistic time for him. The canning business was going well; the printing machine that he and Bacon had developed had just been patented and was about to be installed in the University of Cambridge. Later in the same year, the first two paper-making machines to be exported from England were sent from Bermondsey to the Tzar of Russia for use in the Imperial Paper Mill in St. Petersburg.

In the meantime, Bryan was trying to help an author with the publication of his book. Westgarth Forster had been brought up in Northumberland where his father worked as mining agent to Sir Walter Blackett at the time when Donkin was a boy in the area. Forster was trained as a practical miner, but had developed into a clever geologist, one of the first in that embryo science.[15] He had somehow managed to chart a forty mile section of land, 1,400 feet deep, stretching from

Newcastle-upon-Tyne westwards to Cross Fell in Cumberland. He started by describing the formation of coal seams in the rocks, but had become a pioneer in the recognition of cyclic sedimentation in the carboniferous rocks and its relationship to the formation of lead ore. The first edition of his findings had been printed previously by the author in 1809 and had also been published in the *Philosophical Magazine*, but Westgarth Forster was anxious to make his research more widely known, and through his sister, Mrs Patterson (a Donkin family friend) he approached Donkin for help.[16] His writing skills did not match the quality of his knowledge, but Donkin found someone to make the wording more acceptable. Donkin pointed out that because of the poor state of the paper trade, the printers were not doing well either, and he was not optimistic of good sales for the book. Nevertheless, he did his best and wrote to the publisher, Messrs. Baldwin and Co of Paternoster Row. Less than three years later it was reported that Mr Forster was preparing his much improved and enlarged book for publication, although it was not finally published until 1821.[17] Forster never made any money from his work, but it was considered to be of sufficient merit and importance that a much revised third edition was published fifty years after his death.

It was in Bryan's nature to help people when he could, not only in a professional capacity, but just out of kindness and interest. He procured small things for his friends and relatives. He helped out his brother William by sending one of his own barometers to Northumberland for old John Errington, 'The Chief'; he found William a piano – not quite the new grand piano his brother had requested, but a second-hand upright one for a third of the price and with a better tone, which he had had cleaned and restored – he would keep it himself and look again if his brother was not happy. He procured a 'writing apparatus' – a copying machine – for his old friend Mr Hutchinson in Leith.[18] These things had to be transported from London by wagon or by sea, but Bryan arranged that too.

Donkin's balanced attitude to life meant that his business letters frequently included personal matters; in talking to clients and colleagues he often learnt something which triggered a personal relationship. Conversely, when writing to his family, he kept them up to date with his business problems and achievements, while exchanging family news. Business associates benefitted from his generosity and freely given time, and many became friends. On his travels he was never short of a bed for the night if friends or acquaintances lived nearby. In a quiet way, he was a networker.

In the community of civil engineers, Bryan Donkin was thrown together with other bright young men, most of them members of the same professional societies. Some were co-witnesses in the court cases and enquiries that Donkin was asked to attend; others came together to inspect new engineering developments and give their opinions. Many became firm friends.

A group was brought together in May 1817 for a day of experiment and fun, organised by Joseph Bramah, one of whose specialities was lock-making.[19] He and his sons set up an exhibition of a large number of their locks, made for the Board of Excise, and confidently gave the assembled company four hours to try and pick any one of them. They were a bright collection of twenty three engineers, including Bryan Donkin as Chairman, John Collinge, Alexander Galloway, Peter Keir, Henry Maudslay, Thomas Tredgold and the eleven year old Isambard Brunel. The offered reward of 220 guineas for managing to pick a lock was not won.

28 *Henry Maudslay (1771 –1831).*

Henry Maudslay was one of Donkin's oldest friends in London. They must have met soon after Bryan moved from Dartford to Bermondsey to set up his factory: they worked together in 1806 to patent a piece of machinery that made the use of gears more efficient and was particularly applicable to hoists and lathes (Patent No.2948). Together, in 1806, they had patented this quick-acting gear box, probably for use in their respective factories. It was reported by Alexander Tilloch (the highly respected proprietor of the long-running *Philosophical Magazine,* and a man of many parts) as 'a new and simple method of combining wheel-work together, so as to produce any required proportion of velocity between the weight and the first mover'.[20] In connection with the patent, Donkin went to see Maudslay, to discuss having two models made in case it was necessary for the Lord Chancellor to inspect them.[21] The two men were much of an age – Donkin was about three years older – and had many attributes in common, chiefly their ability to get on well with other people and their skill and love of engineering. Maudslay's career had started earlier than Donkin's: he graduated from being a 'powder monkey', filling cartridges with gunpowder at the Woolwich Arsenal at the age of twelve, to the carpenters' shop and smithy there, where he soon showed himself to be a born craftsman with a genius for solving a problem in a simple and direct way.[22] At the age of eighteen, he was head-hunted by Joseph Bramah, who was looking for a toolmaker to help with his lock-making enterprise. The journeymen at Bramah's works looked askance at the young interloper who had served no apprenticeship, but Bramah tested him by asking him to refurbish a broken bench vice, which Maudslay did swiftly and efficiently, impressing everyone. By the following year, he had become the general foreman. A tall, nice-looking and personable young man, with a large round head and good-humoured face, Maudslay was much liked by all for his lack of conceit and his open-heartedness. After staying with Bramah for eight years, the needs of his growing family forced him to ask for higher wages; Bramah refused, and by common consent they parted company.

Maudslay set up his own small workshop near Oxford Street. It was probably while he was there that he and Donkin met.

For eight years from 1800, Maudslay built the precision machine tools for Marc Brunel's project at Portsmouth Dockyard; these were a collection of forty-five specialised saws and instruments for boring, shaping and riveting the small pulley gadgets or 'blocks' for use in raising the sails of boats.[23] Brunel's patent machinery was revolutionary, and speeded up the production of thousands of blocks in three sizes, needed for the Royal Navy's fleet. Maudslay's skills were crucial to its development; Brunel was a clever designer, but not a brilliant mechanic like the intuitive Maudslay. By the time the block-making enterprise came to an end for Henry Maudslay, he had moved his factory to larger premises in Margaret Street, and then later south of the River, to Lambeth, where the firm steadily expanded to employ several hundred men, constructing machinery for saw mills, flour mills, and the Mint, as well as steam engines. He and Donkin were both fanatical about producing screw threads to perfection – not for small screws, but the large screws that turned lathes and other machinery. Together, they attended projects that needed an expert eye, to give an opinion for a fee. One such occasion demanded an inspection of the ill-designed Springfield Bridge, Chelmsford, built from iron by the rather unreliable Ralph Dodd, who rarely brought an engineering project to fruition.[24] When the bridge opened in 1820, it was highly praised as 'the most classically elegant iron bridge ever erected in this kingdom'.[25] Beautiful it may have been, but its structure was faulty and within months it had to be reinforced with cast iron pieces. Donkin and Maudslay found much to criticise in the construction of the bridge, but agreed that the contactors were not to blame, and should be paid in full for their work.[26] For their appraisal, Maudslay and Donkin earned £38 between them.[27] They had much in common, and were good friends.

While working at the dockyard, Maudslay met Joshua Field, who later became his partner in the business. Because of their recognised expertise in civil and mechanical engineering, Donkin and Field often found themselves in the same group of assessors of newly developed machines, and as witnesses in Government enquiries. One of Bryan Donkin's pupils also became a good civil engineer and, although thirty years younger, a friend. William Gravatt received a thorough training from Donkin at Bermondsey, and later worked as an assistant to Marc Brunel on the construction of the Thames Tunnel.[28]. The project, not surprisingly, was fraught with flooding, and with Isambard Brunel, William risked his life twice to save men caught up by the foul water.[29] On the recommendation of Donkin, he worked for a short while on the Hebble and Calder Canal, where he built several excellent bridges. Working under Henry Palmer, he assisted with plans for the London and Dover Railway, and later worked with Brunel on the Great Western Railway. Gravatt was a good-natured and well liked chap.

Bryan's working notebooks were peppered with facts gleaned from Thomas Tredgold, 'an individual endowed with the spirit of scientific enquiry'.[30] Like many other engineers, he trained as a carpenter, later working in an architect's office, spending his few spare hours educating himself in geometry, chemistry and geology, and becoming an excellent mathematician. His first two major works, treatises on carpentry and the strength of cast iron, were highly acclaimed. When Tredgold became a civil engineer, he continued to write prolifically on a wide range of subjects; his publications were praised in America and France as well as by eminent scientists and engineers in his own country. Careful research and experiment were the basis of his studies, and his overriding mission was to increase knowledge and improve conditions for his fellow men; but he worked himself to death, leaving his family almost destitute. A 'subscription' was raised to help support his poor children, as a tribute to Tredgold, who had given his life to the pursuit of knowledge. He was forty years old when he died, in 1829. He left an aged mother, two daughters in poor health and a son of thirteen. Ten years afterwards, Bryan's son John and one of Tredgold's early friends, Mr Habershon, raised more public money to help the struggling family. A request was made by John to Charles Babbage, to add weight to the cause by lending his name, a call that the great mathematician readily answered, saying that he understood the plight of the young children and supported the idea of securing a place at Christ's College for Tredgold's only son; he was happy for his statement of testimony to Tredgold's 'valuable service to practical science' to be used to promote the success of the cause.[31]

Foremost among the subscribers to the Tredgold family, when Thomas died, were Bryan Donkin and Timothy, the son of Joseph Bramah. The young Bramah was a partner in his father's thriving business in 1813, when the firm was making money from regular orders for Joseph Bramah's patent locks, his water closet, fire engine and patent pens.[32] The aptitude for engineering shown by Timothy, and the firm's interest in steam engines, enabled him to create a central heating system for the garden hot-house at Windsor Castle and similar hot water piping for heating the corridors and baths at the Westminster and St. Thomas's Hospital. He became an acknowledged expert on the subject. He and Donkin were often involved in the same professional activities and were friends as well as colleagues.

In the meantime, yet another scientific society had been formed, which was to play an important part in Bryan Donkin's life. It was founded by a group of young engineers, who got together in 1818 and formed a club to discuss the problems and innovations in their profession. This alliance, despite a shaky start, was the beginning of a prestigious body, the Institution of Civil Engineers. Joshua Field was one of the founder members of the Institution and its first Chairman in January 1818. Two of the instigators had been pupils of Donkin at the Bermondsey factory: Henry Palmer and James Ashwell. Having worked for Thomas Telford from 1816, Palmer struck out on his own career, centred

29 *Bryan Donkin,* 1829, *aged* 51.

round surveying for transport systems – roads, docks, harbours and railways. Donkin probably recognised Henry Palmer as a good mechanician and surveyor, but also as 'self-complacent and indolent', a description given by one of Telford's pupils.[33] James Ashwell was acting as an assistant to Donkin when the ICE was formed. The young idealists had lofty goals, but the Institution did not take flight until Donkin persuaded Thomas Telford to take up the invitation to become its President in 1820. Donkin became a member a year later, serving intermittently on the committee and for fifteen years as a Vice President, sometimes chairing the meetings.[34] At an anniversary dinner, Bryan Donkin proposed the health of the President, Thomas Telford. Afterwards, the comment was made that ' a company combining so much scientific talent and mechanical skill has seldom been witnessed'.[35]

The other Vice President with Donkin in the 1830s was William Cubitt, who had started work as a joiner, repairing mills, but progressed rapidly to make his name in designing and building of canals, bridges and railways, and subsequently gained a knighthood for superintending the working details of the Great Exhibition building in 1851.[36] The human treadmill, used in gaols throughout the country, was his invention.[37] The treadmill was a nasty mechanism, driven by prisoners walking in a line over steps on a revolving wooden wheel for six hours at a stretch. Designated as 'hard labour', it was a barbaric and degrading punishment, of which Donkin would not have approved, and was a sad lapse of judgment in Cubitt's otherwise distinguished career.

Mutual respect between Donkin and Telford, coupled with strong differences of opinion, forged a wary friendship and an effective working relationship. During 1832, Donkin was unable to go to meetings because of ill health; Telford knew that, and wrote at the end of the year to say that the Institution had been deprived of his valuable assistance, and to invite him to stand as an officer in the next session. Telford signed the letter with the words 'I remain always, with much esteem, yours sincerely, Thomas Telford.[38] It seems that Donkin took up the invitation in 1835 and served as Vice President again for at least ten years.

The ever-increasing public thirst for knowledge in the arts and sciences was largely catered for by magazines and periodicals, such as the long-running *Gentleman's Magazine, Mechanics' Magazine* and the *Repertory of Arts, Manufactures and Agriculture.* A new publication was announced in early February 1820: the *London Journal of Arts and Sciences.* It planned to satisfy the public's interest in emerging ideas in practical mechanics and important advances in arts, manufacturing and the sciences. Not only would all new patents be recorded and described, but there would be summaries of scientific information, culled from published journals and essays, as well as original articles on current developments. Several gentlemen of 'the first talent' and 'known ability' had promised to contribute. Notable among them were the Professor of Mechanics John Millington, Mr Brunel, Mr Bramah, and Mr Donkin. Bryan Donkin had a way with words, as good a writer as he was a speaker; his replies when cross-examined in public enquiries were clear and well-expressed, and in his letters to his family his words came naturally to him, the facts interspersed with touches of dry humour. The first edition of the *London Journal of Arts and Sciences* included patents for a skaiting [sic] shoe and portable sugar mills, and included Jacob Perkins's explanation of his method of preventing the forgery of bank notes, which was endorsed by Bryan Donkin.

When William Fairbairn first visited London in about 1809, the guilds and unions held sway, and as a lad from the country, he had little chance of getting a job. Luckily for him, he was taken on by Rennie, but he had to run the gauntlet of the trade societies, and after six weeks of ducking and diving, was declared 'illegitimate' and sent packing. He eventually evolved into a successful civil and structural engineer, building iron ships, and setting up an iron works in Manchester. In 1860, the recently knighted Sir William gave a lecture on the development of engineering in his lifetime. Full of admiration for the pioneers in civil engineering, he said:[39]

> Rennie, Telford and Watt were still living when Bramah, Brunel, Maudslay and Donkin rose to a high position in their respective professions. For nearly forty years between 1790 and 1830, this phalanx of engineering talent had the field to themselves, and scarcely any work was accomplished without one or other of them having been consulted.

Donkin was indeed in good company.

10

Full Steam Ahead

In spite of the dreadful state the paper industry was in ('as well as all other trades'), Donkin was just managing to keep his head above water.[1] But large projects were looming for the Bryan Donkin Company.

The great civil engineer Telford was a good friend to Bryan Donkin, commissioning work from time to time, which kept the firm going through the difficult times.[2] It was to Donkin that Telford had turned for help with machines for the Caledonian Canal. During 1816, work on machinery for the project was already proceeding at the Bermondsey manufactory. So in the midst of his continuing wranglings with Bacon and Wilkin and at a stage where his involvement with phrenology and his son William's antics in Paris were occupying much of his time, Donkin was called away to Scotland to advise Thomas Telford.

The task that Telford had undertaken fourteen years previously, on the orders of Government Commissioners, was to construct a waterway running north-eastwards between Fort William and Inverness, joining the four lakes of the Great Glen, which meant digging out a canal's width for about twenty miles along the valley. The object had been to provide a safer passage for ships than the hazardous voyage round the north of Scotland.[3] Unfortunately the route through the mountains caused the wind to blow along the canal, hampering the progress of sailing boats. There was no space on the banks for towpaths, so Telford had decided to use steam boats to tow the vessels, and had the idea that the steam engines at present in use as pumping engines for making the foundations of the locks could be converted for use on the steam boats. He also needed dredgers to deepen the channels through the lochs and to cut away the land masses between them. He called for expert help from Donkin.

A steam engine was needed in 1815, so Donkin set about ordering one from Boulton and Watt, still the leading name in the field in spite of competition from Woolf and others. Drawings had arrived, but there was some debate about whether Donkin and his men should erect the machine or whether it should be set up by Boulton and Watt's men, who would understand the peculiarities of the engine and could interpret the marks made for putting it together.[4] If the engineer 'upon the spot' had experience of similar machines, he would be able to manage it; if not, a young man from Boulton and Watt's was working in the area and could do the job. Donkin would have passed the question on, for Thomas Telford to decide.

At the beginning of September 1816, Donkin was preparing to make the journey to Inverness to meet Telford. He was 'perhaps a little scared' by the bad weather with high winds, and had decided not to venture by sea.[5] Five massive lengths of good Baltic oak had been cut, ready to be transported from the Thames up the east coast to Scotland. The Baltic timber was strong and durable, and only a little inferior to English oak. Two of the huge logs fitted in the hold, but the longer ones would have to be lashed to the deck. Another ship was ready to take one of the two long ladders that were being made for use in the locks, also roped to the deck. Donkin had made drawings of the canal, ready for approval by Thomas Telford. Preparation was already under way in the factory for the machinery to be used by Telford, who wanted more, including machinery for two steam vessels intended for towing ships through the Canal.[6]

After dithering, Donkin overcame his nervousness and decided to go to Scotland by sea after all; he booked a berth on the two-year-old *Eagle*, captained by George Todd. She was a nicely built smack with the main mast set in the centre, angled slightly to the stern.[7] A passenger boat of 196 tons, which also carried cargo, she had been known to sail the 460 miles from London to Leith in fifty four hours or even less.[8] Able to travel at about ten knots, the boat could sail better than most other coastal vessels, and Donkin hoped he would 'skim over the waves on the pinions of the *Eagle*' to be with Telford in good time. It was not as simple as that.[9]

They set sail on Sunday 22 September 1816 and had only travelled twelve miles down the Thames from London when another boat ran foul of the *Eagle*, causing serious damage to the *Eagle's* mast. True to form, Donkin the master carpenter came to the rescue and repaired the mast but they had lost the tide and it was Saturday by the time they had reached the Yorkshire coast, where the *Eagle* was becalmed. When the breeze came, they sailed on famously, but the wind strengthened off the coast of Scotland, and the gale that ensued took the topmast off again, just above the splice where Donkin had mended it. It took two hours to get the wrecked mast aboard and they had to carry on without an important sail. That night it was still blowing hard and the high seas terrified the other passengers. The captain had great difficulty in navigating into the Firth of Forth without mishap. On the Sunday morning they were becalmed with the tide against them, only fifteen or twenty miles from Leith, and Donkin disembarked from the smack into a small boat, in the dark, and did not land until seven in the evening. After a long week at sea, Donkin probably wished he had gone by land after all, although the passengers had made congenial company. Few had suffered from sea sickness on the journey, but a day later Bryan was still rocking, 'sadly plagued by the fancied motion of the boat'. In Leith, he stayed with his elderly cousin, Mrs Hutchinson, for three days, while waiting for the next coach to Inverness.

Finally he met Telford and spent nearly three weeks with him, travelling up and down the valley between Inverness and Fort William. At Fort Augustus he examined the locks and pumps and at Fort William he took measurements of the three steam engines to see if they needed to be taken to London to be adapted for the purpose intended; he thought, though, that if William Hughes, the engineer who had worked with Telford on the Canal for some time and whose job it was to sort out the practicalities of dredging, would send detailed drawings with careful notation of the dimensions of each part, the steam engines could remain in situ while they worked out how to adapt them for use on the steam boats. Donkin concluded that the scheme would not work, and was anxious because Telford was persistent in his belief that the steam engines could be adapted, in spite of the doubts Donkin had expressed. He was afraid that Telford would report to the Commissioners that the job *was* possible, strengthening his argument by saying that money could be saved by making the adaptations. Donkin was left with a moral dilemma – whether to stand up to Telford, incur his displeasure, and risk losing future contracts, or whether to keep quiet. He wrote to his brother Thomas '... but I will not disgrace myself'.[10]

He had also had the job of constructing the dredgers. Dredging large expanses of mud from the water was a relatively new art. John Rennie was the first to experiment with a 'bucket engine' drawn by horses on the towpath, but it was John Hughes who perfected the floating steam dredger and first used it to clear the Woolwich docks in 1804.[11] His brother William Hughes, also an expert in the subject, had made improvements to the design of the steam dredger and was directing the dredging operations on the Canal. The dredging engine built by Donkin for William Hughes was later described by Hughes' grandson as 'the most perfect ever constructed'.[12]

The vessel, christened the *Prince Regent*, was eighty feet long and twenty three wide, with twenty five buckets worked by a six horse-power condensing steam engine.[13] One of its great advantages was that it never caused any damage to the canal banks by its wash.[14] It was sturdy, but even so, not without problems in practical use. There were some anxious moments when, to cut through a neck of land or the uneven bed of a lake, it was found necessary to adapt the frame holding the chain of buckets so that they stuck out in front of the vessel. Then part of the bed of Loch Dochfour proved to be so hard that even gunpowder would not shift it. The flow of the current of the River Ness was so strong that it was impossible to keep the dredging boat steady. Even Donkin's finely crafted machinery, made of the best Swedish iron, with steel-bushed bolt holes and strong tempered steel bolts, was unable to withstand the force of the water in order to cut into and bring up the excavated clay. The buckets were torn away, cogs were stripped off the wheels, chains snapped, bolts broke, anchors and cables gave way, and more than once, the whole apparatus of chains and buckets fell overboard. Numerous remedies were tried, until finally every other bucket was replaced by a pair of revolving cutters, which loosened the hard clay so that the next bucket could carry it up.[15] Other problems occurred later: each part of the string of lakes presented a different challenge. Two dredgers were used during the operation. Donkin's *Prince Regent* (built on the glacis, or earth slope, at Fort Augustus) dug the first stretch through Loch Dochfour and Loch Ness.[16] It cut out a channel in a twenty-five foot wall of gravel and clay, seventeen feet of which was under water. Donkin was told by David Crabb, the director of operations, that the engineers preferred excavating with the dredging machine to employing men (with spades) as the expense was not so great. It also worked much faster than manual labour, removing up to ninety tons of gravel and clay from the river bed every hour in favourable conditions; Donkin said the average was 534 tons a day. Excavating in sixteen feet of water near Fort Augustus, while men above dug into the ground about twenty-five feet above the water, the dredger soon completed its share of the task and undermined the new bank; when the overhanging soil fell into the water, the buckets quickly raised it – the men could not keep up, so the dredging machine completed the task.[17] Donkin's ten horse-power dredger - capable of raising almost twice as much as the smaller one – was built at Loch Oich in 1816 to finish the job. The sale of the two dredgers and sundry accoutrements earned the Bryan Donkin Company the princely sum of £6,198.3s.5d.[18] Soon after this, Donkin was also asked to construct a dredger for the work being carried out in the Calder and Hebble Canal in Yorkshire.[19]

Back in Leith at the end of October, Bryan stayed with Mrs Hutchinson again. He was feeling homesick after a month away, and wrote to his wife 'I become, my dearest Mary, very anxious to see you and my sweet little ones again, but it gives me much pleasure to hear you are all well'.[20] Along with this sentiment, he sent Mary several instructions for receiving and dealing with money, letters and parcels, including one of clothes he had left in Inverness, which he was sending back to London on one of the Leith smacks because he would not need them on his travels. The letter was addressed to 'Mrs Donkin, engineer'; either she took an active part in the business affairs of the Bryan Donkin Company, perhaps as company secretary, or it was a private joke.

During his stay in Leith, Donkin's phrenologist friend Dr Spurzheim was in nearby Edinburgh giving a course of lectures – Donkin attended some and was highly impressed with Spurzheim's arguments and his spirited defence against his critics. They spent several pleasant hours together, dining one night at his cousin's house. Two weeks later, Donkin was still in Leith, mixing business with pleasure. A trip to Glasgow to see the steam boats on the Clyde turned into a week's sojourn because it coincided with the long weekend of 'the Sacrament'. Although not irreligious himself, Donkin gently mocked the Scots' devotion, particularly when it upset his plans.[21] Far more people in Scotland observed religious ceremonies than in England, but it seemed to him that attending church was a formality rather than a sign of true piety. The behaviour of the Scots on Sundays amused

Bryan; he had witnessed it in Edinburgh. Everyone left their homes at the same time, as if by common consent,

> an immense crowd of neat, clean, orderly, sedate in their appearance, and well dressed people, from the highest to the lowest, moving along in almost perfect silence excepting the noise of their trampling and the ringing of the bells'.

He detected a measure of hypocrisy amongst the Scots; he knew they were said to be an intelligent race, but admitted that he disliked their character and thought they were stubborn, cunning, covetous and selfish, but nevertheless industrious, persevering, and cautious. He was thankful he was an Englishman!

On this occasion, Thursday was a day of fasting, so no business whatsoever was done.[22] On Friday and Saturday, Donkin went on an unofficial visit to Greenock and back on the steam boats (ever alert for information); Sunday was the Sabbath, and on Monday there was preaching again. Finally he was shown the steam boats officially on the Tuesday and Wednesday. The weather was atrocious, bitterly cold and frosty, and as he travelled through the snow-covered landscape on his way back to Leith, he was grieved to see large quantities of unharvested corn left standing in the snow. Much of the potato crop would be lost too, he feared, a calamity for the poor people. 1816 was soon universally dubbed 'The Year without a Summer': a mean temperature of 13.4°C (56° F) and more rain than usual meant that harvesting the crops in many parts of the country had been left until too late.[23] Farmers in Northumberland, already suffering from huge rents extorted by their landlords, were badly hit.[24] In East Anglia, Bryan had noted, the situation was not quite so bad, partly because the farmers had large stocks of the previous year's corn.

England was not the only country to suffer the cold weather. The previous year, the massive eruption of the volcano Mount Tambora (on an island east of Java) had caused an ash cloud so huge that it had masked the sun for months in many parts of the world.[25] Parts of North America were seriously affected, and among the countries in Europe that were afflicted, France, whose economy was still in poor shape from the wars and the Revolution, suffered badly.

On his way south, Donkin could not miss the opportunity to see his three sisters and his brother William in Sandoe; there he stayed for five days. All his friends were well, but the Donkin family's Nanny was sad that her old friend Mrs Hutchinson's mother had not been persuaded to travel back to Sandoe with Bryan. From Sandoe he sent a letter to his wife Mary again, wishing she were there; everyone was asking after her.[26] Donkin updated her with the ongoing saga of the bankruptcy of Bacon and Wilkin, which had been relayed to him from Mr Houlton, a contact in Norwich; the creditors' meeting had been fixed, but he could not be home in time – could Mary help to get it rearranged, through Houlton? The next stop was Durham, where Bryan's lawyer brother Henry lived with his wife Ann and daughter Jane. While staying there, he heard from home that a big order had come in from the Prussian Government, for a dredging machine.[27] This was excellent news in the difficult financial climate, so he arranged to set things in motion in Bermondsey, while he wrote to make arrangements to go to Leeds to order a steam engine for the dredger.[28] He had asked Mary to get his partner, John Wilks, to draw up plans for the steam engine and send them to Leeds. Writing these letters to organise his journey south took another few days, which he spent with relatives of Mary's just south of York. (To complete the circle of visits to his siblings in the North, he had hoped to stay with his brother Thomas in Bishop Burton, but heard that he was in London.) In Leeds, he ordered the steam engine, having decided that a Boulton and Watt one from Birmingham would be more expensive and probably no better than an engine from the Fenton Murray Wood Company.

A visit to Bolton was next on the itinerary, to collect an unpaid debt of £600 from Mr Livesey, a papermaker; unfortunately the client had gone to Birmingham and, after kicking his heels in Manchester for three days while he waited for the man to return, Donkin 'got nothing but fair promises'.[29] Complicated arrangements for paying the money owed by Mr Livesey, an otherwise good customer, involved another wasted journey to Manchester, cash flow problems all round, and the writing of many letters. More monetary difficulties arose back in Birmingham, where a paper machine was being fitted up by one of his men from London, assisted by John, Donkin's nephew. At this mill, Dow and Gold's at Aston Furnace, a steam engine had been erected – a poorly constructed and badly assembled one, in Donkin's opinion –with a view, eventually, to driving four paper machines; this was the first mill to use steam power, if inefficiently.[30] But, perhaps understanding the pressures of business, Bryan Donkin tended to give both these debtors the benefit of the doubt, and optimistically expected that the money would be paid. He was feeling cheerful because of the big order for the dredger for Prussia, which would amount to £3,500. He had been given the impression that more orders of a similar nature might be forthcoming from Prussia, so the future was looking brighter for the firm; at least the contract would see them through the winter.

At last, just before Christmas, he came home to London, where the children gave him 'a jumping welcome'.[31] He had been away for more than three months and was delighted to find all the little Donkins well, although the youngest of the seven, Henry, had been very ill while cutting his last teeth – a late developer at the age of three. Mary was looking better than when he left her; she had continued to help to keep the business going in Bryan's absence, passing on messages to John Wilks about ordering the steam engine, getting on with an order for the dredger and bargaining for payment. After Christmas Day with his family and the unfruitful Boxing Day business trip to Norwich, Donkin caught up with correspondence: he was a prolific writer of letters to his family, friends and acquaintances, as well on business matters. He arranged to visit the Stainton family in Isleworth, where his daughter Maria was staying.[32] He looked forward to exchanging news about his Northern journey, her Yorkshire trip and Mary Ann's to Northumberland; as they had been separated for so long, and because the days were so short, he would take his night-cap with him. 'You must be good girls. And with patience tarry till I come' he wrote. To his brother Henry, Bryan wrote that he had procured him a writing apparatus, and was sending 'best paper' from Livesey's.[33] This had been laid in stock against the debt that Mr Livesey had still not repaid.

On a particularly rainy, miserable day in early January 1817, he wrote a long missive to his youngest brother Thomas, his junior by five years, but clearly a man after his own heart.[34] All his concerns were aired: the continuing problems with the debt owed by Bacon and Wilkin, and his hope that the printing machine account could be kept out of the equation; his work with Telford on the Caledonian Canal, and his anxiety about the outcome; the good news about the order for the dredger; mention of unsuccessful experiments with steam in connection with a potential patent; the sorry state of the country after the war, the poor economic situation, and the starving people in London. He also wrote at length about the controversy surrounding Dr Spurzheim and his ideas on phrenology, which cut him to the quick, as he felt so deeply that Spurzheim was right and that the abuse and venom directed at him by his critics during his lectures and demonstrations on the 'physionomical system' of the brain was totally unjust: 'There is nothing true (I mean natural facts) which it should be dangerous to know, and there are few such truths, I believe, that are not useful when known'.

In his letter to Thomas, Donkin also mentioned that he had been elected as Chairman of the Committee of Mechanics at the Society of Arts, having won the vote over his two rival candidates. He felt it to be an honour, but did not see himself as a natural chairman, although after presiding on a few occasions, he had heard no complaints! The Society had lost its old secretary, Dr Taylor, but he thought the situation was not irreparable, as Taylor had been 'but a humdrum sort of a body'. In private, Donkin did not mince his words. Arthur Aikin, the new Secretary had both scientific and literary talents and excellent character.

At work, Donkin was taking part in a new venture. London was by now the undisputed capital of the world as far as trade and industry were concerned; visitors from Europe and beyond viewed Britain's technological advances with envy.[35] At London's massive docks, goods came in by sea from all over the world: 214,000 hundredweight of coffee and

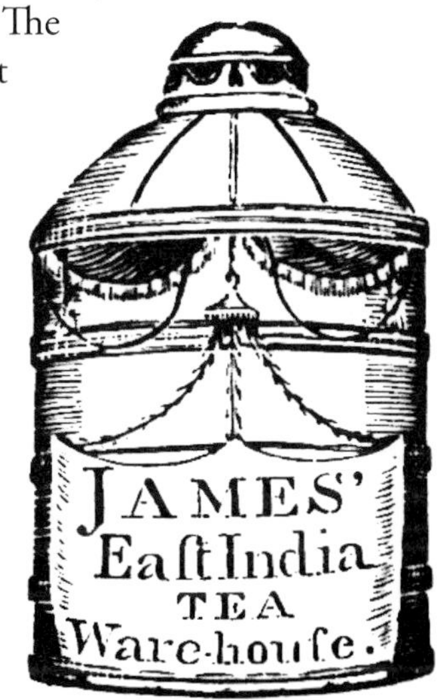

30 *Tea: one of the many imports.*

31 *Entrance to the London Docks,* c.1847.

more than two million of sugar, were imported in 1817, with ginger, pimento, mahogany and logwood brought in huge quantities, as well as large consignments of animal products and foodstuffs, spices, cocoa and rum.[36] The docks had been expanding rapidly since the beginning of the century and incorporated newly-developed steam-driven machinery, and warehouses with still experimental iron roofs and columns.[37] John Rennie was the architect of the new mahogany shed in 1817, building the roof with two 54-foot spans, supported by elegant iron columns; the whole shed was 176 feet long.[38] He had the idea of fitting rails to the huge roof space, equipped with travelling cranes that could grab huge loads of the wood (weighing up to five tons each) from the wharf, and transport them down the aisles of the shed, suspended on chains from the mechanism above, to be piled in stacks in the shed by means of a hand-operated rack and pinion mechanism. These six-ton cranes were constructed at Bryan Donkin's factory, earning the firm £1,450. Later, travelling cranes of similar style, but not made by Donkin, were fitted in another shed – they were not as good.

For long journeys, as well as pleasure trips, travel by steam boat was becoming an increasingly viable option. Since the late eighteenth century, there had been small-scale experiments in France and America in propelling boats by steam engines. After carrying out trials in Scotland in the latter years of the eighteenth century, William Symington constructed a workable paddle steamer in 1802. 'Narrow-minded proprietors of the navigation', predicting that the wash from the boat would damage the banks of the Forth and Clyde Canal, forced Symington to give up the idea and lay up the boat in a creek for several years.[39] Robert Fulton, the American who had been credited with the invention of the steam paddle boat, visited Symington, who invited him and his party on board the abandoned vessel and took them on an eight mile trip on the canal. The boat happily steamed there and back in only and hour and twenty minutes – with no apparent harm done to the canal banks. Fulton was greatly impressed.

The first practical boat, the *Comet,* was launched on the River Clyde in 1812; built by Henry Bell, she was forty feet long, with a three horse power engine.[40] Over the next few years, the Clyde vessels increased in number, size and power; by the time Donkin went there on his travels in 1816, expressly to see them in action, the steam boats were impressive. Typically around seventy-five feet long with a twelve horse-power engine and two paddle wheels, each nine feet in diameter, their speed was roughly four miles an hour in calm weather. The boats could carry two hundred and fifty passengers. Their performance was amazing:[41]

> The distinguishing merit of the steam-engine packets is, that they proceed both against wind and tide with much velocity; but when these are favourable, they use sails also, and then the speed of these vessels is astonishing. While other vessels think it fortunate just to keep off a lea shore, steam boats proudly dart forward into the wind's eye.

Marc Brunel had been one of the first to try out an engine for a steam boat on the Thames.[42] His invention was a double-acting marine steam engine, and the experiment worked – it arrived in Margate in good shape. Brunel was not so lucky; wanting to stay the night, he found he was not welcome:

> So strong was the prejudice which this new mode of communication excited in the minds of the inhabitants, particularly of those connected with the sailing packets that, blind to their future interest, they threatened personal injury to Brunel, and the landlord of the hotel absolutely refused to provide him with a bed.

Passengers on the London to Margate steam boat could promenade on the deck or take advantage of the comfortable facilities in the two cabins and the restaurant; there was separate accommodation for ladies, with a maid in attendance. A library of selected books, magazines and the daily newspapers, as well as backgammon and draughts, helped the passengers to while away the hours. A further pleasure was the music, played by a band, 'when dancing and decorous hilarity render the voyage truly amusing'.[43] The five Thames boats were run by the civil engineer, George Dodd. The first of these, the *Thames*, had been built in Glasgow and tried out for two seasons, plying between Glasgow and Greenock, before being navigated from Glasgow to London via Dublin, a distance of fifteen hundred miles, under the direction of Dodd. She gave good service for four seasons but by the time Bryan made his journey to Margate, larger and more elegant 'steam

32 *George Dodd's steam boat 'The Sons of Commerce',* c.1816.

yachts' had taken over, and the *Thames* had been relegated to the less fashionable resort of Southend.[44]

One of these steam vessels was built by the firm of Maudslay & Field, who by 1818 had established themselves as the premier marine steam engine builders in the capital. The fame and reputation of Henry Maudslay, the firm's founder, was such that he was encouraged not just to build the engines but to allow his name to be used as the engineer in charge of building the new steam yacht for the Margate run, with the appropriate name *The London Engineer.*

The yacht was an elegant craft, adorned with swags along her slim length, with a mast at each end and a very tall iron funnel in the middle.[45] Unfortunately, in the first year of service the boat broke down several times and failed to make a profit. Her new rival the *Eclipse*, with more room and comfort for the passengers, was taking her trade. *The London Engineer* proved to be not very popular, nor did poor Henry Maudslay who was severely criticised and held responsible for its defects. The proprietors commissioned independent reports from Peter Keir and Bryan Donkin to get to the bottom of the problem, but Henry Maudslay was so aggrieved and injured by this action that he retaliated by publishing them, along with a counter criticism of the proprietors and the way the steam yacht had been commissioned.[46] He pointed out that a Mr Courthope designed and should have built the vessel but a Mr Brent had put in a lower bid and was given the commission by the proprietors without his knowledge. Of Keir's findings, Maudslay was very scathing, eventually stating that Mr Keir's report 'is such that hardly ignorance itself will justify, and can serve no other purpose than to expose his utter want of judgement.'

Donkin's report he looked on with far more respect, saying: 'This is certainly a more sensible mode of enquiry' as Donkin, who was assessing the vessel as a whole, rather than just the engines and propulsion gear, quickly got to the root of the problem. Mr Courthope's method of construction had not been adhered to. Timbers of only 4 x 6in. section (approx. 100 x 150 mm) had been used in the construction of the engine room when a 6 x 7in. section (approx 150 x 175 mm) had been specified. This weakness of the vessel and the subsequent vibrations was the cause of breakages to the cranks and other parts, rather than inherent faults in the engines. The proprietors had complained about its inefficiencies. Donkin pointed out that the fire box was far too small, which meant that more coal had to be used to generate the steam required to sail at high speed. He also drew attention to the fact that *The London Engineer* was using estuary salt water in its boilers which 'gives rise to inefficiency'. Henry Maudslay was as pleased as Punch with these comments stating: 'This is completely in unison with the ideas we have always held'.

He was not so keen, however, on Donkin's calculations for the output of his steam engines. Whereas Maudslay, using Bolton & Watt's tables, had rated the output at $60^{8}/_{10}$ horse power. Donkin, using his own calculations, put this figure at $57^{3}/_{10}$ h.p., a full 3½ h.p. less than Maudslay's. Donkin also pointed out a slight defect in the arrangement of the valves, again leading to loss of power, and on a matter of safety, highlighted a need to strengthen the struts that supported the yacht's huge funnel. Another practical suggestion was to remove the heavily carved decorative additions to the hull, to lighten the load by preventing drag as the yacht ploughed through the waves. Maudslay, of course, claimed that he knew these things and would put the ideas in place, along with new paddle wheels. On the whole, Maudslay was accepting of Donkin's criticisms saying they were 'very differently expressed than Mr Keir's'. Donkin and Maudslay had aired their professional views, each using language which prevented the other from losing face. They had collaborated on engineering projects for many years and would continue to work in friendship until Maudslay's death in 1831.

Bryan was a fan of steam boats. His pleasure trip from London to Margate in September the same year had convinced him that it was 'the pleasantest mode of travelling … it is little more than stepping out of one room to another, remaining there for 10 to 12 hours, and stepping out again at Margate'.[47] Another traveller, the editor of the *Monthly Magazine*, did the same journey.[48] Starting from the Tower of London and running against a strong tide, the boat proceeded down the Thames at a rate of six or seven miles an hour, with a band playing, and with 'uninterrupted pleasure'. At Greenwich they met a sailing boat returning from Margate, which had struggled against wind and tide for two nights, whereas the steam boat completed the ninety mile journey in only nine hours. When Donkin sailed to Margate he also wore his professional hat and gained information from observing the engines, which would be useful in the construction of the steam dredgers on the Caledonian Canal. Earlier in the month, he had noted that a steam tug towing an 'Indiaman' down the Thames, had managed a speed of three knots an hour, pulling the sizeable 800-ton sailing boat, carrying cargo to India.

Donkin's first line of expertise had been with the movements of water, but from his early days as a millwright he had been interested in the potential of steam. Early in 1817, he mentioned to his brother that he had started experiments for a steam patent of his own, but had neither the time nor the money to spend on it, particularly when he was not sure that it would work.[49] Bryan Donkin, with a wealth of knowledge gained from assessing and observing other people's steam-raising apparatus, began to formulate his own plan to heat water (or other liquids) utilising super-heated steam. Fully aware of the dangers the workforce was exposed to when dealing with high-pressure steam, Donkin determined to reduce the hazards by raising the temperature of his main boiler to only a few degrees above boiling point, eliminating the fear of explosion. From this boiler, the steam was fed through a non-return valve to a second vessel, where its temperature was raised rapidly. This substantially increased its volume and pressure. From there, a small diameter pipe conveyed the jet of super-heated dry steam directly into the liquid to be heated.

Eventually this patented invention (Patent No.3988) was applied to heat the spherical rag boiler of Donkin's design in which rags of old garments, torn sails and household linens, the raw material of paper, were bleached and softened before being pounded into pulp in the beating engine. This giant rotating sphere, made from strong iron plates hissed and rumbled as it turned on its axis, sloshing its load of rags and bleach about within its belly. Super-heated steam was fed into the rotating vessel through hollow trunnions and although the rags were subjected to temperatures higher than boiling point, safety valves ensured that the workforce was not at risk from explosion. Recognised for its simplicity of operation the design endured into the twentieth century.

Mr Smitherman, a veneer cutter in White Street, Borough, was one of many who made serious mistakes when he ran his engine at too high a pressure, and without a safety valve. The steam engine exploded, demolishing the engine house, scalding a young boy and killing a worker and an apprentice. Donkin's comment was that a high pressure engine was, under the guidance of ignorant persons 'worse than gunpowder'.[50]

On 4 April 1817, a disaster happened in Norfolk. The regular steam 'packet' boat, the *Telegraph,* was pushing out from its moorings in the harbour at Norwich on its way down the coast to Yarmouth, when there was a tremendous explosion: its boiler burst, blowing the roof off the vessel from end to end, and hurtling horizontally through the stern of the boat. Eight of the twenty two passengers were killed on the spot, and six more, who later died, 'had every limb broken'.[51] They were taken to the Norfolk and Norwich Hospital. News soon reached Bryan Donkin, who realised that the pressure in the boiler must have been too great. His instinct was to see the evidence for himself. He rounded up his friend John Collinge, and together they went to Pimlico to call on Timothy Bramah and ask his opinion on whether it would be right to 'interfere' by going to Norwich as volunteer investigators. Bramah's answer was that he would come with them. On arrival, they found that most of the wreck of the steam boat had been cleared away, but the remains of the boiler and the engine gave them a good idea of what had happened. It was evident to them that the boiler had been constructed in two parts and that the explosion of uncontrolled pressure inside had caused the cast iron end to part company from the wrought iron body, with considerable violence. Anxious to look into the whole question of high pressure steam boilers and their construction, and in order to avert another catastrophe, Donkin and his friends enlisted the help of the M.P. for Norwich, Charles Harvey, who took them seriously and immediately set up a House of Commons Select Committee, which met the following month.[52] In the meantime, Donkin, Bramah and Collinge held three public meetings at the Crown and Anchor tavern, each attracting about twenty people; there was much discussion, but no conclusions were drawn.[53] Local magistrates found that the accident had been caused by negligence; the fire had been 'forced too much', during the first few yards of the journey in an illegal race to get ahead of a rival boat, and the weight that should have regulated the safety valve had not been properly set.[54]

The Government Enquiry was thorough. It took place on six days between 13 May 1817 and the 22nd, and the first witness to be called was Bryan Donkin.[55] Under questioning, he reported what he had concluded from examining the remains of the boiler from the wrecked boat: it seemed that for some reason, the cylindrical boiler had been made of wrought iron, but one end had been cut off and replaced with cast iron. He explained why a high pressure boiler would have become dangerous under those circumstances, although he conceded that with careful management, it could be safe – but he would not use one himself. Low-pressure engines were not so flexible or powerful though, and used more fuel. Cast iron boilers were more likely to explode than wrought iron because the metal was more frangible and would splinter into fragments, causing more destruction than wrought iron, whereas a boiler made of wrought iron, in the unlikely event of an explosion, would split. Donkin was able to relate that his brother-in-law, John Hall, had recently had two or three accidents with Woolf's recently invented cast iron boilers at the Dartford works, and that he had heard of a great many explosions of high-pressure engines both in this country and America. He knew of no injurious explosions of low pressure engines, although they did often give way through wear. The questioning was relentless, but Donkin answered up well, responding patiently and professionally and explaining courteously. His was the longest piece of evidence.

During the enquiry, seventeen other engineers were interviewed. Among them was Henry Maudslay, who had recently successfully refitted the *Regent* steam boat for Yarmouth, using a low pressure engine. Bramah and Collinge contributed their knowledge, both of the incident that had caused the enquiry and their experience of steam engines; John Hall, Alexander Galloway, George Dodd and the other eminent engineers gave their opinions. Arthur Woolf, considered by many to be a strong competitor to James Watt in building steam engines said: 'No, I have never had anything to do with steam packets – they are out of my line', but gave a spirited defence of his own invention. Two Cornish mining engineers were called, who both said that in all their years of experience, they had never seen any accident with a high pressure boiler; a chemist who used a steam boiler to prepare his concoctions told of several accidents with cast iron boilers, the first and notable one being Trevithick's catastrophe at Greenwich in 1803. Several men were killed by his high pressure pumping engine.[56] Evidence was taken from two sugar refiners who had witnessed a terrible explosion caused by malpractice by workmen in charge of a badly-built boiler. Alexander Tilloch gave evidence, too; he was the editor of the *Philosophical Magazine* and the *Star* newspaper and was 'sometimes called on to act as an engineer' – in fact, he was a man with numerous skills, who amongst other things was prominent in the development of stereotyping as an aid to printing, and in 1820 entered the competition for a method of foiling bank note forgers, with which Donkin was also involved at that time. He had plenty to say on the subject of steam boilers and safety valves. Each witness had a different point of view, and their opinions were not unanimous. Even so, the committee was able to come to some conclusions: that steam engines could be safely used for driving boats and that high pressure engines were fine, if well constructed from wrought iron, with good safety valves. The disaster at Norwich had been caused by an improperly constructed boiler, an overloaded safety valve and too great a degree of pressure. In order to prevent further accidents, they recommended that all passenger packets should be registered; boilers should be built of wrought iron or copper, with two regulated safety valves and must be regularly inspected; there should also be a Bill to enforce better management of steam packets. All this was the consequence of Donkin's curiosity, diligence and public-spiritedness.

Five years later, as part of another Select Committee's enquiry into the roads from London to Holyhead, the subject of the safety of steam boats was raised again, because the onward journey for mail was now successfully made from Holyhead to Howth by sea, on the way to Dublin. The size and speed of steam boats had increased, and Brunel, giving evidence, believed that the enormous boilers took up too much space; he also thought the paddle wheels were inadequate to their task. Arguments on the merits of cast iron and wrought iron still continued, but Donkin, called again as a witness, was adamant that if enough money was spent on the boilers, 'they can always be got quite perfect'.[57] He (and Timothy Bramah) agreed that boilers were now too large, but said that smaller ones would be as efficient if the surface of the boiler exposed to the fire was sufficient. In any case, the key to preventing accidents was to make sure that the men who operated the engine were diligent, and Donkin thought the inspection and management of the boats was often deficient. Furthermore, Donkin advised on the type and size of the coal used to fire up the boiler; if piled up in large quantities in a damp state, the wrong kind of coal could spontaneously combust. Mr Brunton of Birmingham had invented a fuel-saving rotary furnace: Donkin thought this would be highly suitable for the boats, and safer, because it obviated the need to open the fire door to feed the flames every few minutes. Now that steam boats were taking to the open seas, Donkin reckoned that the engines need to be considerably larger to save fuel, rather than forcing an under-powered engine to work to fullest extent, with the danger of damage to the machinery.

There was no shortage of ideas and opinions from the professionals, and to conclude the enquiry the committee praised them for their opinions on the best ways of improving the Post Office Holyhead Packets. Much public money had been put into building robust vessels, which not only provided better communications between England and Ireland, but had successfully 'established a new principle of certainty and security in the system of steam navigation'. The part played in the development by Bryan Donkin had been considerable.

Telford continued to keep in touch. While working on the Ellesmere canal in Shropshire, he asked Donkin if he could find a second-hand steam engine to drive pumps. Donkin knew of an old six horse power one in a brew-house, with a rotten frame but a good copper boiler, that would probably be cheap, but he had not seen it himself so could not recommend it – he would keep an eye out for another one.[58] With all the contacts that Telford had, he had a choice of good engineers at his behest, but clearly put his trust in Donkin's judgement and resourcefulness.

11

Innovations

Like a Chinese plate-spinner, Bryan Donkin had the knack of keeping several interests going at the same time, ever taking up new projects while having new ideas for the old ones, while managing his social life, never forgetting his family and friends. In early 1817, with the birth of baby Thomas making their family complete, Bryan, Mary and their nine children moved along Grange Road to the bigger house standing back from the line of the other houses, where König and Bauer were among their first lunch guests. After living there for about five years, the Donkins moved to No.80 Great Surrey Street – a sign of prosperity.[1] In this imposing three storey house they made their home for six years. The 1820s, when Donkin was in his fifties, were as busy as ever. The Company was doing well with Mr Donkin at the helm: his son John was working closely with him, and Bryan showed no sign of slowing down. Since taking ownership of the factory in 1811, he had made great strides in the quantity and diversity of goods produced and the works had grown.

Within the walls of the factory was an especially important building: it was tall, hexagonal, and built of wood, and housed a tube-drawing machine, where large metal tubular parts were pulled into shape with the noise of screeching metal. Here the process of tube-drawing was perfected, enabling Donkin to produce tubes with the accuracy in manufacture that was necessary for use in finely-crafted instruments and machinery.[2] Facilities for tube-drawing were few and far between in London, and Donkin's machine was described as 'enormous'.[3]

To make a tube, a brass or copper sheet was first bent and soldered into a cylindrical form; if the outside diameter had to be uniform, the cylinder was pulled through a succession of holes until it was the right size. If the inside shape was crucial, a succession of steel cylinders called 'triblets' was drawn through the tube. Tubes for telescopes had to be made to exact measurements inside and out and so incorporated both processes, sometimes doubling the length of the brass tube; this was carried out vertically, hence the need for a tall tower for use in forming long tubes for giant telescopes. Tubes as long as thirteen feet could be drawn, varying in diameter from one inch upwards. Such highly specialised work demanded excellent technical skills from a dedicated workforce and co-operation at all levels between the men, as it did throughout all departments of Donkin's factory.

33 80 *Great Surrey Street (now Blackfriars Road).*

Tubes were sometimes drawn vertically, by means of a strong chain wound on a barrel and pinions. The tubes were pulled through the dies of Donkin's tube drawing machine by a vertical screw which was turned round by a gearing system driven by six men at a windlass. This machine drew out cylinders for paper-making machines and others, as large as 26½ inches in diameter and six and a half feet long.[4] Several of the most highly-regarded scientific instrument makers came to Donkin for tubes for their astronomical, meteorological and measuring apparatus; the quality of Donkin's workshops was recognised by William Simms and Edward Troughton, who remained good customers for years.[5] Tubes were not only made for optical use, though: customers in other trades benefitted from Bryan Donkin's expertise. Each customer had his own precise needs. A leading engineer and printing machine manufacturer, Thomas Middleton, needed special tubes for his machinery.[6] Robert Wiss of Charing Cross, the inventor of a hydraulic weighing machine, wanted to protect its main parts from the water by placing them inside tubes and in the 1830s ordered dozens of copper tubes and drawn barrels ten to thirteen feet long.[7] The owner of the long-established Hythe End Mill on the River Colne, George Glasscott, needed several copper tubes for his paper-making enterprise, and an engineer and millwright, who rejoiced in the name of William Flowerdew Sadler of Tooley Street, required copper tubes and brass barrels for his

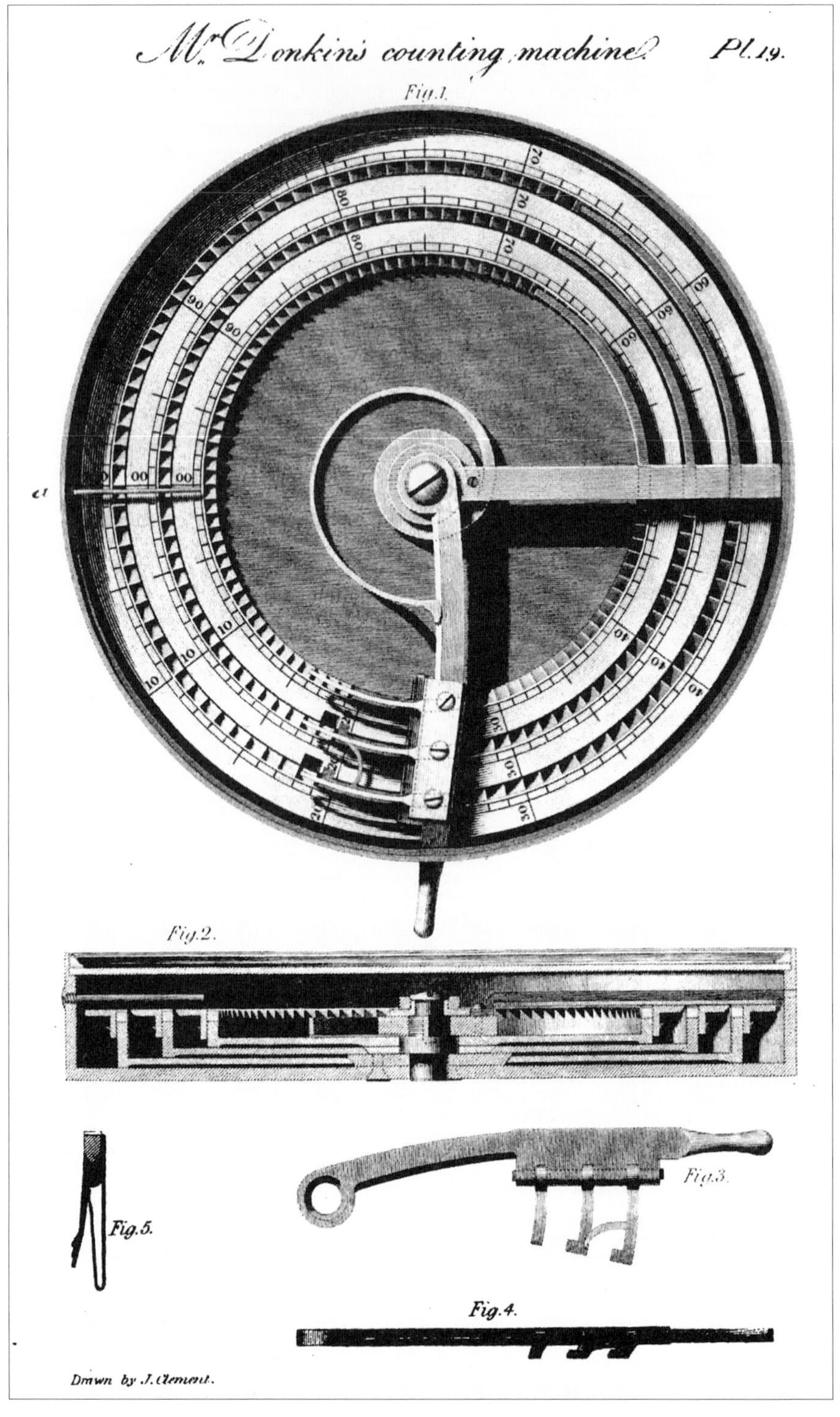

34 *Bryan Donkin's counting machine,* 1819.

everyday work.[8] An order came for sixty copper tubes eighteen inches long, from J. Spiller, a boiler maker from Battersea, and Jonathan Downton, a shipwright who had patented a continually flowing pump for an uninterrupted flow of water, bought a narrow pump barrel, 3ft 3in. tall, as well as copper piston rods for the pumps, all made specifically to his dimensions.[9]

Although run-of-the-mill orders kept the Bermondsey factory busy, Donkin's own creative thinking did not cease. He was always looking for solutions to problems, to make life more comfortable or purely out of curiosity.

While in the throes of trying to get the doomed Donkin and Brightley printing machine into operation in 1819, the ingenious Donkin had been working on a smaller but nevertheless important idea. Bank notes have to be numbered, consecutively and individually, a problem that Bramah had tackled for the Bank of England ten years earlier, when the method of writing on each banknote with a pen had become impractical.[10] His solution was imperfect because his machine could only print units. In 1813, John Oldham presented the Bank of Newry with a similar but much better idea, capable of numbering from 1 to 100,000; it was turned down in Newry, but later adopted by the Bank of Ireland.[11] Donkin's invention, a 'counting machine', was akin to Oldham's, but for a different purpose; it could count the number of revolutions of any machine, by means of a series of notched ratchet wheels and clicking levers.[12]

> The very compact and portable counting-machine invented by Mr Donkin will be found a most useful instrument in the hands of the civil engineer, for registering repetitions of alternate or continuous motions such as the strokes of a piston or the revolutions of a wheel.

Donkin saw it as useful for measuring

> the number of revolutions made by a mill wheel or of the strokes of a steam-engine beam in a given time, or the number of revolutions made by the wheel of a carriage or a perambulator over a certain space.[13]

Its simplicity, accuracy and effectiveness in counting and recording to the tens of thousands earned it the nickname 'tell-tale', as well as another of the coveted Gold Isis Medals from the Society of Arts.[14] (Bryan Donkin became a Vice President of the Society of Encouragement of the Arts, Manufactures and Commerce – an honourable position to hold and a reward for his contributions to the Society.) Another accolade came years later from Charles Babbage, who declared that 'one of the simplest instruments for counting any series of operations was contrived by Mr Donkin'.[15]

A life-long interest in canals and waterways had developed in Bryan, all the more through his experiences on the Caledonian Canal, and in 1819 he learnt of a patent granted to John Bogaerts, for a method of raising and lowering the water of canal locks. Soon after the patent was inrolled, Donkin exhibited a very large working model of the canal lock in the yard at Blue Anchor Road, available for inspection by the public every Monday from 10 a.m. until 4 p.m.[16] Tickets could be bought at several places, including Donkin and Gamble's office in St Clement's Lane, Lombard Street. With permission from the patentee, Donkin made modifications to the lock, which were publicised and praised in the London Journal of Arts and Sciences.[17]

Always intrigued by the flow of water and its implications, he embarked on a series of experiments with Peter Barlow, the brilliant mathematician and physicist; he was Bryan's contemporary and already a fellow of the Royal Society.[18] The aim was to discover the effect on water passing through differently shaped orifices or pipes.[19] The apparatus they used had been made for a different purpose and was rather peculiar; the contraption was rigged up so that water flowed from a circular cistern, two feet in diameter, into a smaller copper cistern and then vertically down a copper pipe just over three inches in diameter and twenty five feet long. At the bottom, a ten foot pipe was joined at right angles, which in turn was attached to a short pipe which could be put into a horizontal or vertical position. To its end, metal pipes of various shapes could be fixed; both ends of conical pipes were used, for instance. Two conical pipes fixed end to end (both ways) could be attached, and flat plates with a hole in them were also tried. The amount of water coming out was measured over a number of minutes, and comparisons made. It is not clear, though, exactly why two grown men spent the best part of six days in November and December 1823 and a further four days the following June, pouring water down oddly-shaped tubes; but the Heath Robinson contrivance may well have been the beginning of the first ever water turbine. The Frenchman Benoit Fourneyron built the first practical water turbine in 1827; it was a more efficient horizontal version of the traditional water wheel.[20] At first they were not popular in this country. However, it is clear that Donkin continued his experiments with using water power more efficiently, and the Bryan Donkin Company was one of the first to use a turbine to replace water wheels for driving paper mills in England. When Donkin turbine equipment was installed during the renovation of Mr Portal's mill at Laverstoke, where the specialist bank note paper was made, it was still a novel feature, even in 1854. It was noted that the turbine was: 'a description of a water wheel but little known, as yet, in this country … It is a horizontal wheel, and to it, in this instance, is attached a beautiful contrivance, rendered necessary here by the constantly varying level of the water at the tail of the mill'.[21]

In his spare time, Donkin patented his new invention, a process 'for singeing, destroying or removing fibres from the thread of the fabric of flax, cotton, silk … composing the fabric usually termed lace-net … .' (Patent No.4842).[22] The singeing process is still carried out on fabrics today, to make them completely smooth by burning off the small downy fibres; nowadays the material is passed

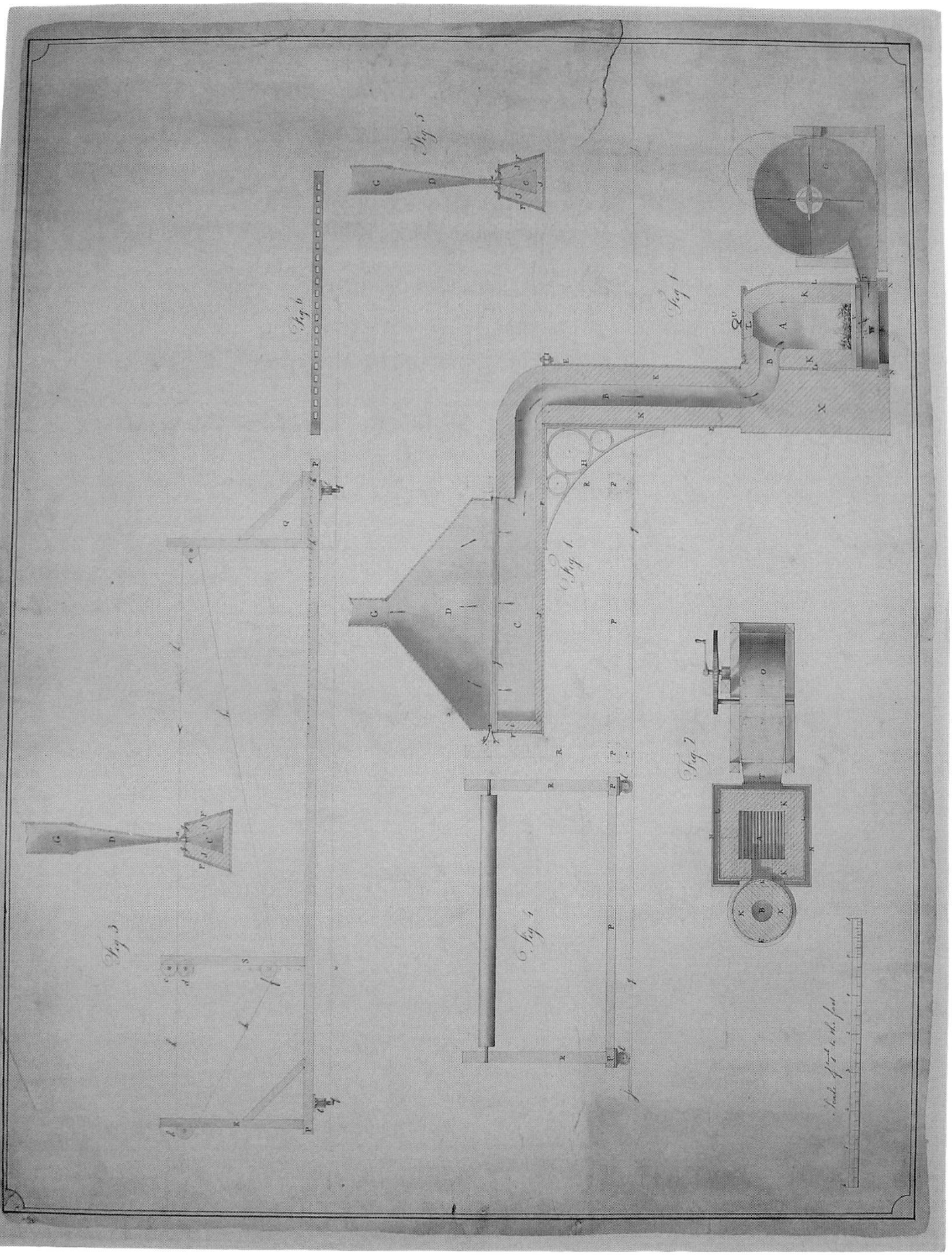

35 *Patent method of removing fibres from fabric, 1823.*

quickly over a gas flame or a copper bar that is heated to a high temperature. The textile trade was booming and methods for dealing with the loose threads in lacy materials (as the patent suggests) must have been useful. In order to perform the tiny task Donkin conceived (and presumably constructed) an enormous contrivance. A fire was built in a stove and fanned, and the hot air passed up through a chimney. Above, the ends of the offending length of fabric were joined together to form a continuous band, which passed round a series of rollers, and over a slit through which the hot air flowed, held taut by a sucking mechanism that kept the cloth close to the jet of air: there the singeing took place. Whether this contraption actually worked is not recorded, but would Bryan Donkin have gone to so much trouble if he was not sure that it was worthwhile?

The state of the country's roads was a source of discomfort and difficulty to travellers such as Donkin. In March 1817, business and family matters were combined again, though perhaps not so willingly on Bryan's part this time.[23] His twelve-year-old daughter Sarah needed to go to Sandoe and the only way to get her there safely was for her to travel with him. The plan was for him to take her in a chaise to Wakefield, where he and his companion, Mr Jessop, had to examine a canal as part of preparation for a court case in York, then on to Halifax to report to the Canal Company committee, and from there to York for the trial. At York he would send her off to his brother Thomas in Beverley, to be collected by her aunt in due course, for the last leg to Sandoe. It must have been a worry for a caring father: travel by land at the time was a bit of a gamble. A healthy man could ride a horse, and for short journeys for two people, it was sensible to drive or hire a chaise, a light carriage drawn by a horse. Scheduled mail coaches, carrying up to a dozen passengers, ran regularly between the cities, but the roads varied considerably in quality, and there could be delays.

Maintenance was carried out mainly by local trusts, who set tolls for the turnpike roads in order to raise money for surveys and repairs. Some trusts were more efficient than others, so provision was piecemeal and patchy. The main problem was the surface of the roads: they were made from different materials, ranging from clay and gravel to uneven stones and chalk, or any mixture of those.[24] The habit of repairing the roads by laying a thick pile of gravel down the middle and leaving the horses to spread it as they passed over it, resulted in dangerous, rough, and patchy roads that were badly drained and uncomfortable for the passengers, as well as being hard on the horses. For a hundred miles around London, the roads were particularly bad, with ruts, potholes and puddles. In North Wales, where Telford's scheme for improving the communications between London and Dublin was well underway, the roads were excellent. Round the city of Bristol, great strides had been made by the surveyor of an extensive trust: he was John Loudon McAdam, a Scot with a deep interest and long experience in road-building even though, by his own admission, he was not a professional civil engineer. He understood the broad picture: he had experimented with different materials, he knew the ways of horses and their drivers, and he recognised the impact of heavy vehicles on the surfaces of roads. McAdam had solutions. His method was to dig up the existing road to a depth of at least four inches and sort the material it was made from, getting rid of any clay or chalk that would 'imbibe' water, and sieving the gravel. Stones would be broken up by women and boys sitting on the ground, using light hammers; the small jagged stones would sit neatly together when laid. The surface would then be re-built in two-inch layers of graded stones and gravel, making the road as flat as possible, but up to three inches higher in the centre so that water would run off the now much smoother and more solid surface.[25] McAdam's success was acknowledged by the Government Inquiry of 1819, and led to the gradual improvement of road transport throughout the country, through the process of 'macadamisation'. (When in 1902 Edgar Hooley devised a method of stabilising road surfaces with a mixture of tar and metal slag, he honoured McAdam's invention by naming his 'tarmac'.)[26]

Donkin, too, applied his mind to the subject. In 1824, he read a paper to the Institution of Civil Engineers, explaining his ideas for a remedy.[27] The holes that appeared in the roads caused intolerable jolting; they damaged carriages and were dangerous to horses, he said. The different sizes of stones used for laying the roadways made them uneven because the foundations were inadequate: when it rained the earth underneath turned to mud, and the smaller stones sank in. In his paper, he carefully considered every aspect of the laying of the road, including his opinion that 'a very slight inclination suffices to drain off water' and that the 'extravagantly high rounded pavement' (the road surface) 'remains a dangerous evil in many of our streets'. (It was Telford's idea to raise the centre of the road to aid drainage.)[28] Donkin's suggestions were that the surface should be made uniform, the materials should be durable, and that the size of the stones and the shape and slope of the carriageway should be taken into account. He put forward a solution: a substratum of hard stone, broken into pieces about an inch across or a little over, laid to a thickness of nine inches to a foot on the earth, and rammed in hard; then a covering of fine gravel or coarse sand, as a 'proper bedding for paving stones'. Macadam's method of carefully graded levels of gravel and stone for roads had been carried out for several years; but Donkin pointed out that the expense and the poor use of materials had hampered progress, and he clearly thought that a permanent surface made of larger, more even stones would be an improvement. He specified the dimensions of the ideal size of each stone: five inches wide, seven and a half inches to eight inches long, and ten to thirteen inches deep for stability. He did not call them 'setts' at the time, but for decades after that, granite stones of this sort were laid as roads in towns and villages throughout the country. And have our modern-day garden patios and driveways reaped the benefit of this man's invention?

John Farey (1791-1851) was an engineer with a similar background and interests to Bryan Donkin, although he was more than twenty years younger than Donkin.

Both their fathers had been land agents for large country estates; they both had had a wide range of engineering experience, and were knowledgeable about patent laws.[29] At the age of nine, Farey was awarded 'the greater silver pallet' by the Royal Society of Arts for his original perspective drawing of the London Water Works; later his many drawings and writings were published in magazines and his major work *A Treatise on the Steam Engine* became a Bible for scientists.[30] As a consultant on the subject of patenting inventions he played a major part in the Government Select Committee enquiry into the state of play regarding patents for inventions in 1829.[31] This time, Bryan Donkin was not one of the twenty witnesses, but his name was mentioned during the proceedings. In answer to the question 'Is not the [patent] specification very seldom prepared by the inventor himself; does he not employ his agent to do it?' the witness, Francis Abbott, replied 'he frequently employs an agent; but in a matter of importance, he frequently employs such a man as Mr Farey or Mr Donkin'. Farey was a professional expert in the field of patent law.[32] Clearly Donkin was in the same league. Later, Farey's nephew, Barnard William Farey, joined the firm of Bryan Donkin and Company.

Being an inventor himself, as well as possessing a facility with words, and understanding patent law, Donkin was often approached to help people who had ideas for new products or gadgets but could not express them in appropriate words for preparing patent applications. One such was Thomas Hancock in 1824, who had been experimenting with a method of making 'artificial leather'.[33] His method was to import raw rubber from Central America in its pure liquid state. It was collected from the rubber trees, extracted in the time-honoured way – as it still is today – by slashing the bark and allowing the sap to trickle into cups fixed round the trunk. He described the rubber as being exactly the colour and consistency of thick cream. The principle feature of Hancock's patent was the manufacture of artificial leather, which he produced by saturating felt, carded cotton wool and hair, and combining it with other fibres such as hemp and flax, and then mixing it with the liquid rubber. When dry, the whole mixture was pressed and rolled under heavy pressure, making a strong material that looked like real leather. It lost its stickiness but retained the ingredients in the mixture. Colour could be added during the process or the surface could be coated afterwards, rendering it suitable for all manner of purposes from harnesses and hosepipes to thin cloth. The advantage of the new material over real leather was its flexibility and elasticity and the fact that it could be formed to any size. One use found for Hancock's artificial leather was during the building of the Thames Tunnel, where Isambard Brunel used very strong straps made of the material on his steam engine, used for sinking the shaft for the tunnel. For his help in preparing the patent, Bryan Donkin received a £5 fee, with an added perk: for decades after the publication of the patent, the deckle straps for his paper machines were made from Hancock's invention, rather than real leather. Thomas Hancock went on to go into an agreement with Charles Mackintosh, who gave his name to the waterproof 'mac'.[34]

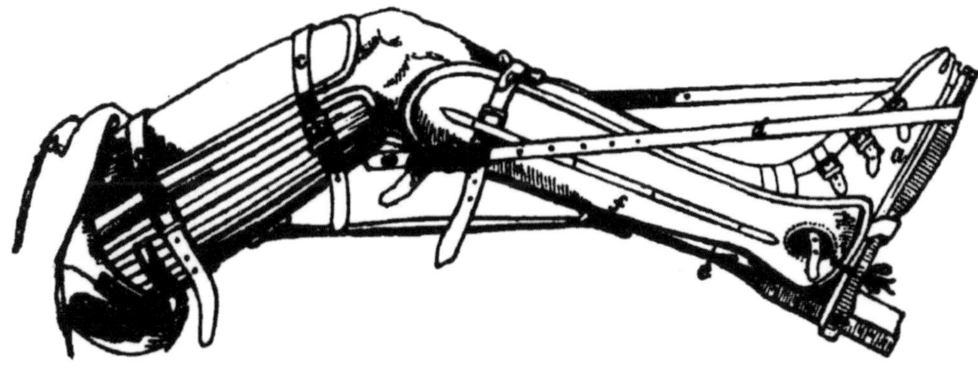

36 *Joseph Amesbury's leg appliance,* 1823.

Inventors of medical equipment also came to Donkin for help with developing contrivances for their patients. As a surgeon, Joseph Amesbury, who happened to be Donkin's next door neighbour at 82 Great Surrey Street, presented a long report about his adjustable leg brace to the Society of Arts in 1823, when Donkin was Chairman of the Committee of Mechanics.[35] It was a clever contraption to help patients who had broken bones in their leg. Unlike ordinary splints which often caused bones to knit in the wrong position, causing pain and deformity, Amesbury's apparatus permitted more natural movement of the limb and quicker healing. Apparatus for helping the recovery of arms, legs and toes was made for Amesbury by Donkin four years later.[36] Mr Griffin of Leicester Square was another inventor whose skills lay in the fabrication of furniture for the disabled rather than in the paperwork connected with patenting them; Donkin helped him with one of his designs and produced the invalid chair for him.[37] Griffin's business flourished and in the 1850s, he was producing a whole range of invalid carriages, including a high-backed padded wheelchair for exercise outdoors and a 'sofa britzka carriage' for persons with spinal complaints, which looked like a large pram, complete with hood.[38]

Through his membership of the learned societies, Donkin was sometimes approached by people from other walks of life who had good ideas for inventions but who were without the skills to perfect them and carry them out. In 1828, one such was John Lewthwaite, who had asked Dr Faraday and other scientific friends for advice on his idea for a harpoon for killing whales.[39] He was encouraged to entrust the invention to 'a very scientific engineer' – Bryan Donkin – who experimented with the design, perfected it and produced six harpoons with levers, joints and recesses, in consultation with Lewthwaite and Captain Kendrew, Lewthwaite's seafaring brother-in-law.[40] Kendrew was on the point of sailing his bark *Ann Elizabeth* to the South Seas on a whaling voyage and agreed to experiment with the harpoons, taking with him the secret ingredient, prussic acid, to be placed in capsules in the point of the harpoon to deliver the deadly blow to the whale. At sea, the first experiment only paralysed the whale for a few minutes, but Kendrew was sure that a larger dose would be fatal. The final outcome is unknown, but although others later claimed to have invented the use of prussic acid for the purpose, it was almost certainly originally Lewthwaite's idea.[41] For the soft-hearted Bryan Donkin, it was a job to be done, but perhaps he felt a few qualms.

The factory, primarily set up to build paper-making machines, undertook any engineering work that came its way, even making machines for cutting furs. One went to a salesman of skins, Mr Borradaile of Great Suffolk Street in 1826; two years later a passport was obtained for a man from the works and his passage was booked to Rotterdam and onwards to set up a similar fur-cutting machine in Offenbach, Germany, returning via Liège after more than three months of work at 9s. 6d. a day.[42] Another large order came from the Government of Norway in 1837, this time for a diving bell.[43] Every part of the 6ft 2in. x 4ft 6in. structure was supplied by Donkin's company – nuts and bolts, pipes, valves, and chains and an 8 inch air pump, but the lenses probably came from one of Donkin's contacts. The whole construction was carefully packed in a large packing case, with a specially made yellow deal cover for the top of the diving bell, to protect the lenses on the voyage to Norway and to serve as a permanent covering when the bell was not in use.

A fellow engineer and Society of Arts member, C.W.Williamson, invented improvements for lathes, but it was Donkin who made the lathe and accessories for him.[44] T.F. Bergin, a Dublin engineer with a host of talents but a particular interest in railways, approached Donkin in 1836 with a request for a model of his latest idea for improvements to railway carriages, which Bryan Donkin made, from drawings that his son Bryan had made after a trip to Dublin.[45]

In 1832, Donkin's Bermondsey 'shops' were visited by an eminent American engineer, George Escol Sellers, who had much in common with Bryan Donkin, particularly as a designer and builder of paper-making machines.[46] To add to his personal knowledge, and to gain a deeper understanding of the state of industry in Britain, he had come to speak to the leading engineers, among them Brunel, Maudslay, the paper-maker Dickinson, and Donkin.[47] Although a confident man with wide experience, he nevertheless approached Donkin with some trepidation, knowing his reputation for keeping his cards close to his chest to protect his business interests. However, he came armed with a letter of introduction from James Swann of Eynsham, Oxfordshire, one of Donkin's oldest and most respected customers and the new owner of the latest paper machine, which Sellers had seen and much admired. On the strength of his credentials, Donkin welcomed him, and willingly took Sellers to the erecting shop to show him 'the widest and finest machine I have ever built'; but he was not allowed to see the tools and materials that Donkin had used in constructing the paper machine. Donkin explained that he had built up his collection of specialised tools – the lathes, drills, milling and shaping machines – over almost a lifetime and he hoped that Sellers would not take amiss his unwillingness to show them. The sixty inch wide Fourdrinier machine impressed the American greatly; he went so far as to say that it was the finest specimen of workmanship that he had seen in England. The secret formula for the composition metal used for the parts was not divulged by Donkin: he did not reply when asked about it. But 'the great inventor' clearly enjoyed showing off his machine to an appreciative fellow engineer, and as the visit proceeded, Donkin began to warm to his guest.

Sellers had brought to England an attachment for a paper-making machine, patented in America by his father; his intention had been to apply for an English patent for this 'pulp dresser'. Now, having seen in action a similar 'grate bar screen' (a strainer that smoothed out the lumps in the paper pulp) made by Ibbotson, he was in two minds. Donkin warned him strongly that he should not show his pulp dresser to anyone for fear that the idea might be copied. Sellars trusted Donkin's advice and discretion: he had been told by his uncle, a well-connected artist, that the epithet 'honest Bryan Donkin' had been applied by no less a person than Sir Walter Scott, who had become an intimate acquaintance of Donkin through their many discussions about the choice of paper for publishing Scott's novels. It pleased Bryan to hear of the flattering description.

With the ice broken, they talked of common concerns: how to make paper without rust spots, and the methods of cutting paper as it came off the machine – guillotine cutters were in common use in America but techniques in England were not so far advanced. Various methods of cutting the paper as it came from the machine at the end of the process had been tried from the outset on the Donkin machine. The first patent had included a device for cutting the dry paper into sheets as it emerged from the last roller; on the later machines, the endless strip of paper was wound into a huge roll, and a cut was made manually right through the bulk of paper at one point to form the sheets. Many paper-makers bought long knives from Donkin for the purpose.

The pulp dresser arrived at the factory a day or two later, but Donkin was not well and looked at it at home; he invited George Sellers to his house, where his guest found him still suffering from a very heavy cold. They discussed the pulp dresser, comparing its merits and costs with Ibbotson's, which Donkin was fitting to his machines: perhaps some agreement could be made between Ibbotson and Sellers? As the two engineers relaxed in each other's company, Donkin began to feel brighter, and the conversation ranged more widely, over subjects unconnected with their professional interests; Sellers was surprised that someone so obviously steeped in mechanical pursuits could be so knowledgeable about art, and so well acquainted with artists. They compared notes on making copper cylinders, on wages, materials, tools and attitudes on both sides of the Atlantic, and Sellers noted that the 'great and successful inventor – certainly the most progressive machinist he had met in England' seemed not to understand how the United States had made such rapid advances. The difference, said Sellers, was partly due to the English resistance to labour-saving machinery and newfangled notions, as well as the division of labour, where men were only proficient in one area of work.

Although he had not expected to be shown the workshops, and in spite of Bryan still not being well, Sellers was delighted to be taken round when he visited the following day. Donkin, evidently impressed by the American's openness, had begun to let down his guard somewhat. In turn, his visitor appreciated being allowed to see the great lathe used for turning the huge drying cylinders for the paper machines. Above all, he admired Donkin's system of uniformity for the beautifully made machine parts. On the first day of his visit, Sellers had noticed that all the parts, from the largest roller to the smallest screw, were standardised, making replacements easy. While he was viewing the precision machine tools, Donkin was called away to deal with an emergency. An accident in a mill – where a worker had dropped a tool into a moving paper machine – had done serious damage to several parts. The messenger from the mill had come by carriage with a description of the parts that had been destroyed. By the time Donkin returned to Sellers, he had already dispatched a competent workman in the carriage back to the paper mill, with readymade duplicates of all the broken parts taken from the shelves in the storeroom, which Donkin showed Sellers with pride. It was the first time that George Sellers, an engineer of wide experience, had seen an efficient system for making and supplying interchangeable parts, and he was vastly impressed. As he later acknowledged, this was an innovation at the time, and the system was not generally adopted for several decades.

Ibbotson arrived in the afternoon, and the three men hatched a plot. They agreed that securing and controlling the rights to the Sellers pulp dresser would be of mutual benefit, but there was a problem. In Kent a paper maker who made good quality tinted paper for such prestigious firms as Dobbs (who did fine embossing) and Thomas de la Rue, claimed to have invented a better and less costly pulp screen than Ibbotson's; however, Ibbotson strongly suspected the mill owner of infringing his patent, and working in secret to avoid payment. They needed to know. The mill had one of Donkin's machines, but when Donkin had sent men to adjust the gearing, they had not been allowed to go into the machine room. Skulduggery was called for. Even with his knowledge of patent law and his careful protection of his own secrets, Donkin was not above a little underhand activity when it came to a matter of suspected unfair dealing. His plan was to procure a letter of introduction from Thomas de la Rue, whom George Sellers knew. (The year before, Donkin had made 'press' for de la Rue's stationery and printing business).[48] With the letter, Sellers would gain entry to the mill in the guise of an American traveller keen to see English factories and once inside, would sneak a peep at the pulp dresser and immediately know whether or not it was an infringement of Ibbotson's.

George Sellers went to stay the night at Ibbotson's home, and during the evening took the opportunity to see the improvements at Ibbotson's mill. Unfortunately a mistake had been made: a valve in the chlorine tank had not been opened, and when Ibbotson opened a sliding door, a stream of 'heavy gas-like water' poured out, engulfing the two men and the mill manager. Poor Sellers, already suffering from stuffiness with hay fever, was overcome and almost suffocated by the chlorine fumes, and had to be manhandled out into the dark night and pummelled back to life.

Back in London unscathed, Sellers took a coach to Maidstone to embark on his mission of espionage. At the gaol-like mill, he met with a surly, silent welcome from workers on his way in, and handed his letter of introduction to the proprietor, a thick-set, bull-like man behind an untidy desk whose face became contorted as his flabby cheeks shook with rage. In his fury, the man demanded to know what right Mr de la Rue had to send anyone, let alone 'a d---d Yankee', to the mill when he knew that strangers were never admitted. Sellers let him rant; but then thought it best to apologise, and asked if he could instead learn something about the management of the hop crops he had seen nearby, without danger of being arrested. 'Crusty', as Sellers dubbed him, retorted that he could go where he liked as long as it was outside the mill. Glancing backwards as he left, Sellers saw the proprietor jump into a gig and drive off at a furious pace, lashing the horse with his whip. While pondering on his next move, the American chanced to see a man, wearing the traditional paper-maker's square cap, emerging from the window of the machine room down a plank and into a nearby cottage. Sellers engaged him in conversation, playing the naive tourist, asking silly questions about the mill. Could he see round it? No – it would be more than his job's worth if the master found out; nobody was allowed in; the boss was afraid people would steal his secrets. Both men were nervously looking over their shoulders, watching the Maidstone Road. Sellers talked more. He promised to take a message from the man to a friend in America, he listened to his life history, gave him a half dollar as a 'rememberencer', and the man relented. Everybody hated the boss like poison, he admitted, so no-one would 'tell on' the intruder, but he would have to be quick. Feeling as guilty as a burglar, Sellers followed the man over the plank, past the paper machines and driers and up to the vat where the suspect pulp dresser was in action. After a furtive scrutiny of the pulp strainer, he beat a hasty retreat, and escaped through a hop field, emerging just as Crusty had passed on his way back to the mill. The pulp dresser turned out to be a definite infringement of Ibbotson's patent; it worked in exactly the same way, by jogging up and down, but was a different shape. It had an addition, a wiper that supposedly cleaned the screen but actually created extra rolls of pulp, so that more frequent cleaning was necessary than on Ibbotson's model. Back in Bermondsey, Donkin and Sellers had a good laugh about the adventure, and the deal between Sellers and Ibbotson was sealed with Donkin's help. Subsequently the pulp strainers made by Donkin sold to paper-makers better than ever before.

During the week that George Sellers was in London he had several pleasant talks with Bryan Donkin, which strengthened his opinion that he was the most advanced mechanical engineer of the time. Much later, Sellers praised Bryan Donkin, saying that the world was indebted to him for developing the crude ideas of Robert and Didot so perfectly that without any essential changes, the great bulk of the world's paper was produced, over a half-century later, on machines 'substantially as they came from his brain and hands at that early period'.[49] Sellers visited the Bryan Donkin and Co workshops more than once, and said later that he had never witnessed a more admirable assortment of exquisite machine tools, even though he had seen probably the best machine factories of the country and the Continent.[50] He was full of praise for Donkin, who had presented him with a foot-long rosewood scale of his own making, calling him 'certainly the most progressive machinist I had met in England'.[51]

12

Home from Home

In 1828, as Bryan reached his sixtieth birthday, his children were all in their twenties and unmarried. When his eldest son, John, married the following year, he moved to the Great Surrey Street house, and Bryan and Mary took up residence at No.6, Paragon, a crescent off the New Kent Road. Sundry jobs in the Donkin house were taken care of by men from the factory and charged to Bryan's personal account. Mr Brewitt, a skilled worker who was capable of producing micrometer screw threads and making alterations to the precious dividing engine, was entrusted to carry out work in the house and garden too, including making a long fence and parcelling up a grand piano; another man made a garden gate, and a third constructed bedroom furniture.

Mary, Bryan's wife, was an ever-present, supportive figure in his life, for whom Bryan clearly had a great affection. Now, she is known only by her portrait – a strong-looking woman with a pleasant, not unattractive face, in spite of a large nose; her brown eyes had a kindly twinkle. Dressed in her best, she wore a fashionable black silk dress with voluminous 'gigot' sleeves and an under-blouse, with a light ruff at the neck. Topping the shiny brown curls (possibly dyed or even artificial) that were crimped round her forehead, a great bow-like confection of stiffened silk adorned her head.

Bryan's first grandchildren, twin girls, were born early the following year, but alas, did not survive long. A decade later, John joined his parents' household in the Paragon with his five children; Bryan Donkin Junior lived there too.

Life went on in Sandoe. Bryan visited his home village whenever he could fit it in with his business trips to the North. His brother William spent his whole life in the area, working as a land agent and steward for the Erringtons, and his sisters Mary, Ann and Jane lived full and happy lives in the village, but by the 1820s all the other siblings were married and scattered. Even when their parents were long dead, the far-flung brothers regarded Sandoe as their second home, and gravitated there when their busy lives allowed the journey to Northumberland. On one occasion, all the brothers except John came to stay with their sisters in Sandoe; later, when one of them died, the other seven all gathered there for the funeral.[1] In 1828, Bryan spent over a month with Mary at Sandoe, even throwing a dinner party while he was there. At that time, together with William, he still held a game certificate so they may well have spent time shooting together on Stagshaw Bank or beyond. Four years later he stayed again for three weeks and throughout his seventies his old home drew him back at least once a year, usually accompanied by younger members of his family. Otherwise, correspondence flowed between the brothers and sisters; they were a close family. Bryan was always pleased to hear news from Sandoe, with the local gossip.

There was deep affection between Bryan and his family. When Mary Ann, his eldest daughter, was only six, she travelled to York in the Paul Jones coach from London with her aunt, Bryan's sister Mary.[2] A poignant note in his diary recorded his emotions: 'I did not think I should have felt so much, but it was parting with a sister and daughter whom I dearly love, and God only knows whether we may ever meet again; may God preserve and bless them.' They did indeed survive the rigours of the long journey, arriving in York a day and a half later, safe from the perils of the April weather, the overnight stay in an inn, and the threat of attack by highwaymen or travel sickness.[3]

The village of Sandoe, though little more than a hamlet, was a microcosm of society. The Erringtons, John ('The Chief of Beaufront') and Henry, were the local landed gentry, providing work in their fields and properties for the local labourers. Both Bryan's father and his uncle had worked for them. Many of the cottages in the village were rented from the Erringtons and other local landowners, and the population spanned the spectrum from rich to poor. The Donkin family was central to the village activities; Bryan's sister Mary in particular played a full part in village life, keeping up with local activities and mingling with families of all classes.[4] It was the habit of several generations of Donkins to call their first-born sons William and John. There was also a confusing plethora of Bryans and Janes.

William Donkin, born in June 1759, was the eldest of Bryan's siblings, his senior by nine years. Very much the country gentleman, he was intelligent, efficient and compassionate – a fine man with wide-ranging interests and abilities. He was happy to follow his father's profession, and throughout his adult life served the Erringtons as land agent. Apart from supervising the day-to-day work on the estate, dealing with tenants and negotiating rents, his many duties included writing to Henry Errington during his absences from Sandoe. One of his letters was about the management of the crop rotation, explaining the virtues of planting clover between the two crops of corn, rather than leaving a fallow field.[5] The system was recognised as innovative. There were problems on the estate to tackle all the time – trouble with John Errington's housekeeper, poachers and the proposed canal to the north of the area. Henry Errington was continually asking him to find servants for his residences in London and Hampshire. It was also his job to buy large quantities of groceries from Newcastle, and once, thirty-six yards of petticoat flannel at a penny a yard to distribute to poor old ladies. One incident, recorded well after William's death, seems to cast aspersions on his name.[6] Allegedly, a bundle of documents concerning the rights of the freeholders of Corbridge was sent to William, who had been appointed to adjudicate on the allocation of fair proportions of land. The papers were never returned to their owners and were found many years later, scattered up and down the neighbourhood. William Donkin's 'neglect or oversight' was cited as a reason for the loss, coupled with the indifference of the freeholders, but the slight on his character was never proved, and it is reasonable to suppose that theft by an unknown person might have been involved; it seems unlikely that William, a man of impeccable honesty, would have had any motive for such a devious action.

William's hobbies were country pursuits. At the Tyne-side Agricultural Society one year, he won prizes of five guineas each for his sheep – 'best tup more than one shear' and 'best shearling tup'; and his prize Shorthorn cow, 'Duchess' was renowned.[7] The red and white bull 'Brilliant' and the roan 'Garland' were bred by William from good stock, as well as the white Shorthorn 'Rhadamanthus' and a whole family of young cows and bulls bred from 'Beauty' and 'Traveller' between 1810 and 1815.[8] William's sheep breeding skills were the envy of the neighbourhood, mentioned alongside stories of his prize-winning cattle by a rival, who happened to be a relative of William's wife: 'The stock, cattle and sheep of Mr Donkin, and his tillage management, were long equal to the best in the North of England'.[9] At home, under his instructions, William's excellent gardener, James Ireland, grew prizewinning vegetables and exotic fruit as well as flowers.[10] Surprisingly, melons and pineapples could be grown outside, in heated pits, and William's gardener was successful enough to win him a gold medal for a melon in the Horticultural Society of Durham, Northumberland and Newcastle-upon-Tyne's July show in 1830, as well as a prize for 'a fine dish of green peas' and a silver medal for peas in the pod in the same year. A later gardener gained a prize for William, for the best eighteen dahlias, 'dissimilar blooms'.[11]

The house where William lived with his sister Mary in 1825 (after his wife's death) was Sandoe High House, a comfortable mansion and the third most imposing residence in Sandoe, after Beaufront Hall and Sandoe Hall.[12] It was rented from a descendent of Captain Henry Tulip of Walwick Hall, who had owned the High House back in the 1750s. (He was the local landowner, notorious for tearing down more than a hundred yards of the seven foot tall Hadrian's Wall, to build a farmhouse.)[13] It seems likely that it had been the home of William's parents, and that Bryan's older brothers and sisters were born there, while Bryan and the younger children were born at the now elusive Fountain Hall.[14]

37 *The High House, Sandoe.*

The High House was spacious. It had originally been built as a farmhouse during the reign of William and Mary, with a roof of stone tiles set in lime plaster; the size of the slabs was graded, with larger stones at the base than at the ridge. Back in the late eighteenth century it had been converted into a comfortable house with a new stone front.[15] An extension had been added to one side, incorporating a two-storey bay window, the three tall casements on each level allowing the sunshine to pour into the rooms. Behind the house were outbuildings, used later as a coach house and stables; at the front a terrace looked down towards Sandoe Hall, supported by a high stone wall dropping to road level. The imposing front door opened into a well proportioned and spacious reception hall with an arched iron fireplace under a stone mantelpiece carved with a simple lattice design. Doors led through to further rooms on the ground floor. In the adjacent dining room, an elegant room with a simply decorated cornice near the ceiling and a fireplace similar to the other, was a cupboard where chamber pots were kept for the comfort of the lady diners: gentlemen made their own arrangements outside in the garden. The library and other ground floor reception rooms were interconnected, while the servants' corridor led discretely across the house behind the main rooms to the kitchen, the housekeeper's sitting room and butler's pantry. A wide, shallow staircase, installed in the 1760s, curved upwards to a further sitting room, the bedrooms and the nursery. Clearly, the family was relatively affluent; but even so, the house must have been hard to keep warm in the Northumbrian winters, and the residents probably shared their space with mice. Nevertheless, it made a good home for William, his sister Mary and their servants in their later years, after the death of William's wife.

Unusually, William and his wife Catherine had no children of their own, but when the wife of his brother John died in 1822, William stepped in to become the guardian of his twenty year-old niece Jane, rescuing her from an all-male family, bringing her to Sandoe and adopting her. Catherine had died four months earlier, but William's sister Mary made an excellent aunt. (Jane later married rather well, to William Smith of Houghton Hall.)

Earning about £200 a year, William was well paid, but also had other strings to his bow. As a partner in his father's brewery enterprise at Hexham, he thought of buying out of the business after his father's death; he disliked the trade, and anyway, it was not doing well at that time.[16] But he remained a trustee of the brewery, joining with George Elstob to whom he transferred two tenth shares in 1817. Under the name of Donkin and Elstob, the Hexham Brewery flourished into the 1830s, and Elstob was still going strong in 1852.[17] With his co-trustee George Elstob, he was a member of the Hexham committee of a nation-wide appeal in support of lead miners.[18] The Donkin family's connections with the Lambtons of Biddick in County Durham led him to gain land and property as trustee and sole beneficiary of the will of John Dawson Lambton; as well, he undertook the guardianship of Phoebe Lambton, who lived with him and his sister Mary in their middle years before marrying Matthew Carr and going off to live in St Petersburg.

William was a landowner, as well as both a landlord and a tenant. His dedication to rearing sheep and cattle meant that he needed the use of much of the local land.[19] As a tenant, he made payments of half-yearly rents to Henry Errington and later to his successor, Rowland Errington, for land at Stephenson's farm, paying £50 for six months when his salary as a land agent was £200 a year.[20] He also rented fields belonging to the Brewery Company that he had previous partly owned. William owned a great deal of the local land himself, including about eight hundred acres called Whiteside, near Walden to the West of Sandoe, which he acquired in 1802 for the sum of £3,500 and let for £160 a year, a good return on his investment.[21] In addition, thirty eight acres round the High House were rented to him by John Errington, and he paid rent on a house and land in nearby Anick as well. The cultivation of fields and the use of land for animal husbandry were formerly subject to payment by tithes by the tenant farmer, who gave the landowner a proportion of his produce, be it wheat, hay or milk. However, by the early nineteenth century it was common practice for the tenant farmers to pay rent instead of tithes, for example:[22]

> 1d. [one penny] per cow whether farrow or calven, in lieu of milk,
> 4d. for every foal fallen,
> 1d. for every cast of bees in lieu of honey and wax,
> 1d. from each occupier in lieu of fowls and eggs'.

Thus William, as an owner of land in Sandoe, received £32 10s. a year from his tenants, in lieu of tithes of corn and grain.

As John Errington aged, his mind became confused. Under a Commission of Lunacy he had been labelled as a lunatic as far back as 1787, when he was not yet fifty.[23] The following year, after appealing against the commission on the grounds that he was enjoying 'perfect and constant sanity of mind', he was allowed by the Lord Chancellor to continue to have the care and management of his estate until 1800, when it was again decided that he had become 'disordered in his senses', and a 'committee' (one person) was appointed to look after him and his land and property. When the 'committee' died, and after some legal wranglings, two local people were appointed to look after the wellbeing of John Errington, and a Newcastle gentleman of the bar, who was given the job because he was unconnected with the family but near at hand, took over responsibility for overseeing the running of the estate: by law, he was entitled to five per cent of the amount of rents collected from the tenants. Naturally, much of the work involved in the management and finances of the estate, and looking after the old man, fell on William's shoulders; he regularly reported to Sir John Swinburne of Capheaton, near Newcastle, but he discovered that no-one was actually empowered to take action over practical problems and often found the situation awkward. Sometimes he had to delve into his own pocket to pay immediate expenses.[24] He and The

Chief respected each other and got on well, and although Errington also had a housekeeper, he seemed to prefer William to attend to his needs. It is likely that he suffered from the condition now called early-onset dementia, which was not understood in the early nineteenth century. He was certainly a benevolent lunatic, giving William a bottle and a half of port one rent day and, to celebrate a wedding day, dispensing port and rum to the servants.[25] When William's wife died in 1822, Errington asked after William every day, gave his trusted friend a basket of fruit from the garden and offered anything William would like from the house.[26] But he could be irrational and difficult. At one stage, when he was 'well in health, but never more crazy than now', he wanted to take over a neighbour's land and grow a new plantation on it. William's deluded employer unpacked pictures and hung them but did not know what they were. He had sent for a house painter from Hexham to clean them, but William, mindful of an episode the previous year when a painter had ruined pictures by varnishing them, had to put a stop to it.

The old chap was erratic, sometimes eating heartily, at other times sparingly, and refusing to eat any food except that from his own farm; he was sometimes quiet, but could get 'high' and bad-tempered. William knew that it did Mr Errington good to get out and talk to the workers in the fields: he was watched over by his butler and the gamekeeper when he rode out. The Chief started hinting to his housekeeper that he had very little money to spend on butter, and she thought he had not much money left. William wrote: 'I was thinking it might be right to offer him some … say £100', adding that he was by no means certain that John Errington would accept it. In December 1826 Errington became very sick and 'continued to puke for a long time'. The doctor came, but the old man refused to see him; William sent him in, but the invalid would not speak to the doctor. At the end of June 1827, having survived to the age of eighty nine, John Errington died. One of the pall bearers at the funeral was William, who carried the coffin to the burial at the church of St John Lee. Henry Tulip the neighbouring land owner, was another.[27] The management of the estate was carried on by William for many more years, until he was well into his seventies.

Changes came to Sandoe after John Errington died. He left no direct descendents and Beaufront was put on the market and bought by William Cuthbert, who dismantled parts of the house and made substantial renovations during 1836 before moving in the following spring. Henry Errington had also died, and Sandoe Hall was inherited by his nephew, Rowland Errington. Mary helped him to settle in, giving him china for his new home.

Henry Errington had harboured a secret. In London, he was quite the man about town, mingling with high society. George, the young Prince of Wales, had around him a galaxy of fun-loving friends; the Prince Regent was known as a flamboyant pleasure-seeker, profligate with his money, and a womaniser, although at the same time he showed good taste in the Arts. Henry was one of his acquaintances, and became a trusted friend. In 1784, Henry attended the opera with his recently widowed niece Maria and his half-brother Lord Sefton (another of 'Prinny's' set.) [28] Also there that night was the Prince Regent, who requested an introduction to the beautiful young widow. In spite of his record with women, it seems that he was seriously smitten by Maria – 'my love, my life, my soul, my all, my everything' – and pursued her ardently. Maria was more reticent. She was six years older than George, and had already lost two husbands: the second was Mr Fitzherbert. The Prince resolved to marry Mrs Maria Fitzherbert; he even staged a suicide attempt by stabbing himself with a sword, then summoned her and procured her assent with further threats of self-harm, making her accept a ring to seal the engagement.[29] Maria, confused, retreated to the Continent. Although attracted to George, she could not commit herself under the circumstances. Like all the Errington family, she was a Catholic, and knew that marriage to the Prince Regent would be illegal. George begged her to return, and enlisted the help of Henry Errington in arranging a secret wedding.[30]

At the Prince's request, the two men met on the road half way between London and Henry's southern country home Red Rice, for a man-to-man discussion, during which Henry advised George on how to proceed. The plan was for Maria to return to England immediately to marry him. She would arrive in the evening; then under cover of darkness, George would either meet her on the road from Rochester to London, or arrive as soon as she reached London; he would creep into her house through the stables and garden, and they would agree on the wedding arrangements there and then, and be married forthwith. The wedding took place on 15 December 1785. A minister, Maria's brother and Henry Errington were the only witnesses, and it was said that the future King George IV's new wife used her own scissors to cut their names from the document so that they could carry no blame.[31] Even Maria's family did not know of the wedding – Henry's advice had been to keep it from them until the deed was done, so that they could not be implicated in the plot. In spite of their unlawful marriage (and a separation while George was unhappily married to Caroline of Brunswick) Maria and George lived together openly for eight years; but eventually they drifted apart, mainly because George returned to his dissolute ways and took up with another mistress. Whether the Donkin family or the other inhabitants of Sandoe ever learnt of their neighbour's involvement in the affair has not been recorded. The friendly relationships between the Errington family and the Donkins may subsequently have brought it to light.

All Bryan's brothers seem to have upheld the family's aspirations; but little is known of his second eldest brother, John. It seems that he was a schoolmaster in Hexham.[32] John and his wife Jane had six children, only three of whom survived more than a few years. His son William became a solicitor in Hexham. John's wife died when their only daughter was a baby of a few months old; it was Jane who was adopted and brought up by her Uncle William and Aunt Catherine, and when Catherine died, Jane lived in Sandoe with her Aunt Mary Donkin. John's second son, also John (Bryan's nephew) became interested in a career as a millwright and was to be found helping to set up a paper-making machine in Birmingham when his uncle Bryan was returning from his stint on the Caledonian Canal in 1817.[33] Nephew John had joined the Bryan Donkin Company, working alongside his cousins.

The three spinster sisters, Ann, Jane and Mary, lived a pleasant and varied life in Sandoe. Mary kept a diary from 1819 when she was forty-eight, a sporadic record rather than a commentary, but enough to document the everyday happenings in the village and beyond, visitors and trips, family happenings, and the highlights in her life.[34] It seems that Ann and Jane always lived together, but Mary certainly lived at the High House with William after his wife's death.

Hardly a mention is made in Mary's diary of her sisters' activities, except to note that Jane had begun to learn grammar and the two Janes (sister and niece) were starting to study French. Household matters cropped up, such as buying bits of furniture (a mangle for £3, a new oven for less, and a bed, chairs and a hen coop from a house sale). At the end of a cold September, she bought material at 17d a yard and made two pairs of sheets to put on her bed at once, for the winter. Her life seems to have been organised and happy. She had time to make gingerbread, and gave Bryan the recipe:[35]

> *Ginger bread cakes*
> A pound of flour
> Quarter pound sugar
> Quarter pound butter
> Nearly 1 oz of ginger
> Make it into a paste with about 1lb treacle.

For Mary, there was no shortage of company. Visitors often came to stay for three or four days; because Mary had two servants, guests were no trouble. One of the first in 1819 was Elizabeth, daughter of the Hutchinsons of Leith who were well known to the Donkin family; Mary was invited back after Mrs Hutchinson died, and much later Elizabeth came to live at Sandoe. Most of the brothers came: Henry was the closest, living in Durham, and he and Mary exchanged visits of a few days at a time. Nephew John came to stay for over three weeks with his wife, Sarah, before going back to London. In spite of long distances by coach, Mary seemed happy to travel to see her friends and relations – several times to the Lambtons at Biddick (where she stayed for three weeks over Christmas in 1819), to Tynemouth for three weeks, and to London. Some of these trips were taken with Phoebe or her sister Mary Lambton as a companion. To visit John and Bryan, as well as Mary Ann in London, a long journey was inevitable; it took fourteen hours by road and longer by sea, a voyage that Jane undertook too, seen off in Newcastle by her sister Mary. In 1826 and 1827, there were several trips by the Londoners and the Northumbrians; Bryan and his wife Mary went to Sandoe, Henry went to London. The youngest brother, Thomas, visited Sandoe with his wife and son, and other members of the large Donkin family came and went. During a ten-day touring holiday in the Lake District, Mary enjoyed the sights of Penrith and Keswick, going on to Borrowdale and walking up to Scale Force, then sailing up Windermere to Bowness and home via Patterdale and Ullswater.

In the spring of 1827 Mary Donkin went for a long stay in Isleworth with her niece Mary Ann, who was living with the elderly Matthew Stainton and his wife; while there, she visited the House of Commons, the opera, and Strawberry Hill, Horace Walpole's former home, which she thought was decorated 'with peculiar taste' and not kept up properly by its new owner, Lord Waldegrave. The strange story of the skull of Alexander Pope the poet, buried in Twickenham church, was related to her by William Day (Mary Ann's husband-to-be) who also lived in the village of Isleworth – and retold in Mary's diary on 14 March 1827:

> In making a vault, the sexton dug into Pope's grave and the end of the coffin fell out and with it the skull, which the sexton took to the curate Mr Carr, and he had a cast taken from it, which made it talked of, and the sexton to avoid suspicion substituted another in its place and gave the original to Mr Peel's butler, who gave it to Mr Day.

It had indeed been talked of. There were rumours that somebody had been induced to swap the skulls with a £50 bribe, that it had been seen in a private collection, and that Dr Spurzheim, the celebrated phrenologist, had it in his possession. It was suggested that whoever had it should acknowledge the fact and put an end to the controversy, and that he might be forgiven if a liberal sum were paid as conscience money.[36] Even the vicar was suspected of purloining the skull, but it was the phrenologists who were blamed the most.[37] No doubt Bryan Donkin examined the skull with glee and fascination.

In the North, there was excitement sometimes too. The annual ball hosted by Mrs Elstob, whose husband had been a partner with William Donkin in the Hexham Brewery, was one of the events that Mary attended more than once. On New Year's Eve 1821, she went to the Newcastle Musical Festival to hear the world-acclaimed soprano, Angelica Catalani – twice on the same day. Once her London season was over, the amazing Madame Catalani toured the provinces, entrancing her audiences with the range and fullness of her fine voice, the speed and energy of her performance, her beauty and her elegance.[38]

Mary's diary entries for 1822 ended on a sombre note: 'Jenny Stokoe's husband shot himself'. This was no accident. The poor man, David Clayter, a private in the Dragoon Guards, had married Miss Stokoe of Sandoe at Gretna Green only a month before. Jane (known as Jenny) was the daughter of the village blacksmith and publican. Her parents disapproved of the marriage, and her mother spirited the girl from the couple's lodgings in Carlisle and sent her to relations in County Durham. Her deserted husband frantically wrote to his young wife but the letter failed to reach her; instead, it was opened by her parents in Sandoe. Clayter, distraught, got leave from the army and made for Sandoe, but not being able to find Jenny, shot himself with a horse pistol in a field next to the Stokoe's house. Tied to his arm before the fatal act was a letter to his wife, blaming her parents for his death, and professing 'the most ardent affection' for her; he also left her a cheque for £300. Another letter, to his wife's brother, enclosed £400, with the request that he would forward the letter to Jenny, as he could trust no-one else to do it. At the coroner's inquest, the jury were deeply sympathetic; the verdict was lunacy.[39]

Through her sixties and seventies, Mary perhaps felt the aches and pains of encroaching old age, and went frequently to the small spa town of Gilsland, twenty miles west of Hexham. The opening of the Newcastle to Carlisle railway during the late 1830s and '40s made travel easy from Hexham to Rosehill station, near the resort.

As a lawyer, Mary's younger brother Henry would have been interested in the case of Jenny Stokoe and the suicide of her husband. However, his work in Durham was of a different nature; from before 1816, he was employed as an officer in the Court of Chancery and Exchequer in the Palatinate of Durham, an ancient administrative area ruled by the bishop, independently of the monarch. For many years he acted as Deputy Cursitor, auditor and examiner, while practising privately as a solicitor at the same time.[40] The post of Deputy Cursitor covered many responsibilities connected with the conservation and use of public records including writs, affidavits of debts, patents and other legal documents.[41] Many had been stored for centuries and were never looked at, but they were carefully filed in wooden cupboards in a strong stone building known as the 'Exchequer', adjoining the gateway to the Bishop's palace, where they were safe and dry. It was Henry's duty to manage his office; he paid his two clerks, who worked with him from nine in the morning till one o'clock, and from three to seven. By 1816 he was well established in the post, and was publicly thanked for enabling ready access to important records.[42] No annual salary was paid to the cursitor or to Henry, but he received fees for superintending the searching, issuing and re-filing the documents – 3s. 4d. a time, and a guinea for appearing at a trial with the relevant records.[43] By 1827, Henry had also taken on the role of County Clerk.[44] The Durham County Court met every fortnight, presided over by the sheriff but Henry Donkin issued all the processes, and the pleadings were held at his office. All the profits from the cases came to him.[45] A man with weighty responsibilities, he was also the deputy auditor to the Bishop of Durham. He lived in a nice house in Old Elvet, Durham, ten minutes walk from his work.[46]

Henry's heavy responsibilities and serious occupations suggest that he was a man of sober disposition. Like his brothers, he subscribed to numerous factual books of local and national interest and probably read them avidly.[47] When the Surtees Society was created after the death of Robert Surtees, Henry joined the learned group of scholars who were interested in continuing the work of the eminent antiquarian in discussing, collecting, cataloguing and publishing books, mainly on religious themes.[48]

A little levity came into Henry's life in April 1832, in the shape of a grand fancy dress ball, held at the Assembly Rooms and attended by the elite of the county.[49] One of the sponsors – and presumably an attendee – was Henry; others included Robert Surtees and John Dunn, who worked alongside Henry in the same court, as Deputy Clerk of the Peace.[50] No expense had been spared: the rooms were lavishly but tastefully decorated with flowers, greenery and banners, champagne flowed and the ladies dazzled in their elegant and extravagant costumes. The partygoers arrived just before ten in the evening to start the ball with lively country dancing, followed by quadrilles, gallops and waltzes. At 12.30 a.m., more than two hundred and thirty guests sat down to a sumptuous banquet, accompanied by the finest of wines: claret, hock and burgundy of the choicest and richest quality. Dancing was resumed at 2.30 a.m. and continued in high spirits until late in the morning. The worthies of Durham certainly knew how to enjoy themselves.

Henry may not always have been the level-headed, ponderous character that he seemed to be. He was evidently a bit of a lad in his youth: at the precocious age of twenty, he had married Ann Flintoff, who must have been great with child. Their daughter was born two months later.

The youngest of Bryan's brothers was Thomas; they were kindred spirits, both intelligent and possessing wide-ranging skills and a love of the countryside of the North. Throughout his life, Bryan's youngest brother displayed numerous far-reaching interests in the sciences and agriculture and 'there were few crafts, from that of a physician to that of a blacksmith, in which he could not have been useful in an emergency.'[51] Like Bryan, he enjoyed the study of astronomy: he too had a small observatory and, using his transit instrument and a clock, kept the neighbourhood informed of the exact time, and was a respected member of the Royal Astronomical Society for thirty three years.

In the early years of the century, Thomas was following the family tradition, managing the Errington estate. Like his father and his brother William before him, his responsibilities as a land agent were onerous: finding good tenants for the land, maintaining the estate's properties, collecting rents, visiting the farms, and surveying and valuing the land and buildings. In short, he managed all aspects of the land and properties on the estate.[52] In his early days as a land agent, Thomas turned to his brother for advice on a variety of practical engineering matters.[53]

After working on the Beaufront estate, Thomas took the post of steward to Lord Mulgrave on his estate at Sandsend, near Whitby.[54] His home was at Lythe

38 *Westow Hall, Yorkshire, by Sarah Donkin, 1837.*

Hall, part of the Mulgrave estate. A military man, Henry Phipps, the third Baron Mulgrave, was Secretary of State for Foreign affairs under William Pitt the Younger for a year from January 1805, before becoming First Lord of the Admiralty; he also held the honorary post of Lord Lieutenant of the East Riding of Yorkshire. Mulgrave Castle was magnificent, surrounded by extensive slopes of grass and woodland, bounded by the sea shore to the east. On the rocky shoreline was a large alum mine, where alum was cut from the rocks and processed into crystals for several commercial purposes, especially for use in the trade of dying cloth.[55] Part of Thomas's job would have been to supervise the mine. Lord Mulgrave, like most of the land-owning aristocracy, was a benevolent employer: to celebrate George III's jubilee – the beginning of his fiftieth year as King – on 25 October 1809 he had entertained over 700 tenants and workers at the alum works, regaling them with roast beef, strong beer and punch, with fireworks to round off the festivities.[56]

While living in the Whitby area, Thomas met his wife Alice, who at twenty three was several years younger than he was; they married in Whitby in 1809 and had eleven children before 1826. (Unfortunately, in spite of their comfortable circumstances, four boys – his first-born son William Bateman Donkin, as well as young Thomas, and two christened Henry – died as infants, and sadly, Mary and James both died in their twenties.) The first child had been born in 1810 in Bishop Burton, about two miles from Beverley, where Thomas acted as land agent on the 4,800 acres belonging to the brothers Richard and Francis Watt.[57] Richard Watt, who also owned Speke Hall, near Liverpool, was a noted breeder of winning racehorses. (Horses bred by Richard Watt won the St Leger between 1813 and 1833.) Thomas would advertise the services of Watt's stallions at ten guineas a time, in the racing journals.[58] There he and his growing family lived for ten years or more, before moving to Elvington, near York, in the mid 1820s. In 1834 Thomas and Alice took up residence at Westow Hall, a dwelling house and fields of land, with an annual value of £50 and upwards 'of which I am the tenant'.[59] Westow Hall was later described as an 'ancient mansion'.[60] From time to time, in his late sixties, Thomas made visits three or four times a year to Sandoe, where he stayed with his sister Mary and helped out with collecting the rents (and perhaps as a consultant) on the estate, by then owned by Mr Cuthbert.

A man of conscience, Thomas put his name to a Declaration in 1819, against a subversive group which, the signatories contended, was abusing the right to hold public meetings, and inciting the least informed classes of society to rise against the Government and the laws, the religion and the constitution of the country.[61] Signed by over three thousand freeholders and inhabitants of the county of York, the declaration likened the uprising to the revolution in France, where the more opulent classes were represented as enemies and oppressors and 'every class of public functionaries are designated as the tools of despotism'. The signatories declared their allegiance to the law and the Constitution of the country they loved and warned their countrymen of the importance of supporting the distressed working classes by speaking out against the revolutionaries who, claimed the signatories, sought to take away their freedom and livelihoods. After the Napoleonic Wars the country was in a poor state – imports and exports had slumped and famine and unemployment affected thousands.[62] All over the industrial areas of the country, huge crowds of unemployed and disaffected men were being marshalled to meetings organised by the radicals, demanding better conditions and the reform of parliamentary representation. Chief among the orators was Henry Hunt. At a huge meeting of over 100,000 men in Manchester, the magistrates sent the cavalry charging in through the crowd to arrest Hunt.[63] In the ensuing mayhem, at least nine protesters were killed and hundreds wounded by the militia's flailing sabres, or crushed and trampled on by the horses and the fleeing crowds. The violent incident, soon named the Peterloo Massacre, did little immediately towards changing attitudes in Parliament and there were many more demonstrations, but it is now considered to have been a turning point in the history of social reform.[64] Thomas and his like, in their comfortable homes in the country, could do little more than sympathise with the plight of the less fortunate; as a Donkin, he would have seen both sides of the argument.

13
Master and Man

The factory was set in the pleasant countrified surroundings of Bermondsey, Surrey, bounded by fields and gardens and approached by a lane leading from Blue Anchor Road, past a few buildings own by a Mr Child, into the left hand corner of the factory yard. It was bordered on two sides by land owned by Mr Betts, a market gardener.[1] Not far away was a glue factory; the whiff of boiling animal carcasses must have somewhat marred the rural atmosphere. The overall area of the works was about 3,600 square yards, with a frontage of 166 feet and stretching 223 feet from front to back.[2]

The area was defined by adjoining buildings, built of timber or brick, set around and within the large yard, with a range of buildings roughly dividing the yard into two. To the left near the entrance were the offices, housed in a two-storey brick building and joined with a covered way along the front to a long open shed with a single storey above, probably the erecting shop where machinery was assembled. At right angles, a clanging brass foundry formed the back wall of the yard with the large timber-built workshop and a stable. There was plenty of space in this front yard for moving wagons and assembling large pieces of machinery. On the third side of the main yard, and almost enclosing it, was a row of buildings – the blacksmith's 'shop', the big three-storey turnery or machine shop, and a store room with a safe room behind it. When standing in the yard, a visitor's ears would be assailed by a cacophony of sound – the rasp of files, the clanking and whining of lathes and saws and the thrumming of drive belts. In the smaller yard behind this block stood the brick-built engine house that provided the steam power for the factory; the walls were substantial, and the building was split down the centre to provide two rooms, separating the boiler from the hissing engine for safety. At the back of the engine house was a covered saw pit, about the same size as the boiler house at twenty feet long and ten wide, where the saw was driven by the steam engine. Small buildings nearby housed more workshops, a store and a second boiler room. The front boundary to the factory was formed by three substantial single storey, brick-built pattern stores; they were long and narrow, and quiet. Here, neatly arranged on shelves for easy retrieval, were stored the wooden patterns for making the moulds that were essential for casting metals into the shapes needed for parts of machines. In these buildings, Donkin's many-faceted business flourished.

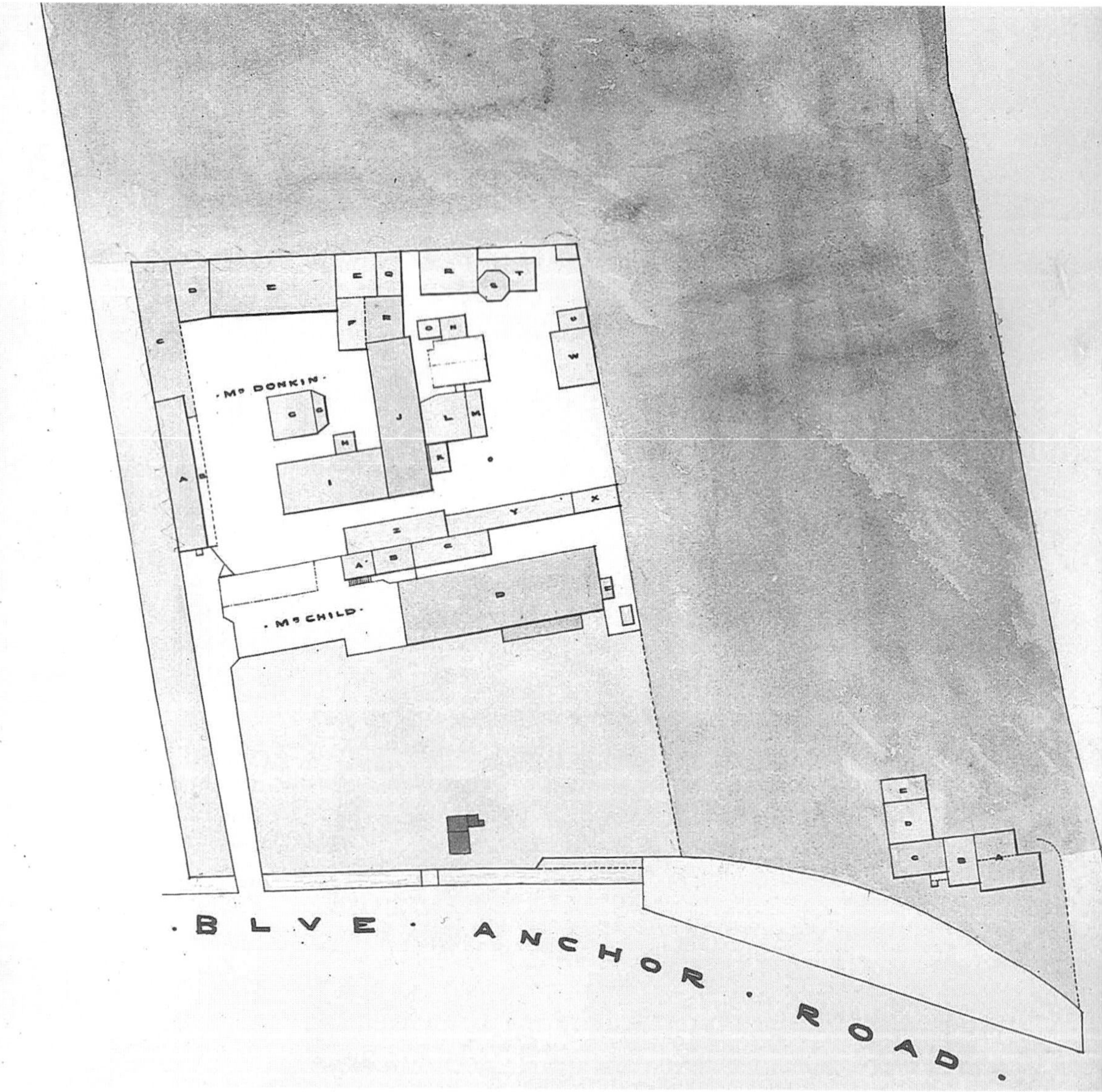

39 *Plan of the Donkin factory and surroundings,* 1836.

For employers of factory workers, though, industrial relations were not always easy. New unions of workers were making demands for higher pay and better conditions, and they were threatening strikes. From the dawn of the industrial revolution, mechanisation of traditional crafts began to have an effect on labour relations. Artisans who had previously earned a good living now found their skills devalued, or indeed, redundant; this often led the workers to break the law and form 'combinations' or unions as a collective method of protecting jobs. Fortunately, in the paper-making industry, many of the workers had been re-trained in the factories where paper-making machinery had been installed, so the situation was not as serious as it had been for cottage industry workers, whose livelihoods had been taken away. Even in his well-run establishment in Bermondsey, Bryan Donkin felt trouble looming in the 1820s, and was anxious to join with other managers and elicit their co-operation in fending off the impending threats. Running a business within the law was fraught with difficulty.

It was not only the employees who collaborated with like-minded colleagues to promote their causes. Employers in industry banded together to counteract the workers' embryonic trade unions. As early as 1799, a group of master millwrights had petitioned Parliament to bring in a Bill to prevent unlawful combinations, or unions, among the journeymen millwrights, and to enable magistrates to regulate their wages; their plea was supported by the social reformist M.P. William Wilberforce.[3] Six years later, Bryan Donkin was a founder member of a new union of industrialists: the inaugural meeting of Society of Master Millwrights took place at the Museum Tavern in London on 7 October 1805, with Donkin as treasurer of the society.[4] Fourteen others attended, paying three guineas for the year for membership. Among them was Mr Moorman, a well-known smith and iron founder;[5] John Penn, who had started as a millwright, and in 1799 set up his own manufactory for agricultural machinery in Blackfriars; and the engineer Peter Keir, well known to Bryan and 'a clever man, though somewhat eccentric'.[6] John Hall joined soon afterwards. The aim of these practical engineers was to sweeten relationships between themselves as employers and the workers in their manufactories. The Society of Master Millwrights lasted for a few years before it was overtaken by larger federations.

In 1813, as a member of another committee, of the Machinists' Society, Donkin agreed that Mr Vansittart, the Chancellor of the Exchequer, should be approached for advice in relation to the ancient 'Statute of Elizabeth'.[7] There was a movement afoot to amend this ancient statute, one of many laws from Elizabeth I's reign which were still in force, partially at least. (Another dealt with 'lewd and wandering persons pretending to be soldiers or mariners'.)[8] The law that worried Donkin related to charitable trusts, and the Machinists were afraid that if it were repealed, the various associations of workers would be able to continue to masquerade under the name of 'benefit societies', which would make the situation worse for their employers. In the old Act were clauses relating to the status of apprentices: rules stating, for instance, that apprentices in London and the important worsted-weaving town of Norwich should be bound to serve their masters for seven years. Some trades still adhered to that rule and other outworn regulations. But by 1814, the law had become so often ignored or flouted, that its repeal was thought to be long overdue, and a petition was signed by the old gang: Bryan Donkin, John Collinge, George Rennie, James Moorman, Peter Keir and several others, calling the attention of the House of Commons to 'the vexatious operations of the said statutes from which they have suffered great inconvenience'.[9]

Donkin was also a member of the committee of The Manufacturers of London and its Vicinity, together with the engineers John Collinge, Henry Maudslay and Alexander Galloway, as well as the leather worker Samuel Bevington and five others, who co-operated in writing an impassioned argument against the four-hundred year-old law, addressed to the Committee of General Purposes of the City of London, and published in *The Pamphleteer*, a publication 'respectfully dedicated to both Houses of Parliament'.[10] They felt strongly that the old apprenticeship laws, passed in a bygone semi-barbarous age when a work-shy vagabond could be branded on the chest with a V and made a slave for two years, were no longer appropriate in modern, forward-looking commerce.

There were advantages and disadvantages in apprenticeships, for both the employer and the apprentice. Employers were assured of a dedicated young workforce, trained to their methods, but they sometimes felt restricted by the responsibilities and feared revolt amongst the apprentices. Parents of young men knew that their sons would be taught the trade in a secure and disciplined environment, but the apprentices were strictly controlled even in their out-of-work hours. Discrimination between the trades meant that apprentices could be taken on, in large towns, in trades that were thought of as the higher rank (such as merchants, mercers, drapers, clothiers, iron mongers, goldsmiths or embroiderers), but only if their parents had land worth 20 shillings (£1) a year. In market towns, the parents' land had to be worth three times as much. For the lesser trades (like thatchers, bricklayers, wheelwrights, carpenters and plasterers), no surety was necessary from the parents, a sure example of Elizabethan social engineering – the lower orders were restrained from entering trades, and encouraged to remain in work on the land. There was controversy about the seven-year apprenticeship scheme and although for most apprentices it was the usual method of learning a trade, many employers used or ignored the law to suit their own purposes. New trades flourished (such as coach-makers, tin-plate workers, paper-stainers, mathematical and optical instrument makers) which were not controlled by the statute and were sought after by parents who wanted to place their children in a good job. Some parents kept their child at school until the age of sixteen, and then apprenticed them for five years. Apprentices could be let off if they reported a case of counterfeiting; the bravery of soldiers and sailors was rewarded by allowing them to work, unskilled, with no apprenticeship at all – these and other anomalies made an ass of the law.

Donkin and the Manufacturers group noted, however, that all the laws had 'been rendered obsolete by tacit consent as totally incompatible with the interests and prosperity of commerce'.[11] They pointed out that it was not unusual for the most ingenious workmen never to have been apprenticed at all. Men such as Arkwright, Brindley, Smeaton and Rennie were judged for their skill, not by indentures, and were motivated by the hope of success and good wages. James

Watt, Joseph Bramah and Marc Brunel had never served as apprentices. (When Maudslay joined Bramah's works, he had not served an apprenticeship, but gained admiration from the journeymen as well as from Bramah, impressing them all with his natural skills.)[12] If the restraints of the Act had been extended to new manufactures how could inventions by men such as these ever have come about? The group argued that the old legislators could not have foreseen the time when England's commerce would extend to the remotest regions of the earth, nor could they have understood the importance of trade in upholding the country's rank in the world.

Demand for the country's manufactured goods had been so great that there had been a sudden and extraordinary revolution in manufacturing;[13]

> but we must never lose sight of the important consideration that we are, to this day, surrounded by powerful and civilized [sic] nations, who are intent of cultivating their manufactures and commerce; and who are the more eager to become our competitors in trade, from having witnessed the astonishing effects of our commercial prosperity.

The old Statute of Elizabeth should not remain on the statute books an hour longer, they concluded: 'if it be not repealed, it will be enforced'. That would be a retrograde step, affecting relationships both in the workplace and on a global scale. Donkin and the others on the Committee of the Manufacturers of London were adamant and ultimately victorious. Later that same year, 1814, thanks to protestors such as Donkin, the statute was indeed repealed. The rule that no young person could enter a trade without a seven-year apprenticeship was abolished by a new statute (54 Geo. III 96). However, the benefits of the discipline of apprenticeship to the employers and to their young charges were recognised, and many manufacturers continued with the practice for decades to come.[14]

As the nineteenth century unfolded and the pace of change increased, the situation got steadily worse.[15] Employment laws were clearly outdated and had not kept pace with the needs of a modernising industrial society.

Added to this was a frustration on the part of the engineering masters with the laws prohibiting the export of certain British machinery and machine tools for making machinery. The crazy law was such that it allowed the export of, for instance, Donkin's paper machines, but steam engines and machinery for the cotton and woollen industries, as well as screws over 1½ in. in diameter, could not be exported (although Henry Maudslay was allowed to send screw-cutting machines to Turkey).[16]

Continental Europe and America were looking enviously at the staggering progress of Britain's manufacturing output. Industrialists across these markets were anxious to mechanise, but the ready means to achieve this – the wonderful machinery designed and built with British skill and endeavour – was kept from them. The machinery manufacturers wanted an end to these punitive laws, to give them the chance to sell into the growing overseas markets. Moreover, while the prohibition was in place, they were seeing their machinery designs stolen and spirited abroad to be copied in great numbers. To rub salt into their wounds, the very artisans who had worked on the machinery were being enticed with high wages to break the law and take their skills to the emerging engineering shops that were springing up across Europe. Something had to be done, and at last, in 1824, Parliament was galvanised into action and a select committee was appointed to look into these pressing issues. Entitled simply *Select Committee on Artizans* [sic] *and Machinery*, it collected evidence from many manufacturing towns in the United Kingdom.[17] On 24 February 1824 Bryan Donkin stepped forward along with his fellow London engineering masters, Timothy Bramah, Philip Taylor, Henry Maudslay and John Hague, to be examined.

On the subject of the ban on exports, the group spoke with one voice. Because of the law, each one had often turned down foreign orders to the tune of tens of thousands of pounds when work was slack on the home market. They were equally clear on their position if the law were repealed: demand would increase, and with that increase, because of the superior quality of British machinery, they would keep their competitive edge and grow their businesses. They all agreed that the skill base of the Continental factories was many years behind Britain, but the need for mechanisation was urging the foreign workshops on, and Bryan Donkin warned: 'By the want of machinery, they have been driven to execute it themselves'.[18]

Donkin was then addressed in his capacity as Chairman of the Committee of Mechanics in the Society of Arts, and entered into an eloquent discourse with his inquisitors. The crux of the questioning concerned the dangerous openness of British scientific institutions, whose aim was the diffusion of knowledge; their publications, including drawings and descriptions of newly-invented machinery, were open for anyone to read, and were circulated throughout the world. Donkin concurred that able workmen could follow these plans and agreed that the prohibition law was fundamentally at odds with the ethos of scientific societies. He also said that the law was prejudicial, futile and demoralising, as whenever new machinery was brought into use, foreigners would use bribery to discover the finer points of its workings. He went on to say: 'A foreigner, or any person, for a few shillings, can go to our record offices and examine a specification containing a description of the best machines that we have ... The offices are open to any man, and copies may be obtained at a small expense'.[19] Donkin concluded his evidence by stating: 'They [the laws] produce no other effect but that of precluding the manufacturers of this country from making a great quantity of machinery and exporting it'.

The committee then moved on to questions concerning artisans, and once again the London engineering masters showed themselves to be forward-thinking and tolerant of the workers' pursuit of fair wages and improvements to their general circumstances. As employers they chose not to come together secretly to combine against the men in order to keep down wages; on the other hand, if the workforce combined for mutual benefit, the owners did not take action because prosecution would cause further resentment amongst the men. The master engineers did, however, prefer a meritocracy, where they were free to reward individual ability, rather than have fixed wages across the workforce. Under this system they had seen a great improvement in the attitude and demeanour of the workers. Led by their progressive employers, this valuable workforce was at the forefront of the new industry – a breed of mechanics and machinists who needed some degree of scientific and mathematical knowledge in order to meet the challenge of new tasks. Bryan Donkin, who was a great supporter of Mechanics' Institutes, put these improvements down to better education and went on to say: 'The moral state of the workmen is much superior to any I have seen before … I have now men who have been with me twenty years, on whom I can place the greatest reliance.'[20]. Bryan Donkin also concurred that the combination laws were not helping, but producing bad feeling between men and masters in all trades.

The views of the engineering masters were then sought on artisans working abroad. Almost all British citizens could hold a passport and were free to travel and ply their trade or business on the Continent. But the new artisans were treated differently; their skill and knowledge was jealously guarded by a Parliament fearful of rival countries getting their hands on British ingenuity. The artisans were barred from working abroad and, as the law stood, miscreants could have their property confiscated and face harsh penalties on their return. Nonetheless, this new breed of highly skilled craftsmen, trained in British workshops, were the envy of Europe, and a significant number were enticed with high wages of up to three times their normal pay, to break the law and work in the new factories in France and Prussia. For instance, The King of the Netherlands (which then included Belgium), was so keen to see his country modernised that he gave Mr Cockerill, an English entrepreneur, £30,000 to recruit men for two factories, one at Liège to produce carding and woollen machinery, and another at Seraing for the building of all manner of steam engines. After the retirement of his father, who had set up the thriving cloth-making business, John Cockerill had erected the gigantic steam engine manufactory, employing 3000 workmen, many of them from England.[21] This outstanding industrialist enlarged his empire to include holding large shares in mining and collieries, and owning cotton spinning and linen-making factories where weaving and printing of fabrics were also performed. Known as an altruistic individual who, in spite of his wealth was benevolent, Cockerill kept an eye on all his enterprises and looked after his workers.

> But what is most striking is a large hall in the centre of the works , with a stove in the middle of it, neatly ornamented like most of the Belgian stoves; and upon this stove, morning, noon and eve, there hangs a kettle filled with warm coffee. It is in this hall that the workmen meet at certain times of day, in the intervals of labour, and take their coffee, men and foremen together, the latter holding a certain moral presidence, which the others willingly acknowledge. They here chat without any noise or quarrelling, until the sound of the clock calls every man to his duties again.

John Cockerill's business sense knew no bounds. Perhaps it was an excess of cotton waste that inspired him to start up a paper factory: in 1827 he ordered a paper-making machine from Bryan Donkin.[22]

What effect on artisans working abroad would be achieved by the repeal of the laws controlling the export of tools and machinery? The buoyant answer from the engineering masters was that demand for British-built machinery would be so great that the boom in business would be sufficient to keep the best of the workforce from contemplating moving abroad. Bryan Donkin added: 'By the repeal of those laws, the employment on the Continent would be considerably less ... It is unlikely that they would go in search of it'.[23] The thinking of the engineering masters was way ahead of that of Parliament. They were arguing for a market free of restrictions, not just for goods but also for labour. Philip Taylor gave an example of how these punitive laws could affect the relationship between employer and employee. Seven of his men were lured away by an agent from France; in doing this, they had broken their contracts, and Taylor sent men in their pursuit. However, on their way down to Dover, the seven thought better of their actions and returned of their own volition. Despite this, justice had to be seen to be done, and the men had to face the magistrates. Taylor eventually managed to intervene and gain their release. The public-spirited employer then allowed the men to return to the situations they had left, and harmony was restored. To emphasise his derision of the law, Philip Taylor added: 'We did not follow them because they were going to France, but because they had broken their contracts with us. Had they left us and gone to Mr Maudslay, we would have done the same.'[24]

All of the masters, some more boldly than others, admitted that as they needed to send men abroad to set up machinery, they were in fact encouraging their workers to break the law. 'We know it', said Donkin. 'I have sent men; we all have done so from time to time, to put up machinery'.[25] 'We were obliged to violate the law', added his colleague, Timothy Bramah, 'We could not carry on foreign business without it'. Clearly, the employers felt safe in breaking this part of the law. 'Mine [the workers], always went without fear and returned without fear', said Donkin. 'They conceive that it is a legitimate employment to go out to put up machinery.'

Finally, the witnesses were asked again their views on the combination laws. Bryan was forthright in his answer. He believed that the laws were ineffectual, because employers were reluctant to rock the boat in relationships with their workers by bringing prosecutions against individuals. He was then asked if at any time he had used the combination laws to punish anyone for leaving his employment prematurely. The sharp-brained Donkin, well known by this date for his sure and steady judgement replied, rather tongue-in-cheek, 'I never have. I have taken to Mr Taylor's method of letting them go, and I am so little of a legalist, I do not know whether the remedy is under the combination laws or not.'[26] The select committee quickly deliberated and presented their resolutions to Parliament. They found the combination laws and the laws restricting the free movement of artisans to be unjust, and on their recommendation, the repeal of both laws was passed by Parliament shortly afterwards.[27] However, the Select Committee recommended further enquiry into the export of machinery, which left that law unchanged. This left the master engineers and machinery builders in a worse position; their evidence had helped to free the working classes from the restrictions of the combination laws, but they now had workers who were at liberty to take their talents to the wider market place of Europe. After all their efforts, Donkin and his friends were still burdened by export restrictions and this law would remain a millstone for years to come, giving foreign competition the opportunity to flourish to the detriment of British manufacturing.

An important point was raised during the enquiry, regarding the behaviour of employees. Donkin, Taylor, Bramah and Galloway were asked whether the character of the mechanics they employed had deteriorated over the last twenty years.[28] All four agreed that, on the contrary, behaviour had significantly improved; fewer of their men now drank heavily or swore at work. The reason was that they were better educated and, as Donkin put it, better informed on the subject of moral and social duties. Galloway added that the best educated were the best behaved, and it was the ignorant who were difficult to manage.

A significant meeting was held at the Crown and Anchor Tavern on Tuesday 11 November 1823.[29] Over two thousand men were present to witness the establishment of a new institution, the London Mechanics Institute. Most of them were working artisans, full of enthusiasm and keen to learn of the benefits. For every proposal, there was applause. For a group so large, it was surprising that the assembly was so earnest and orderly, except for two or three individuals who 'were indiscreet enough to intrude themselves in a state which utterly disqualified them from taking a part in the deliberations of rational men.' They were swiftly dealt with by a group in the audience, who 'lifted the sots gently out of the room'. There was praise for the influential employers, whose liberal attitudes and their respect for the needs and abilities of their workers had overcome the prejudices of the past and who had come forward to lend their support. Bryan Donkin was one of those singled out by name. Other men of wealth and influence had written letters commending the principle of providing opportunities for education and improvement for the workers, such people as Dr Olinthus Gregory, the mathematician, and Jeremy Bentham, the philosopher and social reformer. Dr Birkbeck was the Chairman, but the committee was composed of practising engineers, smiths, a carpenter, a shoemaker, a tailor and other working men. So the Institute was formed, with several agreed purposes, including the provision of a library and reading room, lectures, a school of design and an experimental workshop and laboratory for the mechanics, all to be managed by the men themselves. It was a huge step forward in industrial relations, actively supported by Bryan Donkin.

The Deptford Mechanics' Institution was founded in 1825, with Dr Gregory as its President.[30] At the first anniversary meeting members of the public joined the celebrations and Olinthus Gregory gave them a treat: a florid speech of praise for the achievements of Great Britain, highlighting the 'felicity of being a Briton' with lists of her physical attributes – springs, lakes and rivers ... fruits, herbs, timber ... minerals, fossils, stones ... animals, flocks, hives ... and so on. He described how the arts and sciences enhanced the 'conveniences and embellishments' of this happy spot, and enumerated the advantages of living in Britain: the warehouses were filled with stores, markets and fairs crowded with 'busy rustics', and 'fields, villages, roads and seaports, all contributing to the riches and glory of our land'. Next, he spoke enthusiastically of the latest technical developments – bridges erected, canals cut, ports enlarged, new machines – and mentioned 'new societies for improvement'. Skating over politics and the monarchy, his eulogy came to rest on the merits of Mr König, 'a truly ingenious foreigner', and the invention of his improved printing press, which had encountered a distinct lack of encouragement throughout Europe. He quoted König as saying:

> I need hardly add that scarcely ever is an invention brought to maturity under such circumstances. The well-known fact that almost every invention seeks, as it were, refuge in England, and is there brought to perfection, seems to indicate that the continent has yet to learn from her the best manner of encouraging the mechanical arts.

At the time, said Dr Gregory, Bacon and Donkin had simultaneously been at work on their printing machine, and soon after, Applegath and Cowper, had developed similar machinery; while König had found it necessary to come to England to mature his invention, Donkin and the others had felt no temptation to repair to the Continent to perfect their labours and seek the reward due to their talents. Remarking on the accuracy of the weight of the coins from the Royal Mint compared with foreign production of coins and medals, which needed 'make-weights' to compensate for the lack of precision, Dr Gregory elaborated his theme of British excellence, and challenged his audience to imagine what would become of the country if it were deprived of the results of the science and skill of her great inventors – the 'barbarism and desolation which would then

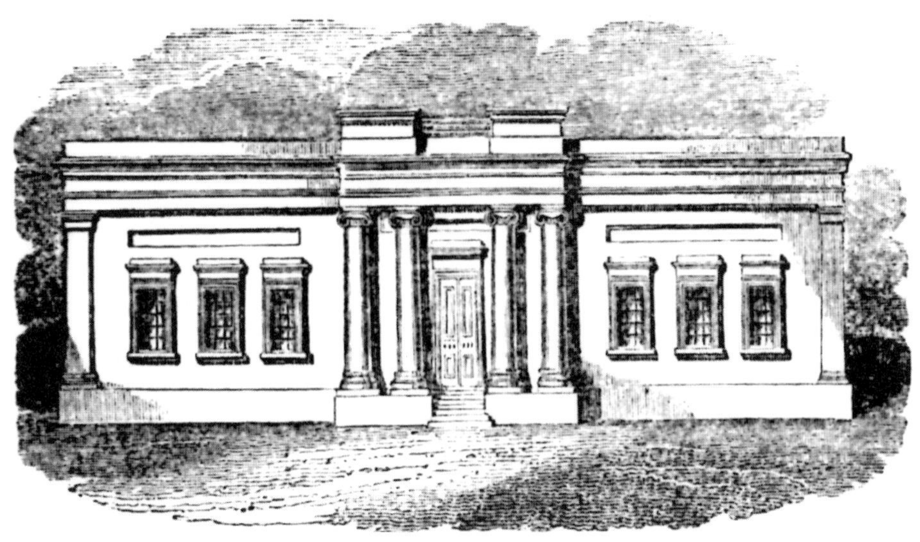

40 *The Mechanics' Institute, Liverpool,* 1838.

reign around'.[31] He enumerated their names: Boulton and Watt, Mushet, Barton, etc.; Smeaton, Brindley, Arkwright, Hornblower, Trevithick, Maudslay, Bramah, Telford, Stephenson, Palmer, and Donkin. The audience must have departed joyfully, buoyed with patriotism.

Fired with hope, the idea of education for mechanics was catching on, and soon afterwards, a well-attended meeting took place in Bermondsey to consider the formation of another Mechanics' Institution, serving the area of Rotherhithe and Bermondsey.[32] Several distinguished patrons of science were present, including Dr Birkbeck and Bryan Donkin. Marc Brunel, who had already agreed to act as President, was ill and could not attend. Birkbeck's declaration that such an Institution would 'add to the sum of human knowledge and happiness' was greeted with wild applause. Education for mechanics through instruction in scientific matters could only enhance their work and wellbeing, it was declared. In spite of an unexpected outburst from a young man named Thomas, who observed forcibly that 'the present fanaticism for educating the people would be the ruin of them and of the State', the resolution to form the Mechanics' Institution was passed. A second motion declaring that 'this meeting acknowledges with approbation the example which the mechanics of the Metropolis have set their brethren at large, in having established an Institution for their own instruction in the arts and sciences' was seconded by Mr Donkin and carried with great applause.

In Liverpool, Leeds and Sheffield, libraries for mechanics and apprentices were opened between 1823 and 1825, leading to the formation of Mechanics' Institutes in the three cities, a trend which spread to towns throughout the country.[33] Following the founding of the highly acclaimed Liverpool Apprentices and Mechanics' Library, a Mr William Paterson, a painter, wrote to a Liverpool magazine, seething with anger because he had found one of his apprentices reading a volume of Shakespeare's works, and on a Sunday too.[34] With ill-written sentences and poor spelling, Paterson condemned the supporters of the Library for encouraging the reading of plays, novels and romances; he would not allow such trash to be read by his family. The Sabbath should be devoted to attending a place of worship. The editor of the *Kaleidoscope* gave Paterson short shrift, pointing out that young men could occupy their time on a Sunday at worse occupations than reading: after last night's drunkenness and debauchery, many spent the day watching 'pugilistic combat' and dog-fights, and playing football, pitch and toss, and other games. Paterson's views were scathingly dismissed, and the evidence of Joseph Lancaster, the school reformer and founder of the Borough School in London was quoted: none of the 4,000 children who had passed through his school (although taken from the lowest classes of society) had been charged in the Courts of Justice with any offence.

At a time when there seemed to be a group representing every echelon in the engineering world from the apprentice to the experienced specialist and the academic scientist, a lone voice cried out for support.[35] Richard Harris, who gave his address as Mr Donkin's Engine Manufactory, Bermondsey, wrote a plea entitled 'On establishing a Society for the Mutual Instruction of Young Men of Scientific Professions' addressed to the editor of *The Technical Repository*, outlining his concerns for a neglected minority. He put the case that there was a need for a Society where young men at the beginning of their scientific careers could meet to investigate and discuss philosophical matters among themselves.[36] The existing learned societies, he said, were aimed at people with a previous and extensive knowledge. His small group was looking for like-minded young men to join them and form a new Society. *The Philosophical Magazine* also published his letter, with a supporting note from the editors, Alexander Tilloch (who had a string of scientific qualifications to his name), and Richard Taylor. They were keen to promote the dissemination of knowledge among all classes of the community and mentioned that societies for artisans had been instituted in Glasgow, Birmingham and Edinburgh. Their recommendation was that societies should provide lectures, experiments and examinations, avoiding 'everything that tends to parade, and vain disputation'. Within days, responses came quickly from members of the public. One gentleman 'A.B.L.' remembered an idea for a 'Society for Scientific Information' twenty years before, which had come to nothing, and wrote a long and pompous diatribe on how to run such a group and publish its findings.[37] A more positive approach came in the form of a surprise invitation issued by the City Philosophical Society, to attend one of their fortnightly meetings;[38] that society had been formed in 1808 by John Tatum, a manufacturer of silver spoons and forks, and had met in his house ever since.[39] Whatever the outcome for Richard Harris, Bryan Donkin would have encouraged him in his venture. It may be no coincidence that a Richard Harris, whose able assistance at the Greenwich Royal Observatory had been highly spoken of by the Astronomer Royal, was appointed as Assistant Secretary to the Astronomical Society in 1844, when Donkin was on the Council.[40]

There was a downside to the apparent success story of co-operation between man and master, which probably gave Donkin cause to ponder the balance between his social conscience and his business interests. In the second decade of the century, the development of labour-saving steam-driven machinery threatened the livelihood of the artisans whose skills in the crafts of spinning and weaving were no longer needed. The Luddite movement was formed by these disaffected textile workers, who vented their anger by forming local groups and smashing up the new machines in wool and cotton mills in Nottinghamshire, Yorkshire and Lancashire, until the movement was suppressed by the Government.[41]

In August 1830, a similar uprising began, stemming from unrest among agricultural workers in Kent: mechanical threshing machines were their target. Times were hard. The unemployed were forced to work in gangs on the roads like criminals, and agricultural labourers earned so little that some died from starvation.[42] Protests spread through Kent and across the counties of southern England to Dorset. These so-called Swing Riots, named after the fictitious Captain Swing, who sent threatening letters to magistrates and landowners, were usually locally organised, centring on demands for higher wages and the abolition of threshing machines, among other grievances. Offenders were sentenced to death or transported to Botany Bay or Van Dieman's Land.[43] For two years, violent riots took place, spreading towards East Anglia.

Disgruntled workers in the paper trade jumped on the bandwagon. In the Wye Valley in Buckinghamshire, where there were upwards of thirty paper mills – many of them recently converted from long-established hand paper-making methods to using Donkin's machine – craftsmen making paper took the opportunity to protest about conditions by rioting, attacking the paper-making machinery with cudgels and metal bars as a last ditch stand against the modern methods.[44] On Friday, 26 November 1830 a large group of paper makers disrupted a meeting of property owners in the Guildhall at Wycombe, then marched in a mob to Ash Mill, High Wycombe, intent on destruction. A passing troop of the Buckinghamshire Yeomanry dispersed the gang by reading the Riot Act, but a mob of 400 – 500 re-grouped on the Monday morning, wielding sledge hammers, crowbars and sticks, and set off to wreck the machinery at Ash Mill; later in the day, drunk with beer and adrenalin, they destroyed more paper machines at the Snakeley and Hedge mills. At Richard Plaistowe's Loudwater Mill at Wycombe, where John Wilks had recently installed one of Donkin's 56½in. paper machines and other machinery, they caused more havoc before passing on to John Fromow's Clapton mill, where the owner was ready to repel the mob with a cannon at the gateway. The rioting reached Norfolk, too, and the paper machine at Taverham Mill was damaged:

at the Sheriff's Jury in Norwich, the following April, Donkin was called to give evidence.[45] In the aftermath of the riots, of course, Donkin's men were employed to repair damaged parts and replace the broken ones.[46]

14
Far and Wide

Orders for paper-making machinery flooded in during the 1820s and 30s. After an initial flurry of sales in the early years, when sixteen machines were built by 1810, the second decade of production had been slower, but sales of paper machines were really beginning to take off by the early 1820s.[1] Two sizes were available to buyers at this time, with wire widths of 44½ and 56½ inches, sometimes described elsewhere as four and five feet respectively.[2] By the time Sellers visited the Bermondsey factory in 1832, the firm had built more than a hundred Fourdrinier paper-making machines.[3]

Naturally, there had been a few teething problems with the very first Fourdrinier machines, causing one of the first keen customers some trouble with the new technology. Charles Martindale, whose mill at Sawston in Cambridgeshire was one of the original seven to be equipped with Donkin's machine, used it to supply paper to the Cambridge University Press.[4] Unfortunately, possibly through his inexperience with mechanical paper-making, he found he could not fulfil his obligations to the university and, in danger of losing the contract, he called on the Fourdrinier brothers to make up the shortfall in paper, but they failed to provide it, claiming that Martindale owed them money for the machine. A dispute rumbled on for months in spite of efforts at arbitration by Donkin.[5] Further difficulties with the Cambridge contract caused the eventual closure of Martindale's mill in 1813, and he asked Donkin to advertise the sale of his property.[6] Four years later it was still (or again) on the market, without a single offer.[7] It was bought by Richard Mackenzie Bacon.[8]

Still very much 'hands-on' as a millwright in the 1820s, Bryan Donkin was often involved in the planning and setting up of new paper mills for clients and for surveying old mills for conversion to making paper by machine rather than by the time-honoured method by hand. One such was William Searle Evans's Postlip Mill, east of Cheltenham, where Donkin spent five days inspecting and measuring up the premises in readiness for installing a 56½ inch wide paper-making machine and matching drying machine.[9] Evans had bought Postlip Hall together with its paper manufactory in 1824 from the Earl of Coventry, and quickly started converting the buildings.[10] With Donkin's machine set to work in 1825, he soon became one of the country's most prolific paper makers.[11] Mr Wilks, Donkin's assistant, went to Norwich to measure up Robert Hudson's mill in readiness for installing a 44½ inch paper machine; it was no mean feat converting and sometimes extending mills to accommodate the forty foot long machines with their accompanying apparatus, and Hudson's mill demanded seventy three days of work for Donkin's men, including inspection visits by Bryan's son, John.[12] Elsewhere, Brandram, Carless & Co spent over £2,000 building a whole new mill, set up by Bryan Donkin's team, and later bought pumps and agitators, and a lot of wood and some cast iron to make a frame on which to stand a steam engine – a sign of progress.[13]

Another paper mill master, one of the many who extended their premises to mechanise the process was John Morgan, who had insured his paper-drying room in 1803; later, he converted his long-established mill in Colyton, near Axminster, and bought a 44½ inch paper-making machine from Donkin in 1825.[14] Up to 1823, the Donkin Company had produced thirty-eight paper-making machines, and by 1829 another forty four had been sold. Those customers who bought machines had to buy their new parts from Donkin to be assured of the necessary quality for the efficient running of the machine and so were clients over many years.

Others were making their own machines by now, but Donkin dominated the scene, providing an excellent service, sending mechanics from the works when necessary and succeeding in a market where there was little competition. Although the paper-making machine was known for ever afterwards as the Fourdrinier, the name of Donkin was, among the paper makers, the byword for precision, efficiency and service.

In 1823 Donkin introduced machines for drying the paper – a series of heated rollers – replacing the old method of hanging up the cut sheets in a loft to dry, and they quickly became an essential and popular attachment to the paper-making machines. J. & H. Matthews bought one for their mill near Exeter, which took fifteen days to install; another Matthews, William of High Holborn, had the next size up.[15] At Moreton Mill, near Wallingford, John Evans set himself up with a paper machine and drying machine and was on Donkin's books for many years. However, life running a paper mill was not a bed of roses, and by 1839 his mill had failed in the hands of his successor, Charles Batten, who was arrested for bankruptcy and incarcerated in Reading gaol.[16]

Bryan's grown-up sons John and Bryan Junior took an active part in the business. John was sent to Bungay to put in a 44½ inch paper machine for William Betts, which had been sent up the coast from London by boat.[17] He was a good customer for many years. He had had a rag-chopping machine from Donkin too, and sometimes needed parts for his well-used machines – replacements were sent via the coach office at the Saracen's Head, Snow Hill, near Smithfield Market, over a period of five or six years (as were parcels for other clients). By 1832 Betts had emigrated to Canada, where he was encountered as the landlord of a tavern in Montreal by a fellow Suffolk man, William Peacock, who had recently arrived in

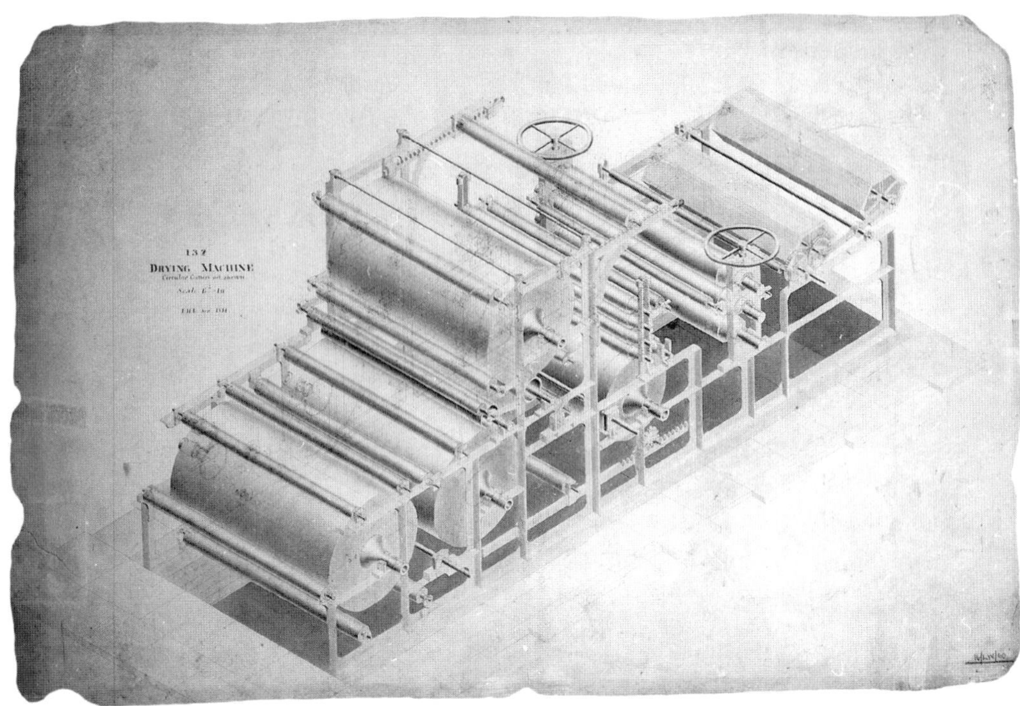

41 *Drying machine,* 1823.

northern Canada to settle, having sailed from Yarmouth to Prince Edward Island. The traveller noticed that Betts was in reduced circumstances, but thought that he could have been kinder: he had rather overcharged his compatriot.[18]

At least one paper machine went to the Scottish borders, perhaps through a local contact of the Donkin family: Wilks travelled to Duns, west of Berwick on Tweed, to measure up at the long-established and large Broomhouse Mill. Four months later, a big paper machine was sent up by sea to Leith. Houghton Castle, where Donkin's niece Jane and her husband lived, had one of his machines, too. (Much earlier, the paper mill, built on the Tyne in the grounds of the castle, had played a vital part in making hand-made paper for printing counterfeit assignats during the war with France, in an attempt to disrupt the French economy.)[19]

By 1832, twenty-three paper mills in Scotland had paper-making machines, producing writing paper, cartridge, printing, brown and newspaper, but still there were fifty-four paper mills there that were making paper by hand in traditional style.[20]

A worrying aspect of the changes in the paper industry was that workers and their children were often reduced to poverty and sometimes almost reached the point of starvation.

One of the paper mills that Bryan Donkin helped to mechanise was at Bledlow in Buckinghamshire, run by Lovegrove and Cubbage, owners of more than one mill.[21] Donkin supplied it with an overshot water wheel (ten feet in diameter) as well as two paper machines. The workforce included Jesse Neal, a sixteen year old orphan earning 2s. 6d. a week cutting rags ready to be pulped.[22] Jesse's mother had 'destroyed herself on account of ill usage by his father', who then absconded leaving five children. The eldest three had found work, but Jesse and his younger brother were consigned to the workhouse, until kindly taken in by George Allen, a farm labourer already struggling to make ends meet as a father of seven children of his own. Luckily, Jesse and his brother found work in the paper mill at Bledlow to contribute to the family income. George Allen was paid from parish funds for his work, according to the Poor Law regulations, and by gathering dung from the roads with a donkey and cart he earned another 2s. 0d. a week to supplement the weekly wage of 7s. 0d.

By 1834 many of the inhabitants of Bledlow had followed the trend for moving to other parts of the country for better paid work in growing industries, and migrated north to Lancashire; the Allen family went too. This arrangement had come about through a happy set of circumstances. In Lancashire, good wages were to be earned by hand-loom weavers in the cotton trade, because labour was in short supply. Edmund Ashworth, a cotton mill owner, described the situation in a letter to one of the Poor Law commissioners. While there was a surplus of agricultural workers throughout the country, to the extent that many had emigrated to the colonies and other countries abroad in search of work, the industrial areas were crying out for labourers and in Lancashire there had been a vast influx from Ireland of 'ignorant, discontented, and turbulent people who, introducing and widely spreading their own habits, have a tendency gradually to demoralise our own population'.[23] Conversely, there were decent poor people in other parts of England, living on money from their parish. Ashworth suggested that it should be made easier for such families to move to where there was work, to earn better wages. Robert Hyde Greg of Styal Mill agreed.[24]

In the same year, 1834, thirty two near-starving men in Bledlow asked a neighbour to write on their behalf to the Poor Law Commissioners; each signed the letter with a cross. They were able bodied and willing to work but desperately poor, and begging for help. Earning only 7s. 0d. a week, they spent 4s. 0d. on bread for the family, 1s. 9d. on bacon and the rest on soap, candles, tea, sugar and other small necessities – and had nothing left for clothes, fuel or rent. Single men earned less than half that, for nine hours' work a week. It was a desperate plight for these paupers. But by June the following year, thanks to the understanding of Edmund Ashworth, his brother Henry and the Poor Law officials, four of the Bledlow families had already made the move from Bledlow to Bolton and found good jobs, earning three times as much as they had in the South. Jesse Neal's earnings increased from 3s. 0d. to 6s. 6d. a week at Ashworth's cotton mill in Turton, near Bolton, and he liked the work better. The mill was loftier and lighter than the old paper mill at Bledlow. He came from Buckinghamshire in tatters, but now had very good Sunday clothes and was decently dressed during the week. The three-roomed rented cottage where he lived happily with the Allen family was a great improvement on the semi-derelict hovel in the south, where the rain had poured through the thatch onto the mud floor. Thanks to his adoptive father, and to Edmund Ashworth of Egerton Hall, Jesse's life had changed. The large modern Lancashire mill was a far cry from the Bledlow paper mill; perhaps the owners at Bledlow had suffered from the change from paper-making by hand to making paper with expensive machinery, and had not been able to fully modernise the mill or offer decent wages. Edmund Ashworth and his brother Henry of Turton, who provided the workers with a village of their own, complete with a school, were good free-thinking benefactors who saw the merits of sharing their wealth for the good of society. Great changes were taking place in industry.

Nevertheless, at mills where Donkin's machinery was making paper, children as young as twelve were at work. Local workers' conditions depended on the attitude taken by individual mill owners. Although he held no responsibility for the working practices in the paper mills that he visited, it sometimes must have grieved Donkin that conditions were not always suitable for the children who worked there. Generally the mills were located in healthy spots beside rivers in the countryside, with plenty of fresh air because of the demands of the paper-making processes.[25] But in some mills, where children were made to sort dirty rags to put in the rag-cutting machine, the air was filled with thick dust. In others though, where finer paper was made, clean rags were used: it varied from mill to mill. Long hours and aching legs were the main problem throughout the industry; sometimes the children fell asleep, especially when working into the evening or overnight, but 'we wets our eyes with water when we feels sleepy'. Children interviewed by the 1844 commissioners for the Employment of Children had low expectations but generally felt that they were well fed, had decent break times and were healthy. Some worked on alternate days and could earn more if they chose to extend their hours. It depended on the mill owner. At that time, the Commissioners found that only two paper factories, Nash Mill and River Mill, had schools attached; other children did not attend school at all, except for Sunday School, where they derived little educational benefit.

Word of the excellence of Donkin's paper machines had spread to the Continent and a steady stream of orders came to Bermondsey from a growing number of new customers as well as mill owners wanting replacement parts or larger machines. The very first export was to Germany in 1818, when a paper machine was sent to Berlin for the Prussian Government; this order followed on from the dredger contract the previous year.

The first supplied to France went to 'M. Canson' in Annonay in 1822.[26] He was a go-ahead paper mill owner who, four years later, adapted part of Dickinson's early process for his own purposes by using suction under the web of paper to speed up the drying process.[27] Bartélemy Baron de Canson was the son-in-law of Etienne Montgolfier, the inventor (with his brother) of the hot air balloon, and one of a long line of paper-makers. Unfortunately, later in the century, his mill was destroyed by a fire that started (as often happened) in the rag warehouse, causing damage to the value of £25,000.[28] The second machine in France was bought from Donkin in 1823 by M. Maupeau.[29]; but although the Fourdrinier had been in use in England for twenty years by then, France was slow to adopt the new technology, and by 1827 there were still only four in the country.[30] In that year, the Montgolfier firm bought a large machine from Donkin, together with a drying machine, and the French market blossomed. Later, when the paper-makers Berthe Hamoir et Cie of Paris needed a new mill, the Bryan Donkin Company sent a drawing, showing everything necessary – the washing plant and all the components for making and drying paper, and a plan and elevation of a mill showing four engines, pumps, the water wheel and the apparatus for the gate.[31] Such enterprises strengthened the economy on both sides of the Channel, but particularly in France, where industry was still recovering only slowly from the wars and the results of the Revolution.

The logistics of transporting the paper machines to the Continent were huge. The machine was assembled in the Bermondsey workshop, then taken apart and packed into a number of large boxes. Additional equipment, for drying the finished paper, or for other parts of the mill, was dealt with in the same way. With the help of a London agent who booked the cargo's passage, the boxes were carried to the London dock on horse-drawn carts for shipping across the Channel. From the foreign port they continued overland on carts, sometimes on difficult roads and in bad weather, to their destination. Trusted men were sent out from Donkin's factory, often for several weeks, to set up the machine and ensure its perfect running.

Among the first of many from France to order a Fourdrinier were members of the Didot family, relations of Léger Didot – the irksome self-appointed engineer who hampered Donkin's experiments in the early years of the development of the paper machine. They were regular clients from 1825.[32] The family was highly esteemed in France, as a respected dynasty of printers, publishers and typefounders. Grandfather François was a scholar and a publisher, who had eleven children. One of the sons, François-Ambroise, was a master printer and type face designer. His brother, Pierre François, born in 1732, was the founder of the paper mill at Essonnes, and the father of Donkin's bugbear engineer, Léger.[33] When Léger inherited the mill Nicolas-Louis Robert had worked alongside him to develop the prototype paper-making machine. Léger was evidently a wild card in the Didot pack; he confused people by changing his name at one point from St. Léger Didot to Didot St. Léger, a strange choice, for who would want to distance himself from the revered family name? Donkin always referred to him as Monsieur or Mr Didot.

The most constant customer for Donkin's paper machines was Firmin Didot of Paris, Léger's cousin and a noted designer of typefaces. In 1825 Firmin Didot bought a 56½ inch paper machine, complete with drying attachment; it was the largest then available – and he bought another eighteen months later. He was a good customer for at least ten years.[34] In 1835, he ordered a left-handed machine! Another Didot, Léger's son Edouard, took after his grandfather as an academic and translated Johnson's *Lives of the Poets* into French, which his cousin Jules (another printer and type founder) printed for him. Edouard also possessed a large paper-making machine, and ordered a drying machine to attach to it in 1825.[35] Not only that: Donkin made him a new overshot water wheel, with cast iron pumps, which all took several months to set up. Edouard del Cambre, also in Paris, had a smaller paper-making machine installed in the same year as Didot: John Wilks went to set it up.[36] The first paper-making machine to be actually made in France was made by an 'an ingenious French mechanic', M.Calla, but under the instruction of Léger Didot, who had managed to obtain a patent for it in France; needless to say, it was recognised as being very inferior to the machines made by Donkin, who continued to supply his own to France for many years.[37] Bryan Donkin Junior spent several weeks in Nantes in 1829, fitting up a large paper mill belonging to M. Blanchard.[38]

In a run-down hamlet near Castres to the east of Toulouse a French entrepreneur transformed the lives of the poor families.[39] Salvages was nothing but a cluster of miserable cottages with only a windmill and a dilapidated building where paper-making was done by hand: these were the only means of providing sustenance for the inhabitants. Then two industrialists arrived; M. Guibal-Anne-Veaute and M. Grasset brought with them their skills as businessmen, and built two factories. The former set up a textile works, and Grasset had a magnificent paper mill built on the ruins of the old one. A paper-making machine was installed, that delivered everything that was expected of machinery: speed, quality and value for money. It came from Donkin's factory in 1831 and was a boon to the community.[40]

Machine No.115 was also made for a customer in France, Adrien Louis de Beurges, an ex-army major who had set up a paper mill in Ville-sur-Sceaux near Bar-le-Duc: Donkin had been to France to survey the plot in 1820.[41] In 1834 de Beurges took out a five-year patent for a mechanical means of making paper.[42] But the following year, he placed an order for one of Bryan Donkin's machines (No.115).[43] Could it be that his own machine failed to perform and he bought the English one to use instead, or to take apart and copy? That very year, Bryan Donkin also filed a five year patent in France, for improvements in machines used for the manufacturing of paper.[44] Donkin was represented in Paris by M. Antoine Perpigna, a lawyer in the French and Foreign Office for Patents, who led many British clients through the process of attaining a patent.[45] Did Donkin sense a serious rival in de Beurges, and seek protection in French law?

Donkin's printer friend König, whom he had met in London, had returned in 1817 to his homeland and set up a factory in the disused monastery Kloster Oberzell, near Würzburg in the northern tip of Bavaria, where he soon started up a prosperous business making printing machines. Almost all the iron and coke used in the foundry came from England because of the poor quality in Germany, but in spite of the high cost that König had to pass on to the customer to realise a moderate profit, there was still a demand for his machinery.[46] Donkin made the journey to visit him in 1823, to advise on the installation of a paper machine for the works. The registration form for travel on the second leg of his journey from London allowed his passage on the Paris to Strasbourg mail coach, with a companion, departing on May 21st and arriving in Metz – a journey of 175 miles – on the 24th.[47] While on the Continent he probably took the opportunity to visit other clients. Two years later König, his partner Bauer and the publisher Johann Friedrich Cotta took the plunge and set up a whole paper mill nearby, ordering a second Donkin machine, which was installed by one of Donkin's men from Bermondsey. It was the first paper-making factory in the Kingdom of Bavaria.[48]

Other paper makers abroad, including Henri Renoir in Liège and the Rauch brothers of Heilbronn in Southern Germany became excellent customers, ordering paper machines and replacement parts such as deckle straps, machine wires and felting for many years.[49] Donkin's first paper drying machine was sold to them in 1823.[50] Five years after the order from the Prussian Government in Berlin, the second machine that went to Germany was delivered to Herr Rauch; at the same time Rauch also bought one of Donkin's very first drying machines.[51]

In Italy, Smith and Megnier of Trieste bought a paper machine 'complete' in 1828, paying £435.[52] In the same year, Agostino Molino had a large Donkin machine delivered to his mill at Borgosesia in Northern Italy; he had visited England, and seemed to be interested in patenting one himself.[53] John Donkin spent three months living there in the summer of 1828, setting up the whole mill, with two paper-making machines, a water wheel and everything else.[54] Six years later, Molino branched out, spending over £900 on expanding his paper mill with all manner of furnishings from Donkin, including two beating engines, a patent rag cutting machine, and a new water wheel.

Poland had its first Fourdrinier by the late 1820s, and its owners, Blanchett Bros in Kleby, ordered several parts during the next few years.[55] Scandinavia, too, realised the potential value of mechanising their paper industry. The Drewson family in Frederiksborg ordered the first Donkin machine to be sent to Denmark.[56]

Inspired by the success of the Danish venture in making paper by machine, the proprietor of a long-established paper mill in Sweden approached Donkin and took the bold decision to mechanise his mill. His name – Sven Magnus Sunnerdahl – was to become familiar to Donkin. The complex at Klippan in Northern Sweden, where paper had been made by hand since 1573, had to be redesigned and enlarged for making paper by machinery.[57]

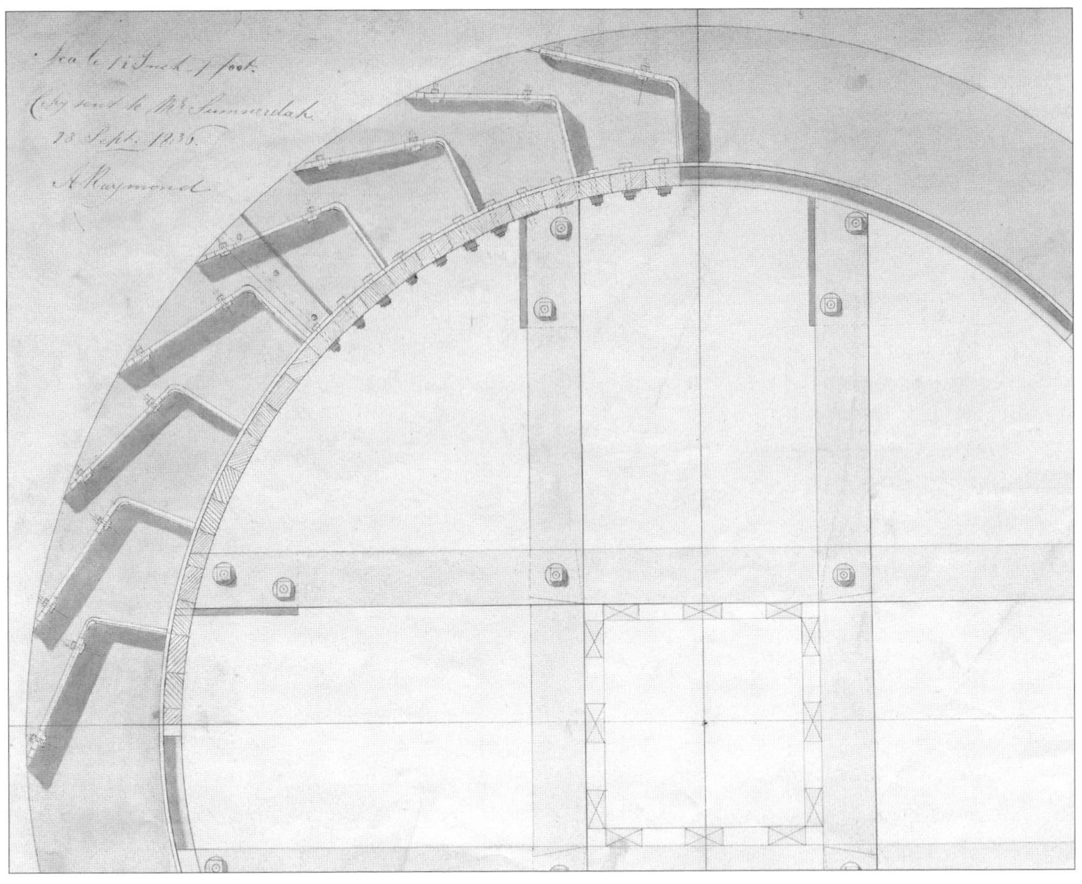

42 *Klippan water wheel,* 1836.

In preparation, new buildings were erected to house the machinery, the entire water system was redirected, and a new overshot water wheel made of Scots pine was built. Drawings of paper-making machinery were sent out to Sweden by Donkin on Christmas Eve in 1831.[58] By October the following year, Sunnerdahl was the proud possessor of the first paper machine in Sweden, with a ten foot boiler for boiling rags and all the necessary paraphernalia to start production. One of Donkin's men, Mr Seamer, arrived on March 23rd and stayed until August the following year to fix up the paper-making machine and its drying machine, and get it all into operation; it must have been exciting but rather daunting for the Bermondsey man to take on such a huge responsibility in a foreign land; his journey home took nearly a month by land and by sea, with a coach hired from Hull to London for the last leg home.[59] Only a few months passed before the Swedish manager was replaced by an Englishman, William Howard, who took up residence in Sweden for five years, managing the Klippan mill and supervising the Swedish paper-makers with such efficiency that the five or six men who first

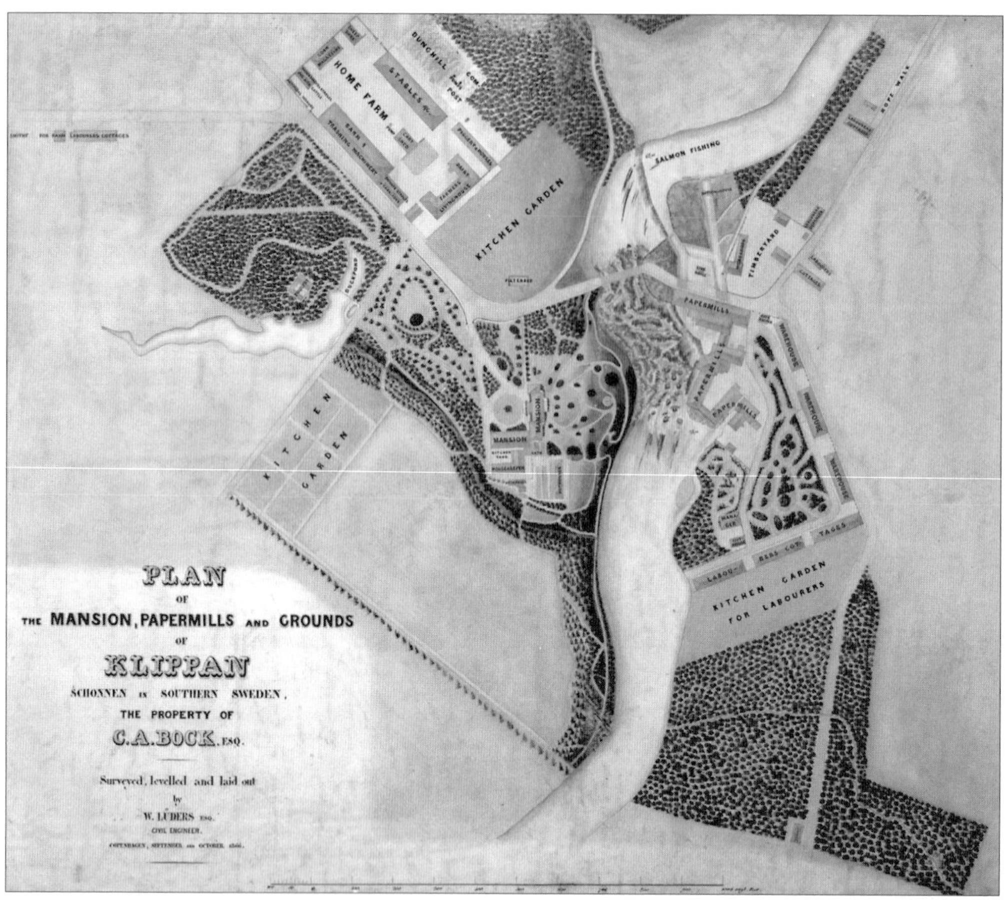

43 *Plan of Klippan mansion, 1866.*

worked the machine were still in their jobs ten years later, although the workforce increased along with the output.[60] Apparatus for glazing the finished paper was sent later, and in the next few years all sorts of materials and parts were provided by Donkin as the need arose: bleaching powder, pipes, wires, rollers, strainer wire, felts and nuts and bolts. Some shipments also contained homelier items, gifts from Bryan Donkin to make life more comfortable for William Howard – books and magazines, drawing instruments, steel pens, a map, and even three dozen table knives with white handles.[61]

So Klippan became a thriving mill. Four big beaters, each with fifty-four steel knives, prepared the 'stuff', and water passed through copper or lead pipes for use in the washing and beating processes; finally the pulp flowed out of a large vat on to the brass wire of the paper-making machine. At the far end, the rollers squeezed the last water out of the pulp and the paper was dried by passing over the five drying cylinders that were now an integral part of the machine, and finally over further rollers that glazed the paper before reeling it up. The paper on the roll was sliced through by hand and cut into sheets. It was a state-of-the-art mill, fitting for the first mechanisation of the process in Sweden. The association between Klippan and the Bryan Donkin Company continued for decades, even after the death of Bryan Donkin. C.A.Bock took over from Mr Sunnerdahl in about 1860, and under his ownership, the mill developed into an attractive community estate, with a mansion, houses for the workers, a farm and kitchen gardens set in green, open spaces.[62]

In spite of the huge cost of shipping, a few American paper-makers bought Donkin's machines. Round about 1827, one of the larger Fourdrinier machines was shipped across the Atlantic from Bermondsey. Henry Barclay, one of the two entrepreneurial sons of a former British Consul, had purchased a large piece of land north of New York, on the Esopus River at Saugerties; there he set up a rolling mill, a cotton factory and a paper mill, using the water power generated by a newly-built dam.[63] His efforts created a vibrant community. One of the three tenants of Henry Barclay's paper mill, by the name of Moses Beach, had been to London to study new methods of production and must have visited Donkin's works.[64] To this exciting new project was sent Bryan Donkin's 56½ inch paper-making machine.[65] It has been said that it was held at the Liverpool Docks for two years before it was allowed to pass through the Customs House, because of strongly-voiced opposition from English paper-makers, who believed that the export of paper from British mills would be jeopardised if the Americans were given the means to make their own.[66] Four young Scots were recruited to install the machine when it arrived. Beach and his two colleagues, Hommerken and Kearney, started it up on 24 October 1827. A second, larger paper machine followed, but it was made by Joseph Newbold, from Lancashire.[67] The reason for the change of supplier is not known.[68] The machinery at Barclay's mill was kept working day and night: it was probably the largest paper manufactory in America. Later, unfortunately, money troubles caused the machines to be neglected and to fall into disuse.[69] The consortium had run the business for about thirty years, and their efforts had created a thriving community, which increased from only twenty-five families in 1825 to a population of over 4,000 in the 1880s.[70]

It seems that two 56½ inch paper-making machines were sent from Bermondsey to the mill of A.C. and W. Curtis at Newton Lower Falls, Massachusetts in 1827.[71] Not all these machines are recorded by the Bryan Donkin Company; because there was opposition in Parliament to such exports to the USA, it is possible that the company used an intermediary. There is also speculation that a paper machine made earlier for one of the Didot family was sent out to America, to Joseph Pickering in North Windham, Connecticut in 1827. By 1829 Fourdrinier-style paper machines made in America and France were already in operation in North America, and during the 1830s, American-built Fourdriniers proliferated.[72] In a discussion with George Escol Sellers about the benefits of an exchange of ideas, when Sellers visited the Donkin works in 1832, Donkin replied laughingly: 'My ideas have gone to America in a machine I sent there to fill an order, and I learn that they have already been copied'.[73]

Bryan's trusted assistant, John Wilks, now had full knowledge of the paper-making process, and brought out his own patent, an apparatus to imitate laid paper by means of a ribbed roller.[74] John Donkin, too, had become a useful and forward-looking member of the team; he submitted, on behalf of Bryan Donkin, a patent for improvement to water wheel gates, to reduce friction, which his father had introduced at an ICE meeting in January 1831.[75] John also contributed a new idea for an improvement to the machine some years later, using vacuum cylinders on large sheets of thick paper, which he also patented.[76]

In the ten years after Sellers's visit, the factory expanded southwards towards Blue Anchor Road, into the land previously owned by Mr Child, and went on from strength to strength. The 1830s were the boom time for Donkin's paper-making machines – by 1843, 133 had been produced. By the time of the Great Exhibition in 1851, the Company had built 191 machines and sent them all over Britain, and to many parts of the Western world.

15
Links

Donkin's work as a valuer and adviser continued. In 1829, he travelled to Hayle in Cornwall to survey a harbour in preparation for providing evidence in a court case involving the Cornish Copper Company.[1] He was called upon to give an opinion on a steam engine boiler in Horse Ferry Road, and to view Ovid Topham's machine for scraping roads, to see if it was suitable for patenting; later, he made copper steam cylinders for it.[2] For a guinea, Donkin examined a new gas engine invented by Samuel Brown, and a steam engine of innovative design by Walter Hancock; both men went on to develop their ideas, Hancock later turning his into a successful steam carriage.[3]

A valuation was required when the Holmes Iron Works in Rotherham was put up for sale. During the frosty winter of 1814 in London the opportunity had been taken to examine Southwark Bridge and because of its poor state of repair, a new one had been commissioned.[4] Rennie was the engineer who designed the huge new iron bridge, with its central arch of 240 feet and two others almost as long. Joseph Walker, the proprietor of the Rotherham Iron Works, took on the task of casting the massive metal parts for the new bridge.[5] He had made a good living from producing canons until the end of the Peninsular War. The whole operation would have been of great interest to Donkin. During construction, tens of thousands of sightseers came to the Rotherham factory from Sheffield and the surrounding countryside to wonder at the new bridge, causing traffic jams (and the invention of a new form of public transport carriage, called a Waterloo). When the bridge was finished and opened in 1819, the factory went into decline – all their efforts had been put into the one project and all other work had been turned down, leaving a void. Another member of the Walker family purchased the Gospel Oak factory in London and moved the canon-making equipment there, and the Rotherham works was put up for sale. Probably because of his connections with Rennie, Donkin was asked to value the premises and answer queries from potential buyers.[6] Later (and closer to home at Bermondsey Wall) when bankruptcy forced the paper maker George Turner to give up his work at Fountain Mill, Bryan Donkin was called upon to take care of the sale.[7]

While he was working on the Caledonian Canal, Thomas Telford was asked to put forward a scheme to bridge the Mersey at Runcorn Gap. On studying the sandy nature and soft state of the river bed and taking into account the narrowness of the shipping lane at that point, he concluded that a suspension bridge was the only viable possibility.[8] His method of planning was to break down the problems of design and construction into individual elements, and to use the services of the best sub-contractors and professionals to resolve them.[9] It is not surprising then, to find that Telford used the talents of Bryan Donkin to determine the strength of the cables intended for the Runcorn Bridge. Through their collaboration on the Caledonian Canal Telford must have heard of Donkin's involvement with a certain Captain Samuel Brown. A former sea captain, Brown had left the Royal Navy and set up an iron cable and chain-making business at Millwall on the Isle of Dogs, not very far from Donkin's works. Initially his main interest was the supply of anchor chains to the Royal Navy and also the manufacture of iron cables, or hawsers, as a stronger replacement for the hemp ropes for ships' rigging.[10]

In about 1812, possibly as a result of reading of the success of chain bridges in America, Brown had begun to look at bridge design and building as a further diversification to his growing business.[11] By 1813, he had erected, within the confines of his works, an all-metal suspension bridge, a demonstration model with a span of just 120 feet, but containing all the design elements and features of a full-sized bridge. John Rennie visited the bridge and was impressed: 'I was drawn in a carriage and found myself perfectly safe and easy … I came out of my carriage and made my coachman drive several times over it, that I might see how it acted'.[12] To earn the approval of Rennie must have been a great boost, but there was still some way to go.

In these early years of the nineteenth century structural theory was not fully understood by the wider engineering fraternity; this shortfall in theoretical knowledge sometimes resulted in embarrassing failures, even amongst the well-known engineers of the day. One such was Henry Maudslay's new erecting shop at his factory, which collapsed in 1826, killing six or eight of his workforce and injuring many more, when the walls evidently gave way under the pressure of the heavy roof.[13] Such avoidable catastrophes as these would not be tolerated in a high-profile public enterprise like a new bridge. A collapse on this scale would shatter the nation's confidence in this new engineering technology. In order to be able to patent his bridge design Brown needed to prove his calculations by establishing the strength of malleable iron and the ultimate force needed to tear apart the individual components. For this he required a known consultant, an independent engineer, well versed in the laws of physics and mathematics, but having a practical attitude to problem solving. His wise choice was Bryan Donkin. Together with Brown, Donkin set up a series of experiments into the practicability of the scheme.

Donkin's collaboration with Telford probably overlapped with his work on Brown's patent. Telford's proposal for the Runcorn Gap was a bridge 2,000 feet long, with a central span of 1,000 feet. Telford and Donkin set in train a number of feasibility studies and experiments in cable design. The trials included more than three hundred tests to establish the tensile strength of malleable iron, using an up-to-date proof testing machine at Thomas Brunton's factory, which was powered by a state-of-the-art Bramah hydraulic press.[14] As one of the leading civil engineering contractors of his day, and one who had the trust of the British Government, Telford had earned his reputation through rigorous empirical investigation and his vision of the grand design. Unfortunately the Runcorn Gap project was abandoned through lack of funds.

However, all this experimental work would be put to good use in the Government proposal for the new bridge to link the north coast of Wales to the Isle of Anglesey, to ease the journey from London to Ireland. This bridge across the Menai Straits, although not as huge as the Runcorn Bridge would have been, was nevertheless a massive undertaking – a bridge of some 560 feet between the enormous supporting towers, and 100 feet above the water. It demanded a new approach to the method of suspension.

Small foot-bridges had been made from fine strands of wire twisted into rope, and this was Telford's preferred method for suspending the Menai Bridge. Donkin had proved that wrought iron, when drawn into fine wire, was more than one and a half times stronger than the original bar; but wire-drawing was still a hand craft and no machine existed that could cope with producing the miles of wire required. The estimated cost was therefore £149, 000, so that was out of the question.[15] An alternative plan was to suspend the bridge from sixteen cables, 'each of which was to consist of thirty six wrought iron rods, half an inch square [in section]'.[16] These small rods were to be packed together in a square form, and then segmental pieces were to be added so the whole might form a round cable nearly four inches in diameter'. The short lengths of iron rod would be welded end to end to form the cable. Donkin had made a sample section, and thought it was 'a very simple and excellent plan'.[17] Again though, the method was in advance of the industry's capabilities, and the cost of making cables from iron rods proved prohibitive so the scheme was abandoned.

At the enquiry of the House of Commons Select Committee into the viability of the bridge, Telford was able to say that it required 'a weight of from twenty-six to thirty tons to tear a one inch square bar of malleable iron asunder'; in other words, the iron had an ultimate tensile strength of twenty-six to thirty tons per square inch (a figure that would hold good today). Bryan Donkin and John Rennie were happy to concur. Telford also stated that although the weight of the bridge was only 342 tons, it would bear 1,674 tons before the cables would break. When Donkin was asked if this figure was accurate, he replied that Thomas Telford was underestimating the strength of his cables, and 'it appears to me that Mr Telford's data are [sic] perfectly safe'. Finally, Telford was asked, probably by an unscientific member of the committee, if he could calculate whether the bridge would stand the weight of two hundred oxen packed tightly from one end of the

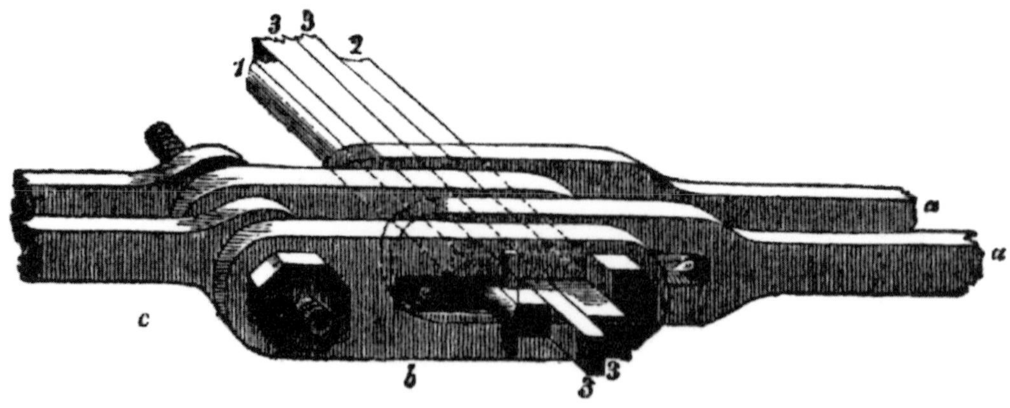

44 *Eye-bar linking system for Menai Bridge.*

bridge to the other.[18] He did the sum, but retorted that it was very unlikely that anyone would drive a herd of two hundred animals 'all in a heap'.

The foundation stone was laid in August 1819, by William Provis, Telford's resident engineer, and work on building the bridge began before the experiments with the cables were completed. Finally, Brown's method, which Donkin had helped to develop, was adopted for making the cables. His innovation was the use of an eye-bar, a flat wrought iron bar of several feet in length with a flattened boss forged at either end and drilled through to accept a connecting pin.[19] The massive iron eye-bars, each 9ft 5ins long, were forged from best Shropshire hammered iron, manufactured at William Haseldine's Upton Forge. From there they were transported to the bridge site by canal and sea. After final machining on site, each eye-bar was tested by suspending it vertically and applying a load of thirty-two tons. Whilst in this position, it was bashed with a heavy hammer and examined for signs of fracture. Finally, as an early form of corrosion proofing, the bars were heated in a stove until 'the hand could only just be borne upon it' and then immersed in linseed oil for a few minutes.[20] After this they were returned to the stove for re-heating, which dried the oil to a thin, hard varnish. William Provis's brother John was acting in the capacity of quality control engineer. After all this rigorous testing, each sound component was stamped with his proof mark, an indented cross. The individual links were then ready to be joined together to form the chain. This was much stronger and more reliable than the conventional short-link chain, and less expensive than the other methods suggested.

It took six years to build the stone structures to support the ends of the bridge, their great arches stretching from the bank out into the water to the towers that would hold up the cables from which the central span was suspended.[21] Finally, at 2.30 p.m. on 26 April 1825, the time came to hoist the first chain cable into place.

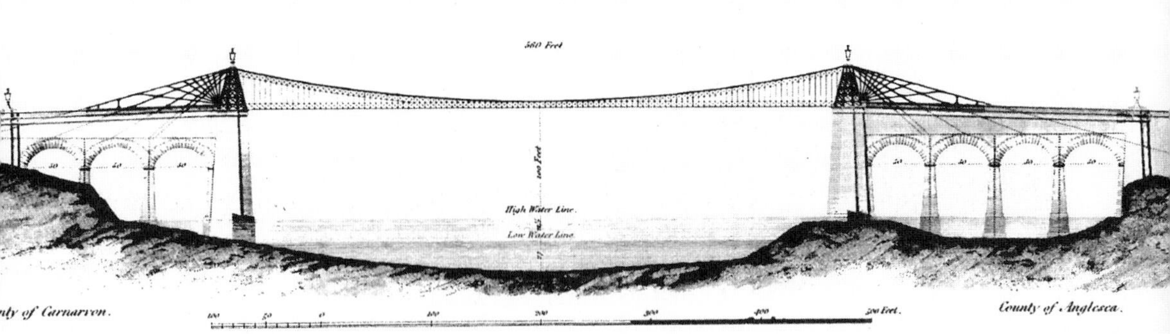

45 *Design for the bridge over the Menai Straits,* 1819.

By means of a 450-foot long raft, the massive chain dangling from the mainland tower was transported across the Straits and fixed to ropes that passed over the opposite tower. Watched by excited crowds on both banks, thirty two men, using four capstans and a block and tackle mechanism, hoisted the immense chain into its position high above the water. To keep the men working rhythmically, two fifers played jolly tunes. The anxious crowds held their breath in silence, and broke into hearty cheers of relief and amazement that echoed across the water as the chain was secured.[22] Three of the workmen (perhaps drunk with exhilaration) 'had the temerity to pass along the upper surface of the chain'. This foolhardy feat was surpassed by a local cobbler who crawled down to the centre of the cable, settled himself astride it and calmly finished making a pair of shoes before climbing safely back to the Caernarvon side.[23] In July the last of the sixteen cables was raised with great celebrations: band players climbed down from the top of one of the suspension piers onto a platform placed across the centre of the cables and played the National Anthem, and workmen marched about up there too, while below, the St David packet boat was the first to sail under the unfinished bridge, re-opening the navigation channel after two months of closure.[24] The grand opening of the bridge, its cinder-covered wooden roadway suspended on vertical inch-square rods from the arc of cables above, took place in the afternoon of Monday, 26 January 1826. Torrential rain had fallen in the morning, but the skies cleared for the ceremony, and more than five thousand people turned out to witness the scene. The toll-gate was thrown open, and first to cross the bridge was the Royal London and Holyhead mail coach, carrying the London mail-bag to Dublin. In the coach was William Provis, the chief engineer, his brother John (who had proof-tested the ironwork), William Haseldine the iron founder and as many of the other contractors as could squeeze in or hang from the side. The jubilant crowds followed, passing back and forth across the bridge for several hours, their faces lighted up with 'joy, admiration and astonishment' at 'this national and splendid specimen of British architecture'.[25] Surely Bryan Donkin was there too, proudly celebrating his contribution to this wonderful achievement!

Together with Brunton, Brown and Telford, Donkin was in the forefront of ironworking technology. Almost a hundred years later, a thorough examination of the bridge was made, and the vast majority of the chain bars were found to be still in good condition, certain proof that their confidence in the theories they had promoted was justified. Although Donkin and Telford never used wire ropes, Donkin's cutting edge experiments had paved the way for future development.

Telford and Donkin maintained their working relationship on smaller projects during this time. In April 1821 Telford passed on an enquiry from Lord Bridgewater about the best way to power the drawing of water from a well. He ended the letter, adding: 'Now as you are a very cunning man, and have yourself had experience in such matters, and may know some respectable well-sinkers, may I request your opinion and advice in this matter? I remain your very humble servant, Thomas Telford'.[26] Donkin must have installed a pump, which for some reason failed a couple of years later.[27] Telford was called and Lord Bridgewater 'in worse humour than usual' complained that the pump 'would not do its office, and … the people could get no water.' Donkin was away visiting Germany, and Telford was busy, so wrote to Donkin on his return requesting him to pay a personal visit to 'this unlucky pump' and let him know what he had done. The hope is that Donkin managed to put it right.

While the Menai Bridge was being built, Telford was carrying out another huge project, this time in Sweden. He was engaged in building the Göta Canal across the country at the behest of Count Baltzar von Platen, a German-born ex-Captain of the Swedish Navy, commissioned by the Swedish Government to manage the construction of the canal. Again, Bryan Donkin was enlisted to help. Unfortunately, instructions were passed from Platen to Telford to Donkin, and letters may have gone astray, causing misunderstandings and criticisms. In November 1821, Telford admonished Donkin for not sending drawings of the dredging machinery to Count Platen; but in the next month they were corresponding about the best types of wood and the method of construction for the boat to carry Donkin's dredging machine for the canal.[28] Telford made suggestions about the strength and availability of fir and oak, but bowed to Donkin's opinion. When the dredger was ready, Donkin had been given no idea where or how to send it and had to point out, politely, that some of his men would have to go out to set the machines up, so their travelling expenses and wages would be added to the bill. In the spring of 1822 materials and machinery, worth £1,500 to Donkin, were put on board in the River Thames – twenty-two strong wrought iron buckets, an eight horse power steam engine and everything else needed to build a dredger. Steam engines, paddle wheels, shafts with coupling links and plummer blocks – to the tune of another £1,800 – were also sent from London to Sweden. Count Platen complained that the buckets and frame on the dredger had been made too short, but had Donkin been asked to go to Sweden to see the canal himself and to measure up, there would have been no cause for complaint. From the beginning though, the dredging machine was praised for cutting through sandy ground with ease and in the end Count Platen was well satisfied with its performance. It is clear that Thomas Telford's esteem for Donkin's abilities was undiminished, and it seems unlikely that the lack of drawings was anything more than a hitch in communication.

The experience with Telford and the Caledonian Canal led to more commissions for Donkin. Near Halifax, work was continually being carried out on the Calder and Hebble canal, which began under Smeaton in 1759. In the early 1820s an order was sent to Bryan Donkin for a dredger.[29] Nearly £1,000 was earned for the company in July 1824 with another order for materials and metal for a dredging machine, and fifteen wrought iron buckets 'steeled at the mouth' for the old dredger, a wood ladder for the side of the boat, and a three horse power engine with an iron boiler, a grate 'within', and a wrought iron chimney. A wrought iron buoy followed. The materials were sent from St Katherine's Wharf by the Tower, and one of Donkin's men, Kingston by name, spent twenty nine weeks from the August to March working up in Yorkshire.

With Peter Barlow, Bryan Donkin spent some time on 15 March 1825 'attending at the Weighing House on the Paddington Canal and at an experiment etc on the Grand Junction Canal', testing the resistance of water to the passage of boats.[30]

With his growing reputation as a scientific engineer Donkin was invited to become an investor and director in a new and exciting venture, Marc Brunel's plan to bore a tunnel under the Thames between Rotherhithe and Wapping Dock Stairs.[31] Throughout 1823, Marc Brunel canvassed financial backers and sounded out politicians and influential military figures who would be helpful to his cause. On 18 February 1824, in response to advertisements and pamphlets, almost 100 people gathered at the City of London Tavern for an inaugural meeting, and the Thames Tunnel Company was born. The M.P. William Smith was appointed Chairman, and a Board of Directors – or 'Court', as Brunel chose to grandly style it – duly elected. Amongst these were the close business associates Bryan Donkin, Timothy Bramah and Thomas Brunton, representing the engineering fraternity. Such was the enthusiasm for the scheme that over £100,000 was raised immediately from the sale of shares at £50 each.

Over the next few months the Board of Directors drew up a Bill to be set before Parliament, outlining the work to be undertaken, and less than six months later a Bill for 'Making and maintaining a Tunnel under the Thames,' with the backing of the Duke of Wellington, received Royal assent. But it was almost another year before work formally started, with the laying of the foundation stone by the

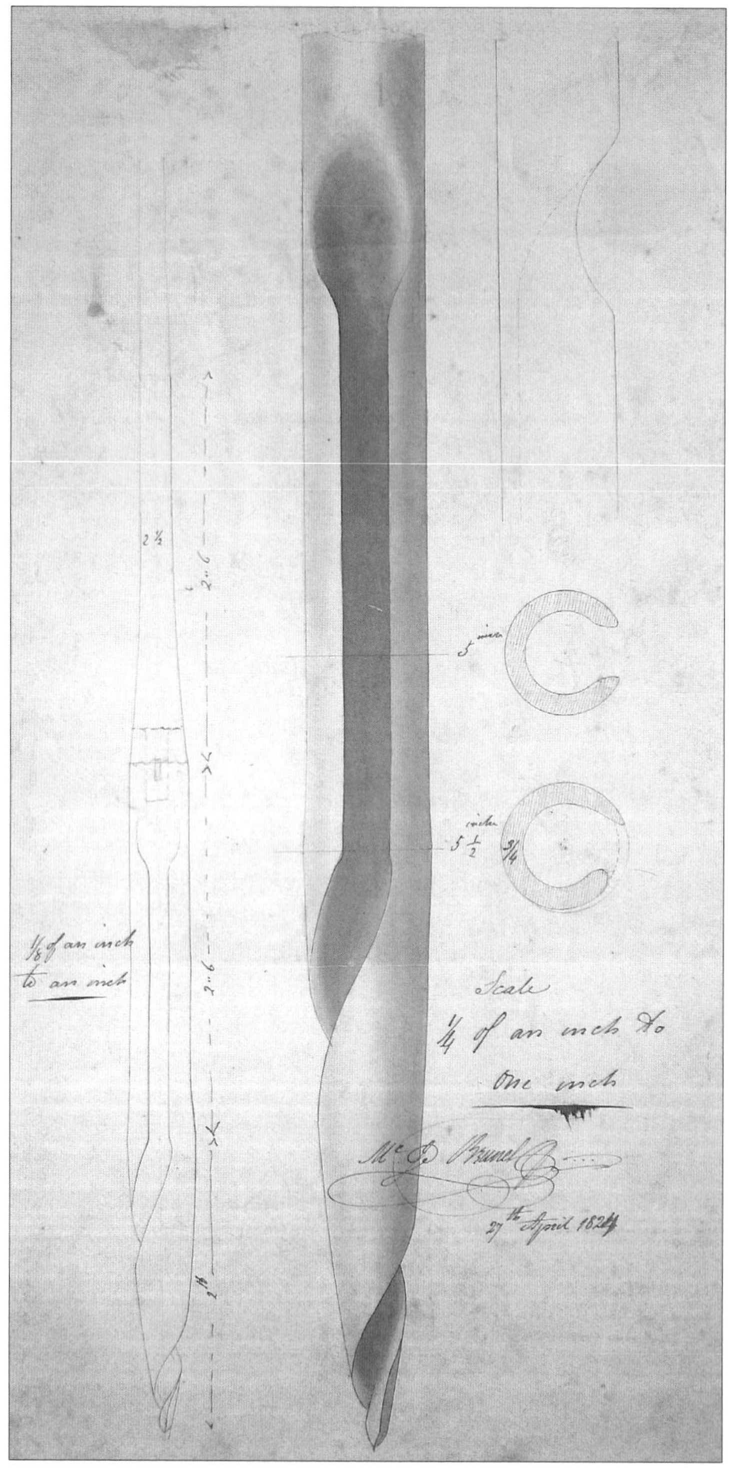

46 *Auger for river bed survey,* 1824.

Chairman, William Smith. Bands played the National Anthem, toasts were raised to the success of the tunnel, a cold collation was provided for distinguished guests and later in the evening the workmen were treated to a supper at the Europa Inn. However, Brunel (confident that his scheme would pass successfully through Parliament) had jumped the gun several months earlier and had ordered the firm of Joliffe and Banks to make a series of bores on the line of the tunnel across the Thames.

Saturday April 24th found Marc Brunel's son Isambard working alongside Bryan Donkin as they made borings into the clay and sand of Cow Court, the starting point of the tunnel in Rotherhithe on the south bank of the Thames. It was not the most gainful of days: the auger was driven down to its first depth and drawn up 'full of clay and sand', but on attempting to drill deeper, the mouth of the auger was jammed by a stone.[32] Isambard noted: 'After loosening, tried every way to get it down, obliged to give up.' They were obviously not pleased with the equipment and used their time instead to go and look at a German auger, which Isambard sketched; this was a large metal 'bit' for boring, intended for making holes through wood, two of which Donkin had acquired on his visit to Germany, and subsequently presented to the Society of Arts.[33] However, the day brightened for Isambard when, after being given a lift by Bryan Donkin, he was dropped off at Blackfriars Bridge where by chance, he met his good friend – and soon to be brother-in-law – Benjamin Hawes.[34] The frustration of the time wasted on the Saturday by Donkin was amply rewarded when, the following Tuesday, Marc Brunel visited Redriff (the old name for Rotherhithe) where he 'made a drawing of an auger to be made at Mr Donkin's'.[35] The surviving drawing shows an auger bit of some seven feet in length and five and a half inches in diameter, with a tapered shank to fit it to the extension rods which would drive it down to the required depth.[36] Manufacturing an auger of this complexity, especially its flute (the spiral that caught the mud) would need the combined efforts and co-operation of blacksmiths, machinists and detail fitters. The drawing serves as a lasting tribute, not just to Marc Brunel's design skills, but also to the versatility of Donkin's workforce.

It was a tunnelling venture on a scale never seen before, but with the great Marc Brunel at the helm, confidence of success seemed to be assured. His plan was bold – first build a gigantic shaft, forty feet tall and fifty feet in diameter, with walls three feet thick (like a squat chimney or the keep of a castle) bound with iron hoops and tied at the base to a ring of iron, called the 'curb' with forty-eight stout tie rods of wrought iron, running vertically through the centre of the wall.[37] Once completed, teams of labourers would dig out the ground from within the shaft and under the iron curb. By this means, the entire structure would slowly sink under its own weight into the ground. Digging would continue until the top of the shaft reached ground level, transforming its appearance from that of a chimney into one of an enormous dry well. A large hole would then be cut in the base of the wall of the shaft, from where the tunnellers would strike out on their long and perilous expedition into the unknown dangers under the Thames. The tunnel starting from this point would be of equally grand proportions, the face of the workings measuring a massive thirty-five feet in breadth and twenty feet high: it would accommodate twin horse-shoe tunnels or archways, each with a roadway wide enough for a horse-drawn carriage and a pavement for pedestrians. Openings at intervals in the central archway allowed movement between the two tunnels.

Amongst the many problems glossed over in this simple explanation there lurked the very real and frightening danger of flooding. In a venture of this size it was estimated that the weight of the river above would induce a constant pressure of around six hundred tons on the roof of the tunnel, a far higher force than the clay bed of the Thames could withstand. To counter this force, Marc Brunel would use his much vaunted invention, the great shield, a strong iron framework corresponding exactly in size to the rectangular face of the tunnel and designed to 'walk forwards on moveable feet with the aid of massive screw jacks.[38] As the miners worked the face, the shield was advanced the distance of one brick, with the bricklayers following, quickly filling this space and constructing a full cross section of the archways, keeping the brickwork in close contact with the shield. The front-to-back measurement or thickness of this structure was around seven feet, and was composed of twelve perpendicular frames, each being divided horizontally into three, making thirty-six strong compartments in which the three dozen miners worked. In front of each compartment was a wooden wall made up of well-fitting oak boards; to work the face, the miner removed the top board and dug out the clay to the width of a brick, about 4½ inches. The board was then replaced and driven forward by long screws to meet the newly-excavated face. The process was then repeated until all the boards had been advanced by the same distance.

After the gala on the day of the opening ceremony, work began in earnest. The ground was cleared and the shaft was fully built in three weeks.[39] A great wooden framework was built across the top of the shaft and a thirty-two horse power steam engine was erected on it. This would first drive a bucket-lift system to extract the gravel and clay that the labourers dug out from within the shaft, and later haul up the vast amounts of putrid spoil from the tunnel, at the same time providing power for the main pumps, used to drain the foul water continually seeping from the river above and from the pockets of quicksand below and in front of the shield. The sinking of the shaft became a public spectacle. Among the crowds were many doubters, who expected it to topple over; but later, as smooth progress was made, members of the aristocracy were drawn to witness its slow descent. Some, including the Duke of Wellington (Brunel's patron), were courageous enough to venture inside to gain a closer understanding of this colossal work of new-fangled engineering.[40]

The concept was working but, teething troubles apart, progress was slow. To build the tunnel in the allocated time of three years, four hundred feet would have to be built each year, or, allowing for holidays and illness, eight feet per week; but in the first month after breaking out of the shaft only eight feet had been covered. Moreover, costs were rising rapidly: a draughtsman, Pinchback, was hired at £62 per quarter; he needed an assistant with a wage of 30 shillings a week.[41] The direct labour force was counted in hundreds, and as conditions worsened, topped 450. Money was haemorrhaging away at an alarming rate, and the Board of Directors was tense and disturbed. Donkin knew the difficulties of managing large projects with spiralling costs; he had, after all, planned and overseen the complete overhaul of the Greenwich tide mill a decade or so earlier, and with a long and respected career as an appraiser and valuer, he was adept at identifying waste and extravagance.

Feeling his responsibilities as one of the engineers on the Board, Donkin spoke out. His argument centred round the lavish use of Roman cement, a relatively new but expensive material, which was quick-dry and stronger than other mortars when set, an ideal material for use in the extreme conditions that would be encountered under the river. But Brunel had constructed the massive vertical shaft using pure Roman cement as a mortar, and had clad its entire outer face with the same material. Bearing in mind that this initial work was at least 150 feet back from the Rotherhithe high water mark, Donkin maintained that conventional cement, mixed with sand, would have been strong enough for this work at a fraction of the cost. Brunel, unused to answering to a Board of Directors, accused Donkin of speaking out of turn, and it took all the political skills of the Chairman, William Smith, to diffuse the situation, vindicating Donkin and appeasing Brunel. The equilibrium of relationships was quickly restored and Donkin continued to make a strong contribution to the tunnel. From the outset, water seeping and sometimes pouring into the workings was a constant problem, and the steam-driven pumps soon had to be augmented with hand pumps. These were made in Donkin's factory and although as a director of the tunnel he had been precluded from tendering for the manufacture of the great shield, he none the less provided men and expertise to rectify defects in its performance. Between 1827 and 1832, Donkin sent his men to Rotherhithe on several occasions – four men spent twelve days 'chipping shields'; then, twice, two men spent eight days there helping out with various jobs.[42] One worked on a lighting apparatus, another repaired and cleaned the counter, or 'tell-tale' and several others cleaned and repaired the many pieces of tunnelling equipment. Donkin made a cement mixer to a design drawn by Marc Brunel.

Despite the fact that he had already committed himself body and soul to the Thames Tunnel, Brunel never passed up the chance of a commercial opportunity. On his regular visits to the Royal Society, that melting pot for all the many disciplines of science where the diffusion of knowledge was openly encouraged, he learnt of the latest joint experiments of Michael Faraday and Sir Humphry Davy.[43] They had been conducting laboratory studies into liquefying carbonic acid gas (carbon dioxide). Their thought was that by reversing the process, with just a small amount of heat, the great expansion of gas could be used to drive a piston, in a similar manner to a steam engine but at a much smaller cost. With Faraday and Davy's encouragement, Marc Brunel took out a patent. Described formally as the differential engine, it quickly became known as the 'gaz' engine; because of his workload, Marc Brunel adroitly passed the burden of its development to his son Isambard. He in turn called in the able Bryan Donkin to assist in the many trial and error experiments. Though complex, and reliant on precisely fitting parts, the engine itself presented few problems for these two indomitable engineers. What did prove confounding was the means to drive it – the conversion of carbonic acid from its gaseous form into liquid; it was commercially unviable and so was abandoned, in spite of many days having been spent on it by Donkin's workforce.[44]

The gas engine was a mere sideshow in the main endeavour. Throughout 1826 the tunnel was pushed along at a painfully slow rate. Despite the merits of the great shield, many unforeseen pitfalls were encountered. The resident engineer, Armstrong, was struck down along with a great number of the miners and bricklayers, by tunnel fever, a debilitating illness with symptoms of nausea, skin complaints and temporary blindness as well as rotting fingernails. The condition was caused by the putrid gasses which escaped with every shovel of detritus-laden mud removed from the tunnel face. Armstrong's ill health prompted Marc to promote his son Isambard to the post of resident engineer, with two assistants, Richard Beamish and William Gravatt. Their role was to take charge of each shift, but in practice the demands were so great that they were often at their posts for days at a time, catching the briefest of naps in the damp and dangerous atmosphere. Water seepage had risen to the unprecedented level of one hundred and eighty gallons per minute, putting greater pressure on the labourers to keep the tunnel from flooding.

Funds were so low that, despite the dangers at the workface, it was decided to admit the public to view the completed part of the tunnel. It proved a great attraction, with as many as seven hundred people per day paying a shilling each for the privilege of walking along the finished part of the archways. With typical aplomb, Isambard celebrated his twenty-first birthday on 11 April 1827, with a concert in the western archway; but just ten days later, the tunnel was breached. The roof of the tunnel was so near to the river that all manner of rubbish – coal, butchers' bones, fragments of china – flooded in before it could be stopped with bags of clay thrown into the hole from above. A diving bell was borrowed from the West India Dock Company and, with Isambard and William Gravatt perched inside, it was lowered to the bed of the river, directly above the great shield.[45] Once they had established that the clay was holding and there was no immediate danger of inundation, Isambard, with the confidence and swagger of youth, took a great risk, and proceeded to push a tube down through the clay roof of the tunnel in order to make direct contact with Nelson, one of the best and most fearless miners, crouching in the top box of the shield. This act of derring-do gave much needed positive publicity to the tunnel project; the stunt must have been premeditated, as gold pins (probably cravat pins) were passed up the tube to be distributed later as mementoes of the occasion. One worker criticised the foolish escapade. William Peace wrote to John Donkin at the factory to explain that he had been absent from work for two weeks with (so he said …) a bad case of smallpox, and took the opportunity of mentioning what he thought about Gravatt and the young Brunel:[46]

> We may now laugh heartily at Gravatt and the other oracle. All their puffing has come to this. Had Armstrong or any other man of experience been there, no such thing would have occurred; they are not competent to [manage] such an important undertaking …

Peace thought that they should have practised their technique somewhere other than the Thames, because 'yon Frenchman was too confident and too grasping and a very careless fellow'.

With the inundation once again reduced from a rushing torrent to a steady stream, tunnelling was resumed, but as the tide rose on the evening of May 18th disaster struck, when water burst through the shield with an unstoppable force, tumbling the miners from the staging. Bricklayers, labourers, miners and engineers ran for their lives along the five hundred and more yards of tunnel, back towards the safety of Cow Court. William Gravatt and the young Brunel forced themselves through the rushing water in a rescue mission; the surging torrent rose rapidly around them as they struggled on to save the men: it was a heroic endeavour by both young men. By their efforts and sheer good fortune, no-one perished, but this time it took hundreds of tons of clay and several months to stop up the massive hole in the bed of the Thames. Eventually, with the steam-driven pumps working flat out, the water level in the tunnel was reduced to a point where the damage could be assessed by Isambard and Beamish, taking the most hazardous of journeys along the tunnel, first by punt and then scrambling over the bank of debris deposited by the flood, to reach the damaged shield.

Donkin had foreseen further problems and suggested that the shield should be split vertically into two. In this way, each archway or tunnel would advance separately, one leading the other by several yards. By this simple alteration the pressure on the shield would be reduced considerably. Once again, Marc Brunel shunned Donkin's advice. A correspondent to the *Mechanics' Magazine* agreed with Donkin's assessment; the Editor endorsed his view:[47]

> The plan which he proposes of excavating only one archway at a time, is particularly deserving of attention; and not the less so, that the same thing was suggested by Mr Donkin, engineer, shortly after the former accident, but rejected, like almost every other piece of advice which Mr Brunel has received from men of talent and experience on the subject.

The prospect of a tunnel under the Thames had initially thrilled the general public, but with each setback, enthusiasm waned. The latest catastrophe was met with general derision, prompting many letters to the newspapers. The London theatres added to the mood of ridicule by staging spectacles of the disaster; once such was entitled *The Interior of the Thames Tunnel with its Curious Machinery,* and had a cast which included fish, water sprites and eels.[48]

Some confidence was restored when, after four months, the tunnel was cleared and work recommenced, but time and money were running out. Marc Brunel estimated that he needed a further quarter of a million pounds to finish the work. To raise this capital, a new Act of Parliament would be needed. Again the lawyers were set to work drafting a new Bill, but their labours were in vain. Early on the morning of 16 January 1828, Beamish mounted his pony and rode poste-haste to wake Marc Brunel with the news that once again the great shield was breached, and the tunnel flooded. Six brave miners lost their lives that night. Isambard survived the inundation but sustained injuries that troubled him for the rest of his short life.

Once again, great effort was made to raise the necessary funds to continue. The Duke of Wellington contributed £500 from his own purse, and made a fine speech to rally new investors.[49] Every director, including Marc Brunel and Bryan Donkin, pitched in a further £100 each, but this gesture to encourage further investment resulted in a meagre sum of £9,660 being added to the coffers, not one twentieth of the money needed to complete the work. Time passed without progress and in 1832 the Board of the Thames Tunnel Company changed. William Smith was replaced as Chairman, first by George Wollaston, with Benjamin Hawes as his deputy; but after Wollaston had a serious stroke, Benjamin Hawes took the Chair. In this period, the engineers Bryan Donkin, his friend Timothy Bramah and Thomas Brunton all resigned and were replaced by John Buckle, a London ship owner, J.A. De Riemer, a friend of Brunel, and John Brown, who had made a fortune from diamonds. Also at this time Benjamin Hawes junior, the son of the Chairman and son-in-law of Brunel, was promoted to the Court. At last Marc Brunel had a compliant Board of Directors, and his engineering decisions would go unchallenged by his peers. The Brunels continued to use Donkin's services as a consultant in many future ventures, but Bryan Donkin was now free to devote more time to his own engineering interests.

It was not until late 1833 that the Duke of Wellington, Brunel's most ardent supporter, after years of lobbying, secured a loan of £270,000 to finish the Tunnel. But tunnelling did not resume until 1835; progress was still slower than expected and as the Tunnel lengthened the build-up of deadly gases became almost unbearable, with miners fainting in the stalls of the shield and the bouts of temporary blindness increasing. There were three more major floods before the archways were joined up to the newly built pedestrian descent tower at Wapping. The project, estimated to finish within three years, had in fact taken eighteen, but at long last they were through. The fickle press changed its tune from one of derision

47 *The Thames Tunnel,* c.1830.

to that of admiration, joy and jubilation. Marc Brunel received a knighthood for his achievement and at four o'clock in the afternoon of Saturday 25 March 1843, the 'great bore' was opened with a procession of dignitaries, following the band of the Fusilier Guards playing 'See the Conquering Hero Comes' down the spiral stairway at Rotherhithe; from there the cavalcade progressed along the western archway, resting in the daylight at the top of the Wapping shaft, before returning to Rotherhithe by the eastern archway. Within fifteen weeks of opening, a million people had passed through the company's turnstiles, paying twopence each for the thrill and convenience of walking under the Thames. Stalls were set up in the roadways, selling fancy goods and souvenirs, while street performers brought a fairground atmosphere to this sub-aqueous grotto. The young Queen Victoria visited with a retinue that included Prince Albert, the Duke of Saxe-Coburg and Gotha, as well as Lord Byron, and expressed her admiration for the work. On the surface, everything looked well, but an essential part of the original plan had been to build large descents at either end of the Tunnel beyond the existing pedestrian stairways. These spiral roadways would be the only means by which traffic of all kinds – from flocks of sheep and loaded carts destined for London's growing markets, to mail coaches, private gigs, and consignments of rum, spices and teak from the docks – could take the short cut under the Thames. Without them, the Thames Tunnel Company was starved of its potential toll revenue and could not even pay the interest on the Treasury loan.

Marc Brunel lobbied the Directors to raise more capital; but after eighteen long years of inundations and tribulations they had grown weary of the tunnel and its problems. The great descents were never made, and the tunnel, once hailed as a wonder of the modern world, began to fall into disrepute, as although it still attracted foot passengers during the day, by night it became the haunt of footpads and prostitutes. London's down-and-outs soon discovered that for twopence they could while away the night hours in the relative comfort of the depths, earning it a reputation as the cheapest doss-house in town.[50] The British and European press continued to extol the merits of the tunnel long after its opening; this extract from *Cruchley's New Guide to London* gives a typical opinion:[51]

> Though it has not answered the expectations in a commercial point of view, it is not the less admirable as a monument of engineering skill and adventurous enterprise, and must be regarded as the most eminent of Sir Isambard Brunel's successes.

However, our American cousins, who by mid-century were challenging Great Britain's supremacy as the most advanced industrial nation, took a more realistic and hard-headed view. Alfred E. Beach, himself a tunnel builder, and promoter of the pneumatic railway system, had this to say:[52]

> The Thames Tunnel Company deliberately selected, at the outset, the most ponderous, massive, costly, and difficult scheme of construction that could possibly have been chosen, and then adhered to their choice with the dogged pertinacity characteristic of John Bull.

He goes on to write that a much simpler plan could have been used; he was referring to the Thames Archway Company's original scheme for tunnel-building of more than half a century earlier, when Wyatt and Hawkins had experimented with the sinking of prefabricated cylinders: Bryan Donkin had played an important part in the trials by assessing the merits of what proved to be a successful experiment, but which was not taken up at the time.

The Thames Tunnel had proved to be a brave but ill-conceived venture. From the outset, Marc Brunel had seriously underestimated the costs; even if everything had gone according to plan, he would have had a shortfall of cash, but in the event, he had no capital in reserve to deal with the many unforeseen problems of inundation, quicksands, illness and poor surveying. Apart from its brief moment of wonder in the year or so after its opening, the tunnel languished in a poor state; a few stalls were scattered through the space, and the occasional exhibition was put up or musicians played, but 'sooth to say, though a wonderful triumph of engineering, it is, as a promenade, immeasurably dull and wearisome.'[53]

The tunnel was eventually bought in 1861 by the East London Railway Company to form part of a connection between Liverpool Street and New Cross stations; and in 1913 it was incorporated into London's Underground system at Rotherhithe, where the arches are still visible.[54]

16

Onward and Upward

Another new learned society had been founded in 1820, and with it came new interests for Bryan. The idea of a society to promote astronomy had been mooted for several years by William Pearson and Francis Baily, and on 12 January 1820 a group of fourteen men, a splinter group from the Royal Society, met at the Freemason's Tavern, Lincoln's Inn Fields, to form the Astronomical Society of London. Among these bright men were John Herschel (whose father William had discovered the planet Uranus) and the idiosyncratic Charles Babbage (mathematician par excellence). Over eighty men applied to join, many of them Fellows of the Royal Society, men of great knowledge and eminence. Bryan became a member six months later and in 1824 was elected to the committee. The members of Council of the Astronomical Society were elected annually; Donkin was on and off the committee several times for over two decades.[1]

The Astronomical Society was no mere club for stargazers. Some of its members were scientists whose minds could tackle data and concepts that ordinary people could only wonder at. As explorers travelled the world, the understanding of the heavens expanded and the need for navigational instruments increased. The Astronomical Society became a melting pot for academics and knowledgeable practitioners alike. This fledgling society was encouraged by the Government's Board of Longitude, for although the problem of finding longitude by day (by the predictable noonday sun) had been largely solved with better sextants and Harrison's chronometer, navigation at night was still difficult, and would remain so until the distances between the night stars could be accurately measured.

For Donkin, astronomy started as a recreation, a hobby that he practised in a neat little observatory at his home in the Paragon. There he was able to regulate his clock by means of a transit instrument as well as observing the occasional eclipse and the occulation (or obscuring) of a star by the moon.[2] The astronomical instruments that Donkin used were only the very best; he would never work with an indifferent tool of any kind if it were possible to procure a good one. He was a good judge of a telescope, and possessed two of the best ever made by the renowned maker, Charles Tulley the elder. Meeting and conversing with the most eminent practical astronomers and instrument makers broadened his knowledge and brought him new friends and new work.

Robert Brettel Bate was an instrument maker in the burgeoning trade, making finely crafted and accurate telescopes, slide rules, drawing instruments, thermometers, and orreries.[3] All these required exact measurements, divided into fractions of a degree, an issue that Donkin understood well and delighted in. Some of Bate's work was for the Government's Ordinance Department, but many of his scientific instruments went to land surveyors, seafarers, architects and other professionals, including many members of the Astronomical Society. One of his specialities was the hydrometer, for measuring the specific gravity of liquids, and he designed a saccharometer – a set of devices that could calculate the sugar content in wine or beer – which he supplied to the Excise Office.[4] While instruments for measurement were his strong suit, Bate had many talents and was also interested in eyeglasses and spectacles. He patented a short-handled model that could be hung round the neck: a hinge in the bridge allowed the two lenses to be folded together for use as a magnifying glass.[5] A more dubious contribution to society was a gyrometer for the use in prisons, to enable inspectors to see exactly how much work had been done by the prisoners.[6] Although undoubtedly brilliant at his trade, Bate was not an easy man to work for. Spells of mental illness (probably manic depression) caused suffering to him and his workpeople. Often overbearing and tyrannical, he would storm round his shop, threatening and chastising his 'damned rascally' workmen; the next day he would skulk about, worn out and unable to do or say anything.[7]

One of Bate's commissions from the Government was the provision of models for new standard weights and measures. The problem of inexact measures of all kinds had exercised the minds of scientists for some while and it was decreed that new standards should be set, on which all others should be based. As with the standard yard, attempts had been made for centuries to agree on the capacity measures for vessels holding liquids, and on exact weights; but without a given and accepted standard, variations existed all over the country.[8] In August 1824, following an Act of Parliament, Robert Bate was approached by Captain Kater, who was to superintend the production of new weights and measures, and asked to produce accurate models of vessels for the measurement of capacity. (Edward Troughton had declined the undertaking: he was very elderly.) In the London air, brass was liable to be damaged by corrosion, so Bate experimented with mixtures of tin and copper. Finally, at the beginning of September, he turned to Bryan Donkin for help. The two men were already collaborating at this juncture: in the same month, for instance, Donkin supplied Bate with two feet of stout brass tube, 6½ in. in diameter.[9] It was the bushel measure, being the largest, that caused Bate particular difficulty.

Evidently Donkin let several weeks go by before declining the offer of taking on the job of turning the model for the bushel. Perhaps he was not confident that he could achieve the difficult task or, more likely, did not feel comfortable with working with the moody and difficult Bate. It was not in Donkin's nature to turn down work without a good reason, or to be awkward; he preferred to withdraw with dignity. The task of casting the bushel models was passed on to twelve of the best foundries in London, but only one proved sufficiently sound to be used – the others were full of small holes from poor casting.[10] Solving the problem took over two months. In the meantime, Robert Bate completed the set of small measures of capacity, and all the weights, both troy and avoirdupois. The episode did not sour relations between Robert Bate and Bryan Donkin, and Donkin continued to produce other metal parts for Bate for many years including, the following January, a 'triblet' (or mandrel) 11½ in. in diameter, being the inside shape of another capacity measure; he also billed Bate for a 'brass measure' and the 'loss upon brass for three more measures', so had evidently managed to produce some of the standard measures by then.[11] Bate also ordered a number of 'triblets and holes'.

Under Donkin's direction, his factory was able to handle work that ranged in size from huge metal rollers for the paper-making machines and parts of dredgers, to tiny components for delicately-balanced instruments requiring microscopic accuracy. His own talent for precision work developed to encompass the world of astronomical and optical instruments, where his willingness to experiment with new materials and technology could be applied. The tall, hexagonal workshop at the factory came into its own for drawing out brass tubes, made to measure for the customers who needed them to make telescopes of all sizes for their clients from the field of astronomy.

It was through his connections with the Astronomical Society that Donkin's skills in tube drawing and minute precision would be recognised in his contribution to that branch of knowledge which was essential, not just to astronomy but to all disciplines of science: that is, fine, accurate and repeatable measurement. The accuracy of the standard yard of Great Britain, made in 1760 and held in the Houses of Parliament, had long been discredited by men of science, and its method of manufacture brought into question.[12] Nonetheless, Donkin was financing his own research into exact measurement, but entered the field from a different angle. In 1826, engrossed in precision, he built an 'engine', essentially a screw-cutting lathe, which would generate the very accurate screw threads increasingly needed to control the movements and settings of ever more complex machinery and machine tools. Both the Bank of England and Bank of Ireland were early customers for screws cut on these machines.[13] However, Donkin had designed the machine to be quickly converted into a very accurate linear dividing engine.[14] Still using the precision lead-screw of the machine (or, as it was more accurately called at the time, the 'leading-screw'), an unmarked ruler of boxwood, ivory or brass, was moved with microscopic accuracy below a cross slide which carried a fine-pointed diamond. As each division to be marked was reached, the diamond was passed across the rule, or scale, scribing a line into its surface. The use of a very clever compensating device ensured both scales and screw threads could be cut with phenomenal accuracy, with errors never greater than one thirty-thousandth of an inch.[15] Donkin made many standard scales for his own use and, when George Sellers visited him, presented his American guest with a twelve inch boxwood rule that he had graduated, which Sellars later said was in constant use and highly valued by him.[16] Previously, at the Greenwich Royal Observatory, Sellers had seen Troughton's great mural wheel that had been turned at the Bermondsey works and graduated by Troughton, using one of Donkin's screws. Donkin spoke enthusiastically about the work that Maudslay had done towards establishing standard screws, but indicated that there was still room for improvement when using the screw as a dividing engine.

Joseph Whitworth, later Sir Joseph, was one of the greatest and best known machine tool builders of the nineteenth century and a pioneer of the standardisation of screw threads. Recognising the significance and accuracy of Donkin's dividing engine, he purchased one of Donkin's yard scales, marked out on this machine, together with one made by Edward Troughton. [17] From a comparison of these two standards he was able to make his first thirty-six inch standard length gauge. Whitworth's own 'one yard end measure' would serve as his master reference standard for many decades.

The story by no means stops there. In 1831 Donkin, with his long experience of fine tube drawing, conceived an entirely new and revolutionary method of producing a yard scale. Instead of a flat bar, he would use a cylindrical brass tube, which was far less liable to bend. The tube measured 5ft 3in. long, with an outside diameter of 1$^{5}/_{8}$ in. Drawing a tube of this length was no easy task, but to add to the difficulty each tube was meticulously constructed from three tubes 'drawn one upon the other' (to add rigidity).[18] After relieving the stresses of manufacture by passing each finished tube slowly over a charcoal fire, they were found to be perfectly straight, a triumph of precision and a testament to the skills of Bryan Donkin's workforce. The yard scale was then struck off on the middle three feet of the tube, using Donkin's dividing engine.

In 1833 the Royal Astronomical Society was trusted with the onerous responsibility of establishing for the nation a new standard yard, and a committee was formed under the leadership of Francis Baily, a brilliant mathematician and treasurer of the society. Donkin was also on the committee and although never mentioned as the architect of the scheme, it was his method in its entirety that was adopted in the quest for the new yard. Donkin drew five new tubes to his unique design, but it was the firm of Troughton and Simms, with their long-established reputation as scientific instrument makers, who were given the task of marking off and numbering the scales.

Through the necessity of his trade, Edward Troughton, the great mathematical and navigational instrument maker, had previously made his own yard scale based on the standard yard but using a dividing engine of his own design. Scales

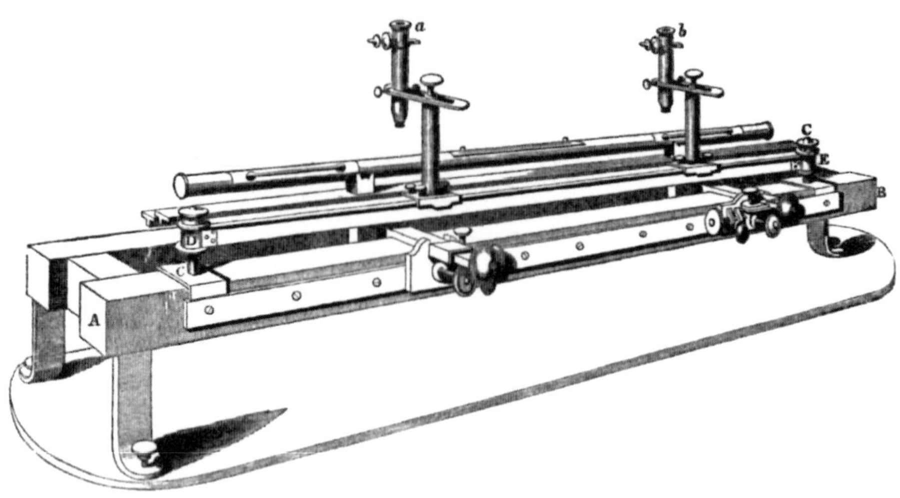

48 *Testing the tubular standard yard.*

divided by this precise machine were far more accurate than the hand-calibrated equivalents. Troughton kept this scale for his own use but made others, one of which was commissioned by Sir George Shuckburgh; another was bought by the Royal Society, and the far-sighted authorities of the city of Aberdeen also chose to buy one of Troughton's.[19] Over the ensuing two years the firm of Troughton and Simms marked off the scales on Donkin's five tubes, and numbered them from 1–5. No.1 was kept by the Royal Astronomical Society; nos.2 and 3 went to observatories in Denmark and Russia; no.5 was kept by Francis Baily. No.4, which was slightly longer than the rest, was taken on Francis Chesney's 1835 Euphrates expedition to aid in the surveying of an overland route to India.[20] In January 1834, scale number 1 (the Astronomical Society's tubular standard yard) was taken, together with the flat scales belonging to Troughton, Shuckborough, the Royal Society and Aberdeen, as well as several yard measures made by Troughton and other makers, to Committee Room 11 of the House of Commons, which had been set aside for the express purpose of making scientific comparisons between these scales and that of the accepted but mistrusted Standard Yard of Great Britain – or at least, those parts of it that had not been damaged by years of maltreatment.[21]

Experimental methods and equipment were both sophisticated and precise. By measuring the scale, first after immersion in melted ice and again after being boiled in a water bath, Baily's committee (of which Bryan Donkin was an active member), established that a variation of one degree Fahrenheit would cause a difference of 0.000377 inches in the length of the yard. In this respect Committee Room 11 was particularly suitable. It had only one window, north-facing and, measuring 24 x 24 ft, it was large enough to accommodate all the standard yards to be compared. Also, its temperature could be maintained at an almost constant 62 degrees Fahrenheit. For the months of the comparisons of the various scales, Committee Room 11 of the House of Commons became the very first 'standards room' in which Baily, along with his co-experimenters, laid down many of the ground rules and conventions of the science of measuring, or 'metrology'. The 'frame' on which the scales were compared was both novel and complex. Thermometers mounted at three points along its length recorded the temperature to an accuracy of one tenth of one degree Fahrenheit, whilst length measurements were made using especially designed microscopes, fitted with micrometer scales, each division equal to one twenty-thousandth of an inch.

Eight prominent members of the Astronomical Society, including Bryan Donkin and his son Bryan, worked in random pairs to take the observations of the various yard scales, and for any one pair of scales, upwards of five hundred observations (measurements) were made. The study took from late January 1834 until April of the same year and at its conclusion, Baily could say with great confidence that the new tubular scales were consistent in their accuracy and extremely close to each other in length, differing one to another by not more than a few tenths of 1000th of an inch; he said that they 'may at some future time be brought to bear on the important question of the figure of the Earth' – in other words, these standards were accurate enough to enable map makers to measure the Earth.[22] At the conclusion of the tests, the committee room was vacated and the original standard yard was reclaimed for the Treasury by the Speaker of the House of Commons. Amongst the masses of data recorded was a detailed description of the Parliamentary standard yard, which was very fortunate because, within weeks, the Houses of Parliament – together with this national relic – went up in smoke.

At about six o'clock on the evening of 16 October 1834, a 'conflagration' broke out on the north bank of the river Thames:[23]

> The wind blew briskly from the south-west; the flames shot up with fearful rapidity; and the crowds of people who clustered upon the bridges and banks soon ascertained the scene of the 'great fire' to be the Houses of Parliament at Westminster'.

The cause of the fire was traced to the burning in a cellar of two cartloads of old notched wooden tally sticks, an antiquated system of calculation used in keeping the accounts in the Treasury, until it was abandoned in 1826. The terrific heat from the flames in the furnaces had been underestimated and the iron pipes under the floors became red hot, igniting the wooden floors and setting the whole building alight. Bryan Donkin witnessed the spectacle.[24] Although it was a Thursday, Bryan had enjoyed a pleasantly sociable day at home; his brother Henry had come down from Durham and Mary Ann and her husband William Day from Isleworth had dined with them all. They were sitting comfortably 'at tea' just after seven when Bryan's brother John rushed in to bring them news of the raging fire. William Day, Henry, and Bryan's sons Bryan and Thomas rushed off together but, arriving at the scene more than an hour after the fire had started, they found their way blocked by soldiers and police, and soon returned to tell the tale. Bursting with curiosity, Bryan joined the four men and they all crammed into William's post chaise and rode to Westminster Bridge, where they had a good view of the blaze. It was 12.30 a.m. before Bryan got to bed. Instead of leaving for the North in the morning as planned, he went back to the scene of the 'extraordinary occurrence' of the night to 'see what mischief had been done', and mingled with the immense crowd of gazers; smoke was still issuing from the ruins and the soldiers were keeping the spectators well away. Rumours were rife, but at least it was reasonably certain that the contents of the library had been saved. Bryan's planned business tour was postponed until the following day; he had bought a ticket for the coach to Stony Stratford next morning and intended to go on to Birmingham later that day, then to Derby, Manchester and Preston, and onwards to Lancaster, Penrith, Kirkoswald and Alston Moor. The final destination was Hexham, where he would be met to join the 'Sandoe circle'. Never one to miss a trick, Donkin once again managed to organise a workable combination of business and pleasure. The whole journey took ten days, but once in Sandoe, he stayed for over two weeks.[25] No doubt the story of the fire carried him through many a social event while in the North.

The destruction of the Palace of Westminster was a tragedy for the nation, but the fact that the old standard yard was badly damaged and rendered useless was something that did not bother Frances Baily: 'There probably never was a measure so totally unfit for the purpose of a definite standard, … and certainly, in a scientific point of view, its loss is not to be deplored'.[26]

It was a further four years before the Government appointed a Commission, once again chaired by Baily, to oversee the construction of a new official Standard Yard of Great Britain. Although Donkin's tubular scale had proved its worth in scientific circles, the Commission favoured a return to the traditional solid, flat bar, probably on the grounds of its strength and durability over time. Trial bars of gun metal, each varying slightly in composition, were cast and Donkin and Simms tested the strength of each bar by loading it to destruction. Once the best composition had been found, forty bars were cast, machined and prepared as standards. Each was then loaded into a tank of heated water, in order that its rate of expansion could be measured. There followed the almost interminable task of measuring and comparing these forty scales, a chore that could only be entrusted to the few scientific figures capable of taking the microscopic measurements: they were William Simms and his son, Warren de la Rue and Bryan Donkin. In 1844, not long after the start of these trials, Francis Baily died and was replaced as chairman by the Reverend Doctor Richard Sheepshanks. Under his meticulous guidance, the trials dragged on until his death in 1855. Airy, the Astronomer Royal, then took charge and on finding that the observers had taken almost

200,000 readings, swiftly brought the proceedings to a close, concluding that they were as near to the old standard as physically possible. Of the forty bars prepared, the one which most closely matched the 'lost' standard was chosen as the new Imperial Standard, to be kept once again in the Treasury offices. The others were distributed to the manufacturing cities of the United Kingdom, where they were made accessible to tradesmen and the public for checking the accuracy of their own rulers.

Running in an almost parallel timescale with the long years of experimentation to establish the definitive standard yard, and once again inspired by the needs of the Astronomical Society and the Board of Longitude, was Babbage's work on his 'difference engine'. Bryan Donkin became embroiled in this shambolic venture.

The full story of the usefulness of this revolutionary machine, and the impact it should have had on a society that was reliant on commerce and industry to keep its competitive position in world trade, is well documented.[27] By the abject failure of successive Governments to recognise its potential and steer the project to a successful completion, a crucial opportunity was missed. It is sufficient to describe here, in broad outline, the events from its first conception to its tragic end in Britain and its re-emergence on the world stage as the Swedish difference engine.

In 1820 the Astronomical Society commissioned a set of mathematical tables that would accurately predict the true position of stars, as noted at the Royal Observatory, Greenwich. Each set of figures for these tables was calculated by two mathematicians, or 'computers', working independently, who then compared results. Charles Babbage, professor of mathematics at Cambridge University and a leading member of the Society, came to the conclusion that human error could only be removed from the equation by the invention of an automatic calculating engine, or 'mechanical computer'. After making a small prototype, he outlined his plan in an open letter to Sir Humphrey Davy, which became a widely reproduced pamphlet, stating that his machine would both save labour and eliminate errors; moreover, it would calculate almost any kind of table, astronomical and naval as well as mathematical.[28].For an admiring public, there was a magical element to Babbage's machine, and to add to its mystery it would, while the calculations were being made, simultaneously punch the resultant figures into soft metal printing plates, and a built-in press would provide instant hard copies without the fear of compositors' errors. Fellow scientists were impressed with the speed and accuracy of the first model, and at the request of the Government, the Royal Society set up a committee to advise on the feasibility of the project and monitor its progress. However, large amounts of public money would be needed for Babbage to realise his dream of building a fully functional difference engine. With the intervention of a few influential friends, public finance was finally secured from a reluctant Chancellor of the Exchequer, once Babbage had convinced him of its importance to a maritime nation. In August 1823, a grant was made, with the verbal promise of further advances as the work progressed; the Treasury wrote to the Royal Society informing them that the Lords of the Treasury 'had directed the issue of £1500 to Mr Babbage to enable him to bring to perfection an engine for calculating mathematical tables'.[29]

As a theoretical mathematician Charles Babbage had none of the skills needed to convert his brilliant ideas into a working machine. On the recommendation of Marc Brunel, he hired the services of Joseph Clement, a former employee of Henry Maudslay, described by Babbage as 'a most excellent workman and draughtsman … . [Clement] ought to be well paid'.[30] Babbage proved not to be a good manager and little progress was made in the first few years. Personal setbacks, including the death of his father and his wife, and Babbage's subsequent nervous breakdown, resulted in a lack of supervision for Clement, who spent much of his time building specialised machine tools for the project. Things went from bad to worse. There were endless wrangles about payments and misunderstandings between the two stubborn men; Babbage was always out of pocket and the Treasury seemed unable to grasp what was going on. By then it was the end of 1828 and in desperation Babbage wrote to Wellington, the Prime Minister, who in turn passed the problem back to the Treasury. Mr Stewart of the Treasury stirred the Royal Society into action by questioning their current view on 'whether the progress made by Babbage in the construction of his machine confirms them in their former opinion, that it will ultimately prove adequate to the important objects which it was intended to attain'.[31] The committee set up by the Royal Society had met only twice in 1823 and had failed to mediate during the intervening years. More Government money was needed urgently to keep the project moving: another failure at this stage might scupper the endeavour and leave the blame at the door of the Royal Society. The Council reacted by strengthening the Babbage Engine Committee and included for the first time 'several of the first practical engineers and mechanicians in the country', among them John Rennie, Marc Brunel, John Penn and Bryan Donkin. Once again, Donkin, with his great breadth of knowledge, and although not yet a fellow of the Royal Society, was called upon to conduct a full enquiry by examining the machinery and inspecting 400 square feet of elaborate engineering drawings. The committee's report was accepted and more money was found. Clement was still not satisfied with his lot.

Fortunately, Babbage recognised Bryan Donkin as a friend who could see the basic problems and help to tackle the financial difficulties by rational thinking and a calm approach that had more success with Clement than Babbage's own confrontational manner.

Babbage was so deeply at odds with Clement that he needed professional advice and an appraisal of the situation to winkle out the truth. He approached Bryan Donkin and John Rennie in a most deferential manner, asking them to act on the matter; he wrote to Donkin: 'Will you do me the favour to name some time which may be convenient to you and I shall be happy to meet you wherever you may appoint? … I shall be at the Royal Society tomorrow evening and at the Astronomical Society on Friday night.'[32] Babbage needed answers to fundamental questions. Who owns the tools? Who owns the patterns and drawings? Who takes the risk? Ought the tools and drawings to be insured? How secure is Clement against his creditors? What is the value of the work already done?

Donkin reported back within days with answers to all Babbage's questions and a promise from Clement that 'he would prepare full details of time, labour and materials from the start to the present'.[33] Despite these drawbacks, work was progressing; most of the components for the calculating part of the engine were lying ready for assembly. Nearly all the design drawings were finished and the end should have been in sight. But in his examination of Clement's accounts, Donkin found that Clement's house, tools and stock had not been insured; and he recommended that Babbage should insure his own property. Clement could not have cared less. Eventually, to overcome this problem, and with the help of the Royal Society, Babbage persuaded the Treasury to fund a purpose-built fireproof workshop in the garden in his new home in Dorset Street, to house the difference engine, with accommodation for Clement.

Although a thoroughly competent engineer, Clement was both strong-willed and obstinate, and valued his own opinion highly. He was still failing to report the progress of the work or present regular and detailed bills. The Treasury officials could not release more funds without up-to-date accounts. By the middle of 1829, relationships between Babbage and Clement had almost broken down completely. Clement had done, by his own estimation, more than £5,000 worth of work but was still owed more than £2,000. Babbage, thoroughly aggrieved by Clement's attitude, refused to pay this sum until a better arrangement for reporting the work done was set in train. Incensed, Clement stopped all work. This stalemate lasted a year, and again, Babbage pleaded with Donkin for help, asking him to name any convenient time either to call on him or meet him to discuss the machine.[34] Eventually, with an intervention by the Duke of Wellington, more money was found. Also, at long last, the Treasury acknowledged that the calculating machine was public property, thus lifting the yoke of financial responsibility from Babbage's shoulders. With money on the table Clement, still dissatisfied and wary that he might not receive his full payment, was persuaded to have his bill settled by arbitration and appointed Henry Maudslay to represent him. Babbage, looking for an equal to balance Maudslay, appointed as his representative the somewhat reluctant Bryan Donkin, who had already given him advice and who was not sure whether becoming an arbitrator would be appropriate; but Donkin agreed, and asked to see the terms of the arbitration bond drawn up by Babbage's lawyer.[35] One can almost picture the scene: Maudslay and Donkin, busy professional engineers of the first rank, who had both on more than one occasion been called to give evidence on Parliamentary Commissions, now met in the less salubrious

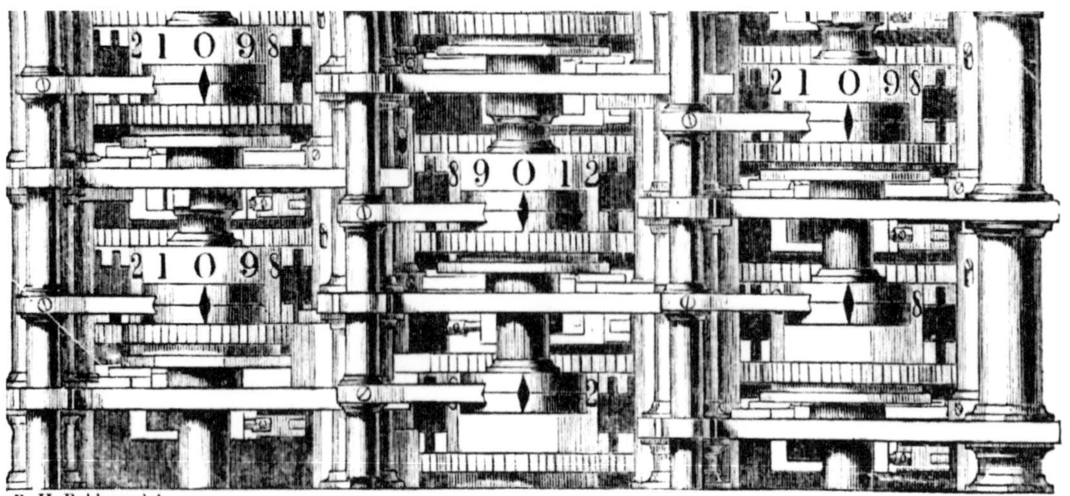

49 *Part of Babbage's difference engine.*

surroundings of Clement's workshop near the Elephant and Castle to try to make sense of his rudimentary accounting system and rummage through boxes and boxes of gear wheels, spline shafts and all manner of components to establish the true worth of Clement's work. Agreement was soon reached and Donkin quickly isolated the sticking points, making suggestions that seemed to appease both sides.

A truculent Clement received his money in full and work recommenced in mid-1830. But Babbage the theorist, instead of satisfying the Government and his loyal colleagues at the Astronomical Society by concentrating his efforts and finishing the machine as first conceived, embarked on a series of design changes to increase its calculating power, with the obvious consequence of pushing back the date of completion.

In January 1831, Charles Babbage asked Donkin to audit the accounts to sort out yet more cash flow difficulties, with assistance from Field (who had taken over when Maudslay became ill; Maudslay died in mid-February). Babbage was really hoping that he could look forward to the machine being finished within two years.[36] He thanked Donkin for 'the trouble you have already taken in assisting me in this affair'. Donkin must have heaved a sigh of relief that the end was in sight.

Clement continued making parts for the engine at his factory and, at Babbage's request, had already assembled a vital section of the engine, to demonstrate its powers. (This was a small calculating part of the engine, which is now exhibited at the Science Museum, London). But, after less than two years, friction between the two men was once again at boiling point. By now, the fireproof workshop had been built in Babbage's garden but Clement was demanding £600 per annum in compensation for having to move there against his will. Babbage seethed inwardly and reported the position to the Treasury paymasters, who asked Clement to present another claim; this he failed to do. Donkin and Field were once again requested by Babbage and the Treasury to intercede in the matter and save the project. In discussions with the Treasury, Donkin won concessions, which should have smoothed the way. Donkin instructed Clement to withdraw an offensive letter; he informed Babbage that future payments would be made directly to Clement and that Clement could remain working in his own workshop, but should transfer the finished components to Babbage's premises.[37] He must also state that he agreed with the conditions. Knowing full well that Clement's response was unlikely to be favourable, Donkin offered his assistance, together with Field's, in shielding Babbage from any 'repugnance' he felt in communicating with Clement. A flurry of correspondence between Donkin and Babbage during the first half of 1833 highlights the difficult task of arbitration that Donkin had been asked to undertake. A smouldering stalemate ensued.[38] Donkin did his best to calm the waters, while both parties issued ultimatums. A trivial 'pertinacious' demand from Clement led Donkin to believe that, once that was settled, 'my mission with him is at an end'.[39] On 30 March 1833, after another furious row with Babbage, Clement dismissed his workforce and work stopped. Another round of arbitration and valuation ensued, during which Donkin and Field were once again key players. Despite the valiant efforts of Babbage and the two engineers, work was never re-started. More than £15,000 of public funds had been spent on its development, with, from Parliament's point of view, little to show for it. The momentum had been lost, and without the vigorous backing of senior politicians, the project could never recover.

It must have been a huge disappointment for Bryan Donkin; for years, he had given objective advice and performed the difficult task of mediating between the two disparate and obstinate men and an ineffectual Government department. All sides accepted his judgements, but eventually to no avail.

Babbage, though bitterly disappointed, continued to design further calculating engines, none of which got further than the drawing board. With only a few more months' work the difference engine could have been finished and Britain could once again have laid claim to a true breakthrough in scientific discovery. Instead, the distinction of producing the first fully functioning difference engine fell to Georg and Edvard Scheutz (father and son) of Stockholm who, enthused by an 'elaborate disquisition on the merits and construction' of Babbage's engine, published in the *Edinburgh Review* of July 1834, took up the challenge.[40]

Edward Troughton, twelve years older than Donkin, was also an expert in instrument-making and specialised work with lenses.[41] He and his brother John had prospered by building dividing engines and using them to graduate sextants and circular instruments for other makers. Access to Fleet Street from their premises in Peterborough Court was through a low and narrow passage under the houses, which became a problem when they started to receive orders for large apparatus, such as their big equatorial telescope and other observatory instruments. Back in 1809, Troughton had designed a mural circle, an astronomical instrument set vertically against a wall which would enable astronomers at the Royal Observatory to turn a telescope to follow the passage of stars. The huge six-foot circle was far too big to handle in their own workshop, so it was both cast and turned at Bryan Donkin's works.[42] This had been an early introduction to astronomical instruments for Bryan, in the first decade of his work as a civil engineer. Sharing common interests, the two men's paths crossed many a time after that, and together, much later, they tackled a problem brought about by Troughton's friend James South.

Accustomed as he was to dealing with tricky customers, Donkin was always tactful and tried to please his clients. James South, though, was an especially difficult man to please. A man of means, he had his own observatories in England and France; Troughton provided and maintained the instruments there.[43] In late 1829, not content with his existing telescopes, James South acquired a gigantic 11¾ inch lens from Cauchoix in Paris, which he wanted to incorporate into an equatorial telescope: this would enable him to follow individual stars steadily, by turning it on an axis parallel to the polar axis. (The axis of the earth points to the North Star, so the axis of the equatorial mounting of the telescope must do the same). He asked Troughton to provide the telescope; he and his younger partner, William Simms, started work on the difficult design and produced a model, and then another, which at six feet long was a quarter of the eventual size. It was guarded in great secrecy in Troughton's bedroom. Meanwhile, Bryan Donkin used his tube-drawing facilities at the factory to produce the two brass tubes for the telescope; they were 5ft 2in. long, each composed of three tubes that fitted into each other, held with steel rings. Hurried on by James South, who lacked the patience to wait until the equatorial mounting was ready, Donkin went with South to select a block of mahogany for the telescope's support. In May 1830, Troughton and Simms received from Donkin the sphere (20 inches in diameter) for the centre of the declination axis, on which the telescope would rest, and the following January, Donkin supplied several more specialised parts that were too large to be made in Troughton's small workshop.[44] He also suggested modifications to strengthen the structure with cast iron ties. Throughout this time, South followed every development and made a nuisance of himself, watching Troughton's every step and meddling with the design of the parts, pestering the cabinet maker, and frequently calling in on Donkin when he was trying to work. Against Troughton's advice and Donkin's common sense, South insisted that the inside of the sphere should be turned, an operation that Donkin thought was a waste of money.[45]

South threw his weight about; yet this devious and annoying person had managed to ingratiate himself with the French Government, who had granted him free travel back and forth to France, where he planned to live permanently in his house in Paris, and he was charged no payment of duty on the huge telescope that he intended to take with him. In turn William, the new King of England, on hearing that he had changed his mind about leaving the country, took the opportunity to praise South's 'honourable and disinterested zeal in the cause of science, and especially your unwearied and successful exertions to perfect and increase our knowledge of the position, distances, and relations of the heavenly bodies,' and on 21 July 1830, knighted him.[46] Sir James South's cavalier behaviour divided the Royal Society and the Astronomical Society into factions and caused a great deal of backbiting between his supporters and those who neither liked nor respected him. As President of the Astronomical Society, he was instrumental in gaining a Royal Charter for the body, but created such bad feeling that he was forced to leave, and Bryan Donkin had the honour of chairing the meeting in 1831 at which the Astronomical Society gained the Royal Charter, becoming the Royal Astronomical Society.

A vociferous opponent to Sir James was the Reverend Richard Sheepshanks who, as a good friend of Edward Troughton and a prominent member of both the RAS and the Royal Society, became entangled in the controversy over the equatorial telescope. (There was a history of bad feeling between the two men within the Royal Society.) A few years back, Sheepshanks had escorted Troughton to South's home in France, taking with him South's pointer dog; the frail Troughton was unable to look after himself, let alone someone else's dog, and it was Sheepshanks who had to take on the troublesome commission, coping with the unfortunate Dido, strapped in her basket on the back of the carriage – one of the many grudges that Sheepshanks held against South, which rankled for years.[47]

The relationship between Troughton and South deteriorated badly after the equatorial telescope was delivered to Sir James's observatory in Camden Hill. The trouble was, the whole thing was too big. South had insisted, against all advice, that the new version should be scaled up from a normal equatorial telescope, but that presented problems. When it was delivered, South's own builder managed to drop the huge instrument and the lower end was damaged badly, while the upper section hit the dome of the observatory. Joints were loosened, so that when the telescope was eventually righted, observers looking through the eyepiece saw stars wobbling and wavering through the sky. Troughton and Donkin tried to rectify the fault by reinforcing parts of the instrument, but all the experiments failed. South accused Troughton of constructing a 'useless pile' and went off to France. Troughton quoted Pope:

> See! Heaven with laughter the vain toil surveys
> And buries madmen in the piles they raise.

Nothing was done for several months and on his return South made further work extremely difficult by imposing ludicrous restrictions on the visitors who were trying to solve the problems, insisting on their making appointments and then not letting them in. Troughton and Simms kept trying to rectify the problems but finally, because South refused to settle his account, brought a law suit against him.[48] Sheepshanks, as a former barrister, was brought in to help his ageing friend Troughton.

The situation did not improve. When Sir James did deign to be present at the trials he strutted about, whistling tunelessly, getting in the way with his family and dogs. [49] His friend Joseph Gwilt acted as a security officer when Troughton and Simms needed to visit to take measurements, and when Professor Airy came to look at the telescope unannounced, Gwilt insisted that in the future, appointments to visit should be made in advance, listing the names of the visitors. In July 1834, the list of names sent to Gwilt included Pond (the Astronomer Royal), Timothy Bramah, Francis Baily, Dollond and Donkin; Peter Barlow also came to advise. Sir James lurked in the background, whispering and tittering with Gwilt. As time ran out for the assessors to have access, they were still forced to work under the same sort of duress. Meanwhile, Simms fought on and his case against South was won. This and other encounters strengthened relationships between Troughton, Simms and Donkin. It has been said that Simms first met Bryan Donkin at the Society of Arts, forming a friendship with him that was the foundation of his career.[50] It was Donkin who, in 1833, made the zenith sector designed by Troughton for the Royal Observatory at Greenwich; three years later, he constructed a mural circle over five feet in diameter for Simms.[51]

South's telescope itself, however, was eventually a complete failure and in spite of all efforts to rectify its problems, it ended up as a heap of scrap.

17
Going Strong

An awkward assignment challenged Donkin soon after his 60th birthday. Benjamin Lewis Vulliamy, clockmaker to the King (and later to Queen Victoria) was in demand as a designer and maker of large clocks for public buildings. After visiting Paris to see the city's public clocks, Vulliamy made a very large and beautiful turret clock for St Luke's church in West Norwood, south east London. It was of a simpler design, but superior to any that had been made before.[1] In the spring of 1828 he was asked to design and construct a similar clock for the new parish church of St Mary Magdalene being built in Bermondsey. The Chairman and members of the church committee employed two eminent engineers, Messrs Bramah and Donkin, to survey the clocks of Norwood, St Paul's and several others; they reported their approval to the Committee and Vulliamy was told that he would be given the contract.

There were delays and it turned out that behind Vulliamy's back a Clerkenwell clockmaker by the name of Moore had also offered to make a clock, identical to the Norwood timepiece, but for half the price; his offer had been accepted. The enraged Vulliamy, knowing that his clock for the Norwood church was unique, agreed to twenty guineas in compensation from the committee for the loss of his contract, on the express understanding that it would not prejudice him from taking steps to prevent Mr Moore from seeing the Norwood clock in order to copy it. Moore agreed a timescale for the work, which was to be surveyed by

50 *Church of St Mary Magdalene, Bermondsey,* c.1840.

Donkin and Bramah, and agreed that if the new clock did not match the quality of the Norwood one, he would not be paid. But Mr Moore had already covertly sent his foreman to sneak in and make a plan of the Norwood clock ('with Mr Vulliamy's permission', he claimed). Fortunately the sexton had not allowed him to stay in the tower, and Vulliamy instructed the churchwarden to deny Moore and his spies any further access.

Mr Moore completed his clock the following year; but it was nothing like Vulliamy's, and the construction, workmanship and materials were deemed by Bryan Donkin and Timothy Bramah to be inferior. However, all Vulliamy's requests to see a copy of their report were refused by the authorities. Donkin felt, with regret, that he and Bramah would be compromised professionally if they released the report to Vulliamy, although there was 'no disinclination on our parts' to do so; indeed 'it would give us both great pleasure if it could be made the instrument of contradiction to the false reports you complain of'.[2] Moore had lied about making a clock exactly like the Norwood clock, because he had not seen the original; he had even had the audacity to ask Bryan Donkin what the differences were between the two clocks, so that he could amend his – no doubt he received a dusty answer. Bramah had remarked that although the new clock must have cost the contractor much more than he had estimated, he was certainly in strong support and sympathy for Vulliamy. He slated the church committee for accepting the lowest tender for the contract 'which surely ought not to prevail in matters of mechanical science'; the case was 'amongst the numerous instances that occur'.[3]

Years later, when Benjamin Vulliamy was designing the new Big Ben for the Houses of Parliament, he was asked to submit a cardboard model, a request that he dismissed as impracticable and enormously expensive.[4] As he had already made several clocks for the Government and was in the process of constructing a smaller one that would be not unlike a model of the proposed Great Clock, he suggested that his work of many years should be examined, instead of making a useless cardboard replica. As evidence of his abilities, he quoted a letter from a panel of assessors, written nearly twenty four years previously. The testimonial was fulsome in its praise for the great superiority of a large turret clock made in 1823, applauding the ingenious design and accuracy of workmanship of 'this beautiful specimen of mechanical contrivance and execution'. The signatories were Marc Brunel, Joshua Field, Timothy Bramah, Thomas Hoblyn, John Pond (the Astronomer Royal), William Congreve (of compound-plate printing and rocket fame) and Bryan Donkin. Even with the testimony of this illustrious line-up, Vuilliamy failed to win the contact, which was given to Edward John Dent in 1852; unfortunately he died the next year, but the work was completed by his adopted son.

Following the successful introduction of steam boats, steam locomotion on land was being developed.

In 1825 there was much controversy over the proposed Liverpool to Manchester railway, planned to provide cheaper transport for the public and a faster link for goods. Strong objections came from landowners and merchants with a vested interest in the canal network. On 15 March 1825, Donkin, Barlow, Palmer and others took part in an experiment at the Weighing House on the Paddington Canal and, on the same day on the Grand Union Canal. On March 20th, Donkin had a discussion with the lawyer Mr Harrison at his chambers, about the opposition to the railway, and on the next two days was called to give evidence before a committee of the House of Commons (for which he earned five guineas a day).[5] Previously, Donkin and his former pupil Palmer had worked together in carrying out experiments commissioned by Telford, on the Hetton Railway and on boats on the Ellesmere Canal, to discover the relative resistance of steam-powered trains and horse-drawn canal barges.[6] Their results showed that the ratio of efficiency strongly favoured canal transport, but this efficiency could only be exploited at low speeds, two and a half miles per hour being the optimum … 'as this is the pace at which horses usually walk', with four and a half miles per hour roughly the maximum speed … 'otherwise the boats would drive the water out of the canal'. Their results were also used in evidence in the 1825 Parliamentary enquiry.[7] The Bill was presented to Parliament and was defeated, but it was passed in the following year, and work on the Liverpool to Manchester Railway began. The speed of the steam train had finally won against the steady plod of the draught horse.

The Liverpool to Manchester was the first passenger railway and was opened in September 1830, after George Stephenson's struggle to overcome the boggy terrain

51 *Robert Stephenson's 'Rocket', built* 1829.

of Chat Moss that lay between the two cities.[8] The opening ceremony was marred by a terrible tragedy. On one of the two parallel tracks the *Northumbrian* puffed along, carrying the most prestigious dignitaries, including Sir Robert Peel and the Duke of Wellington, while seven other engines pulled carriages full of guests alongside on the other line, in the same direction. When the *Northumbrian* stopped to refuel, the Liverpool M.P. William Huskisson alighted between the tracks to shake the hand of the Duke of Wellington and, failing to notice the approach of the *Rocket*, fell with his leg caught across the rail: 'The wheel went slantingly over the thigh up to the middle of it and the muscles were laid bare in one immense flap; the bone was so dreadfully crushed as to resemble powder'.[9] He died from his horrific wounds that evening, in the local vicar's drawing room. However, in spite of the tragic circumstances of its first trial, the railway became a success, bringing in the era of rail travel for all.

Plans for the building of the London and Birmingham Railway, again under George Stephenson's direction, were published by Act of Parliament in 1833.[10] Details of land ownership, work to be done and materials to be used were carefully thought out and checked. A six-arch brick viaduct was to be constructed at the mid-point of the railway, across the Wolverton valley in Buckinghamshire, where the River Great Ouse ran through. The engineer representing the trustees of the will of John Radcliffe, who had owned the land on each side of the route at that point, was Bryan Donkin.[11] He approved the plans for the viaduct and made 'sundry journeys' to examine the progress of the work, earning £77 2s 0d.[12]

Throughout the 1830s, experiments with the velocity of steam engines on rails, and the behaviour of the carriages in their wake were being carried out by George Stephenson, Isambard Kingdom Brunel, and Dr Dionysius Lardner, who were trying to come to agreement over the best gauge for the railway lines.[13]

Attention also turned to steam travel on the roads; after all, there seemed no reason why a boiler on wheels could not propel a steam carriage on an ordinary highway, without rails to guide it. Experiments had been made for many years. James Watt had dabbled in the idea of a mechanical road vehicle, and at the end of the eighteenth century several engineers had patented their inventions, notably Murdoch (whom Donkin had met at the Boulton and Watt factory), who was probably the first to actually construct one, and William Symington.[14] Trevithick and Vivian, working together, produced an ingenious and successful conveyance propelled by high-pressure steam in 1802, but turned their attention to railway engines, because of the poor state of the roads at the time. One of their experiments ended in flames when the engine, left in a shed after breaking down on an uphill test, heated itself up while the inventors ate roast goose in a nearby inn, and set fire to the building and everything in it.[15]

Patents by others soon followed. Steam carriages were patented by Julius Griffith (1821), David Gordon (1822), Burstall & Hill (1825), Josiah Easton (1825) and others.[16] The first to run a regular passenger service was Walter Hancock (brother of Thomas, the patentee of artificial rubber); his ten-seater steam coach, the

Infant, plied between London and Stratford from 1831 and made a trial trip from London to Brighton the following year, achieving speeds of around ten miles an hour.[17] Neck and neck with Hancock was the entrepreneur Sir Charles Dance, promoter of a steam carriage invented by Goldsworthy Gurney, a Cornish doctor and engineer, with whom (and four others) the patent had been taken out. While Hancock started his coach service round London, Dance ran a successful steam carriage business, travelling the nine miles between Cheltenham and Gloucester four times a day. After only four months, he was forced to give up, when horse-coach proprietors who were opposed to the enterprise covered the road to a depth of eighteen inches with loose stones, making it impossible for any traffic to pass.[18] However, in 1831, a Select Committee of the House of Commons instituted an inquiry into steam carriages in general and came out in support, although no legislation was passed.

Sir Charles then started new experiments and collaborated with Joshua Field to patent a new boiler; Dance put it to the test in September 1833, taking his steam coach to Brighton and back with fourteen colleagues and friends on board, including John Maudslay and Joshua Field, from whose factory in Lambeth the journey started.[19] Henry Maudslay, founder of the firm, had died in February 1831, at the age of fifty nine. Two of his four sons had already been partners in the business for some time; John became a partner shortly before his father's death. The fifty mile journey south from London to Brighton took five hours and sixteen minutes, plus four stops for water and coke, and the return trip was slightly quicker – all achieved without mishap. News quickly reached Bryan Donkin and his engineering friends. Fascinated by the success of steam coaches but wanting to test one for themselves, a group of engineers persuaded Charles Dance to let them find out whether a journey to Birmingham from London might be possible, and on 1 November 1833, Bryan Donkin set off with Telford, Timothy Bramah, Joshua Field, six other civil engineers and a highways official.[20] The other engineers were John Thomas, John MacNeil (Engineer to the Holyhead Roads), Alexander Gordon and William Carpmael; as well, J. Simpson (Engineer to the Chelsea Works), C.W. Pasley (Lieut. Col. Commanding the Royal Engineers, Chatham; the party included John Rickman (Secretary and Commissioner of Highland Roads and Bridges).

The journey was plagued with misfortune: the weather was awful, the road surface was difficult and after five miles the engine sprang a leak. The carriage managed to get as far as Stony Stratford, fifty two miles from London, and then gave up. Nevertheless, the experiment was considered a success by Donkin and his fellow travellers, who wrote a glowing report: the average speed had been seven miles an hour and, given a more powerful engine and better road conditions: 'there can be no doubt that … a steam carriage conveyance between London and Birmingham at a velocity unattainable by horses, and limited only by safety, might be maintained'. It was not to be. Some steam coaches

52 *Maceroni's steam carriage,* 1833.

continued to carry passengers on the roads – Francis Maceroni's efficient new carriage caused bitterness in competition with Walter Hancock's in the 1830s, for instance, and Maceroni ended up penniless.[21] However, the high cost of turnpike roads and competition from the developing network of railways had put paid to the scheme altogether by the early 1840s.

Known as an expert on the flow of water, Donkin was often called on for advice on the subject. Since the early eighteenth century, schemes had been put forward for improving London's water supply by taking water from surrounding rivers.[22] In 1821, Donkin had been asked to survey part of the River Colne for the owner of Glasscott's copper mill; and a month later, he had given evidence to the Commons Select Committee on the supply of water to the Metropolis.[23] Plans were crystalised in 1831, when the directors of the Grand Junction Water Company suggested a massive scheme for building a new canal to convey water to the metropolis from the River Colne, thirteen miles away, involving aqueducts, reservoirs, footbridges, drains and tunnels as well as the huge canal itself and vast sums of money. Thomas Telford was commissioned to conduct a survey, amid accusations of partiality, competition from other water companies and disagreements over his fee.[24] Telford supervised the survey, but the work of laying down the maps and sections, measuring water and calculating quantities was carried out by Bryan Donkin and William Cubitt, with three others, Casebourne, Neil and Turnbull. Specific advice on the loss of water to mills was given by Donkin and Cubitt – it was a perennial problem for mill owners, who found their water stolen by changes made to water courses or diverted by mills further up river. Quarrels broke out between Telford and his assistant; Mills publicly damned his employer by saying 'Mr Telford never saw any more of the country than what he could see out of a poste'.[25] Worries about impure water compounded the difficulties. The scheme came to nothing, as did Robert Stephenson's idea for boring a well in the chalk near Watford in Hertfordshire, to solve the same problem of providing water for the Metropolis.[26] Donkin knew the Grand Junction Canal well and was the right person to go to Stony Stratford in June 1833, to work out what effect was produced by the canal aqueduct across the valley of the river Ouse; he went more than once, and wrote a report, returning the next year for more work there.[27]

At the same time, the Chelsea Water Works was in dispute with several of its users. Being a go-ahead company, the Water Works was the first to install, in 1829, an invention by its engineer James Simpson (who went with Donkin on the experimental trip in Sir Charles Dance's steam carriage). Since the beginning of the century, the possibility that diseases might be water-borne had caused increasing concern, a matter that Simpson addressed with his innovative sand filter beds.[28] London's 1831 epidemic of cholera served as a stimulus to the slow process of providing clean water to the metropolis. Many breweries took their water from the Thames and its tributaries, supplied by the Chelsea Water Company, and Donkin spent several days from the end of January 1831 until the end of March on surveys and assessments for the company.[29] At Elliot's Brew-house, he and Bramah (Timothy or Francis) took three days to make a valuation of the machinery and equipment and, immediately afterwards, visited the large distillery in Millbank Street, Westminster, of Seager and Evans, where they valued all the stills and other apparatus. Other visits that week were to survey pipes and mains, and a reservoir in Green Park, as well as equipment elsewhere belonging to the Chelsea Water Works, in order to give evidence before an arbitrator of the value of its property.

In 1834, together with William Cubitt, Donkin assessed the expenditure on the Western branch of the Montgomeryshire Canal (which terminated at Newtown in Wales) and found that the money had been wisely spent.[30] Their evidence was referred to when the question of raising the tolls on the canal was brought to the House of Commons four years later.[31]

Light relief came in the form of a Donkin family outing in June 1834. Back in 1784, a festival in commemoration of Handel had been held in Westminster Abbey, sparking a surge of music festivals all over the country.[32] Fifty years on, the London event was recreated, with a four-day programme of mostly choral music, spread over two weeks and consisting mainly of Handel oratorios, but with selections of works by noted composers including Beethoven, who had died only seven years previously. Richard, the elderly Earl of Mount-Edgcumbe, had attended the Royal Musical festival of 1784 and wrote a critical comparative

53 *Music Festival, Westminster Abbey,* 1834.

report.[33] Before each performance was an open rehearsal when the seats were half price – Bryan Donkin and Mary, with Mary's mother and two other ladies had enjoyed hearing Handel's oratorio 'Israel in Egypt' and selections from Haydn, Handel, Beethoven, Mozart and others, at the Abbey on 25 June. Bryan Junior was in charge of the family's arrangements for arriving at the performance of Handel's *Messiah* on Tuesday, July 1st, and he took his duties seriously, rounding up the family, relations and friends and keeping track of plans that changed several times because of illness and a business meeting that failed to materialise.[34] There was confusion over a proposal that the senior Donkins should go to Isleworth for the weekend before the concert – the ladies by coach and Bryan Donkin with a servant and luggage by steamer; the idea that everyone should assemble at Mr Cubitt's in order to make sure of arriving at the concert together seemed to complicate matters, as did the fact that both Bryans wrote well-meaning but contradictory letters to Isleworth on the same day.[35] The main thing was to arrive early and keep together. 'Now be good girls and come early' said Bryan, Jun. Reserved seats at two guineas accounted for two thirds of the space in the Abbey, but the Donkins had tickets at a guinea for unreserved seats, so had to take their chance, although the doors opened early to reduce the crush of 2,500 or more concertgoers arriving together.

No doubt everyone enjoyed the event in the end. The females in the Donkin party, worried that they might wear the wrong thing, had been reassured by their organiser that bonnets would be worn by all the ladies. The Abbey was full; some people had paid up to ten guineas to get in. The galleries were hung with crimson cloth and the Royal box, draped in crimson and gold, looked splendid. King William and the young Queen Adelaide were present once again; they had attended all the concerts.[36] The elderly but still talented John Braham opened the *Messiah* with a fine rendering of 'Comfort ye, my people'; the choruses were extremely well performed by the massed choir of over 350 singers and an orchestra of more than 220. Sir George Smart, the instigator of the festival, conducted. It was the first time that most of the audience had witnessed a conductor beating time with a baton, an idea newly introduced from the Continent; previously the role of leader of the orchestra had been taken by the organist or an instrumentalist.[37] It was an afternoon to remember.

The younger Bryan had hoped to enjoy 'the pleasures of Isleworth' two days after the concert, but was 'vexed' to find that his father expected him to go to Stony Stratford on business instead, probably to look at the viaduct.

In 1834, Bryan Donkin was drawn into a controversial patent case in the Court of the Exchequer. On behalf of the plaintiff (Mr Russell) he acted as a witness, together with Marc Brunel. Opposing them for the defendant (Cornelius Whitehouse) were Mr Clegg and Timothy Bramah.[38] The case hinged on methods of welding iron tubes and whether Russell's 1825 patent was an original invention; if so, whether Whitehouse had infringed it. Donkin and Brunel went to inspect Russell's works, to watch the procedure in action. Next day, they visited the defendant's factory to compare the two processes. Bramah and Clegg went the following day, when the differences were again noted. Under cross-examination, Donkin said that before 1825, he had not known much about welding cylinders by rollers – the method under dispute – but he had experience in welding in general. After much discussion of technical details, the patent was declared void on the grounds that too much had been claimed; most of the patent went over old ground and only a small part of it was new.

Discussions of technical matters in connection with patents provided work for many of the best and most experienced engineers such as Donkin and his colleagues, who were called in as witnesses to give their opinions on one side or the other in disagreements over patent specifications; these were important matters in interpreting the legality of patents and for setting precedents. The year after the dispute over welding methods, Donkin was called to the Vice Chancellor's Court for another such case, this time to help to decide whether an improvement to paddle wheels for steam boats was an infringement of a patent originally taken out by Elijah Galloway and sold to Morgan and Lucena. John Seaward, an engineer who had invented an improved steam boat paddle wheel, was accused by the patent holders of copying their idea. Bryan Donkin and John Isaac Hawkins (a colleague since the days of the Thames Archway experiments thirty years back) jointly gave evidence for the defendant; they pointed out that Seaward's wheel was 'much superior for strength, durability and economy to any other wheel made agreeably and according to the specification of E.Galloway ...' but with new and useful additions. Timothy Bramah and Charles Collinge agreed, and Marc Brunel also gave his opinion. After a discussion that spread over three days, the Vice Chancellor concluded that while he had sympathy for the plaintiffs, they had been too specific in their patent and that the defendant had simply found a new and better mechanism to produce the same effect; he left some room for manoeuvre in his verdict. In the event, the case was taken to court the following year, when Hawkins came under fire for lack of knowledge and Donkin for contradicting himself.[39] The lawyer for the defence, Sir Frederick Pollock, quibbled with the wording of Donkin's answers and his 'ifs and buts', adding 'I cannot help saying, though I have known him now many years and found him a man of integrity, I was ashamed of the manner in which he shuffled with those questions'. The Bramah brothers, Bryan Donkin Jun. and Collinge suffered similar criticism. The judge, Baron Alderson, stood up for Donkin and vindicated him, calmly teasing out the strands of the complicated case; the jury returned a verdict for the plaintiff.[40]

During the early hearings in the patent case, a name that was familiar to Donkin was mentioned. John Oldham was a surprising man; he was an Irishman, who trained as an engraver, and became well known as a painter of miniatures.[41] As well as his artistic skills, he possessed a strong interest and ability in engineering and in 1809 had invented a numbering machine that counted and printed in hundreds, tens and units. (Ten years later, Donkin was praised for a counting machine of his own invention.) In 1812 Oldham's mechanism was put into use by the Bank of Ireland, who were so impressed by Oldham that they appointed him as their engineer and chief engraver. His device automatically numbered the finished bank notes printed by the bank and was later adapted to attach to the printing press itself to record the number of impressions taken. (Oldham was in the forefront of printing bank notes from engraved steel printing plates, a process perfected by Jacob Perkins.)

One day in 1829, Donkin's phrenology friend, George Combe, was shown round the Bank of Ireland by one of the Directors, and during the visit met one of the employees – 'a respectable-looking man, above the middle period of life'.[42] Out of interest – and perhaps as a test – the Director asked the phrenologist to examine the man's head and describe his qualities. Combe, who had no idea who his subject was or what his capabilities were, felt the man's head, measured its various areas and gave his phrenological reading: the man, Combe said, possessed notable indications of intellectual, perceptive and reflective faculties, and strong abilities in tune, number, language and benevolence. He also, said Combe, possessed a general capacity for painting and a mind that 'if turned to mechanics or any other similar pursuit was so constituted as to excel' – a remarkably fitting description of John Oldham. After identifying Oldham as the subject and introducing the two men to each other properly, the Director showed Mr Combe Oldham's machines, a steam engine of his own design and the printing machine registering bank notes. John Oldham himself showed Combe two water-colour portraits that he had painted and told him about another of his inventions, an organ that could produce sounds like human speech – further substantiation of the phrenologist's diagnosis.

At the time of the patent paddle wheel case, in 1835, Oldham's name was mentioned because he had been one of the first to patent a new modification to conventional paddles for steam boats, whereby the actual paddle could revolve to decrease the water resistance – another product of this talented man's fertile engineering brain. Oldham moved to work at the Bank of England in 1836 with the grand title of Mechanical Engineer and Principal of the Engraving, Plate Printing, Numbering and Dating Office. Bryan Donkin, still working at the factory in his late sixties, supervised the construction of Mr Oldham's machine, for use at the Bank of England for printing bank notes.[43] He also provided John Oldham with two very similar steel engine-cut screws, for the Bank of England and for the Bank of Ireland.[44] These were precision-made parts for machinery, 18 in. and 18½ in. long, both under an inch in diameter and with fourteen threads to the inch – tricky for the ordinary worker to make, but well within the capabilities of Bryan Donkin's skilled operatives, using precise machinery of Donkin's manufacture.

Donkin was still physically and mentally alert at this time, although the day-to day running of the works was now largely in the hands of his sons. Speaking at the Institution of Civil Engineers in February 1837, Donkin passed on news of somebody else's invention: Henry Guy had found a way of making completely spherical balls of hard substances such as metal, glass, and agate, by means of a lathe that caused the material to spin in all directions against a static tool.[45] In another talk, at the Royal Astronomical Society in April the same year, Donkin admitted that he had thought some years previously about inventing a levelling apparatus for use on telescopes, based on the principles of an instrument called 'Hardy's Noddy' (an inverted pendulum that wagged on a spring), but had been aware of the almost insuperable difficulties at that time of making a sufficiently accurate spirit level to fit to his invention.[46] After much experimenting, he was now able to present his 'spring-level', which he described with his customary thoroughness. Naturally, he had made one for himself, to attach to his own transit instrument (a telescope) in his observatory at the Paragon.[47] It was a precise and delicate instrument and incorporated a spider's-line or cobweb (amazingly, a real one!) to aid the fine measurement. Troughton and Simms, who regularly used spider threads in their telescopes, collected the line by winding it round a two pronged fork – with the spider still hanging to keep it taut – then pressed it on to the correct position and attached it with varnish.[48] In 1827, a proposal for artificial cobwebs had been reported in the *Mechanic's Magazine*, invented by C.R. Goring, M.D. who described his process of spinning very fine threads from caoutchout, or rubber.

Donkin's former pupil, William Gravatt, also invented a highly acclaimed 'level', for use in surveying, parts of which were made by Donkin.[49] The 'dumpy' – named for its compact construction - was effectively a sophisticated telescope combined with a spirit level, and was popular with its users; it also won Gravatt the Telford Medal at the Institution of Civil Engineers.

54 *Bryan Donkin,* c.1830.

55 *Mary Donkin,* c.1830.

18
Three Score and Ten

Surprisingly, it was not until Bryan Donkin was nearly seventy that he was finally awarded the highest possible tribute to his distinguished career: Fellowship of the Royal Society. After many ups and downs, the Society was regaining its reputation as the most prestigious scientific body in the country.

The process of welcoming a new Fellow began with the writing of a certificate, which was 'suspended' in the meeting room at Somerset House and signed by those proposing the candidate. For Donkin, 15 June 1837 was the day it happened. The citation read:

> Bryan Donkin, Esq., Civil Engineer, No 6, Paragon, Kent Road, Fellow of the Royal Astronomical Society, Vice President of the Society of Civil Engineers and ... [sic] a gentleman zealous in the support and extension of science and intimately versed in practical mechanics, being desirous of admission into the Royal Society, we the undersigned recommend him as a proper person to become a Fellow thereof.[1]

Many members of the Royal Astronomical Society were also Fellows of the Royal Society. The signatories who proposed Donkin as a Fellow included George Biddell Airy (the Astronomer Royal), Francis Baily (President of the Royal Astronomical Society) and Richard Sheepshanks, another prominent astronomer. Among the other sixteen supporters were Henry Palmer, Joshua Field, George Rennie and Marc Brunel – a galaxy of stars. Seven months later, on 18 January 1838, a ballot was held and Donkin was formally elected into the Society.[2] The following week, he duly paid his admission fee, agreed to pay the annual contribution, signed the Obligation with a quill pen in the Charter Book, and was admitted into the Society. It was two months before his seventieth birthday.

Meetings of the Society took place every week from January until June, when a long summer break stopped proceedings until November.[3] Each gathering began with a list of 'presents', mostly scientific articles donated to the Society by fellows and others anxious to promote their work or advertise their talents as writers on matters of scientific interest. A wide range of subjects was covered: birds, meteorology, magnetism, the training of pauper children, antiquities, anatomy, pumping engines and even a treatise on Aesop's Fables in Chinese. Even then, when education in the mechanical sciences was beginning to be offered and 'science'

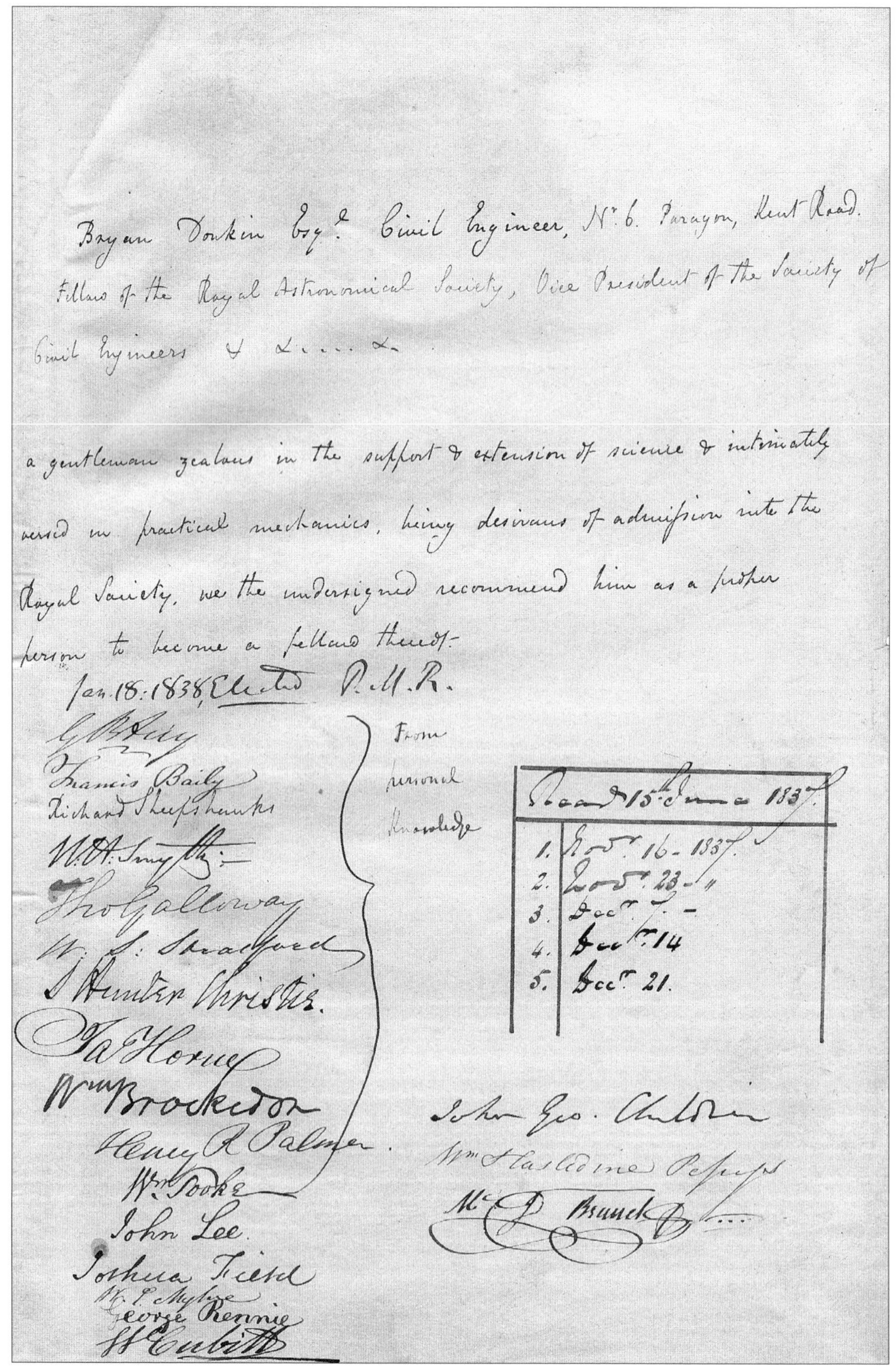

Bryan Donkin Esqre Civil Engineer, No. 6. Paragon, Kent Road.
Fellow of the Royal Astronomical Society, Vice President of the Society of Civil Engineers & &.... &.

a gentleman zealous in the support & extension of science & intimately versed in practical mechanics, being desirous of admission into the Royal Society, we the undersigned recommend him as a proper person to become a fellow thereof-

Jan. 18: 1838, Elected P.M.R.

G B Airy
Francis Baily
Richard Sheepshanks
W. H. Smyth
Thos Galloway
W. S. Stratford
S Hunter Christie
Ja. Horne
Wm Brockedon
Henry R Palmer
Wm Tooke

From personal knowledge

John Lee.
Joshua Field
W. P. Mylne
George Rennie
W Cubitt

Read 15th June 1837	
1.	Novr. 16 - 1837
2.	Novr. 23 - "
3.	Decr. 7 -
4.	Decr. 14
5.	Decr. 21.

John Geo. Children
Wm Haseldine Pepys
Mc I Brunel

56 *Royal Society proposal,* 1838.

was falling into more specific categories, the interests of the Royal Society were diverse. After the presentations there were usually talks and discussions. It was the custom and privilege for members to be allowed to invite a guest to a meeting; many of the 'strangers' later became Fellows. Thus, in 1834, Marc Brunel had first introduced his Thames Tunnel assistant Richard Beamish as a stranger – Donkin knew him well, both as an engineer and later as a fellow committee member of the Phrenological Society; and Peter Barlow, the great mathematician, had brought his son, Peter Barlow, Jun., who in turn introduced Henry Palmer as his guest: all became Fellows.[4] Less than two years after his induction, at the annual November 'Anniversary' meeting, Bryan Donkin was elected to the Council of the Royal Society, under the new President William Whewell, a true polymath and the first to coin the word 'scientist'.[5] The following month, Donkin invited his brother Thomas as a guest to the Society, but he did not become a Fellow; instead, his brilliant twenty-four year old son William Fishburn Donkin (Bryan's nephew) was elected as a Fellow in 1842, in the same year as becoming Savilian Professor of Astronomy at Oxford. Donkin himself added his signature to the list of proposers of nine new members in the 1840s. One of these was James Tulloch, a man of taste and education, who had been helped by Donkin to patent a marble-cutting machine two decades earlier and who had also just become a fellow member of the Society of Arts.[6] John Farey, an expert in steam power, was well known to Donkin, too, and William Simms was one of Donkin's friends from the world of astronomy and instrument making.[7] He was the last person whom Donkin recommended as a Fellow; clearly Bryan, at almost eighty four, was still attending the Society on occasion, but his handwriting was shaky and sometimes his signature, though still bold, was spidery and smudged.

The Royal Society had been through a bad patch during the first two decades of the century. Being the longest established and most highly respected scientific society, it had at first attracted truly experimental and academic men, but towards 1820, Fellows were being admitted who were not all practitioners of scientific learning.[8] In the following decade the strict policies of the Royal Society had been blurred to allow members of literary and antiquarian groups to be drawn in, as well as amateurs with money and social status, some more interested in the Arts than the Sciences. By 1830, three great pillars of the Society had passed away: Sir Joseph Banks, William Herschel and Humphrey Davy had died, leaving the Royal Society in some disarray.[9] In a lack-lustre election for the presidency, apathy reigned and only a third of the members turned up to vote; the Duke of Sussex, a non-scientist, was chosen by a small majority over the more obvious candidate, John Herschel. The Duke had a difficult task ahead. Into the fray stepped Charles Babbage, that extremely bright but tetchy and unpredictable mathematician who, while working on the difference engine and having difficulty in funding it, found time to write a furious attack on the Government's lack of support for science, the low level of respect for scientific achievement and the failure of the Royal Society to promote the subject and uphold its values.[10] It was time for a review of the state of science and a re-think of the categorisation of the subjects within it. In an appendix to his *Reflections on the Decline of Science in England*, Babbage noted that in Germany, meetings of an 'academy' had taken place in different cities for the past eight years, bringing together men of science; at the first meeting in Leipzig only those interested in the fields of medicine and botany were present, but such was the success of the annual meetings that the membership expanded to include 'the cultivators even of pure mathematics'. Babbage had attended the Congress of Philosophers in Berlin in 1828, and enthused about the ethos of the congress: he saw great potential for emulating the idea in England.

The germ of the suggestion took root and in 1831 a new society, the British Association for the Advancement of Science was formed, with Babbage central to its management. It was a good move: the Royal Society was able to take moral support from the British Association, many of whose members belonged to both, so that scientific proposals gained more weight and pressure could be brought to bear on the Council of the Royal Society more effectively than if put forward by any individual.[11] In fact, the noble President, the Duke of Sussex, slowly but surely breathed new life into the Royal Society and reformed it, building up a strong Council to raise standards and so regain respect in the eyes of the Government and the world of science, so that when his term of office ended in 1838 (when Bryan Donkin became a Fellow), the Royal Society had re-emerged as the leader of scientific opinion.

The British Association, as it came to be called, flourished, meeting every year in a different city. The eighth annual meeting of the British Association was held in Newcastle in August 1838 and attended by Bryan Donkin, FRS. He had attended the conference the previous year, in Liverpool, when he had been appointed to a committee 'for ascertaining the amount of duty actually performed by the consumption of one bushel of coals in steam engines employed in pumping water', as well as to another group which was to experiment on the strength of cast and wrought iron: each committee was granted £100 to spend on the trials and expected to report their findings to the British Association.[12]

The 1838 meeting was an important one for Donkin. In preparation, Bryan had spent a few days staying with Mary in Sandoe, before they both went to Newcastle for the conference.[13] He had been approached by Charles Babbage, a big noise in the Association, with the proposition that Donkin should take over from him as President of the Mechanical Sciences section for that year.[14] The Association met in a different town each year, and tradition dictated that the President of each group was a 'local' man. George Stephenson and George Buddle (an influential mining engineer) had already turned down Babbage's offer; it seemed that nobody wanted to take on the responsibility for chairing meetings where Dr Dionysius Lardner was speaking, for fear of controversy. Lardner was a talented but misguided man, with strong and contentious assertions, particularly

57 *Central Exchange, Newcastle,* c.1840.

on the subjects of the gauge of railway lines and the inadvisability of Atlantic steam voyages. Donkin evidently felt it unwise to risk unpleasantness and also turned down the offer, accepting instead Babbage's invitation to become one of the Vice-Presidents of the group, as well as acting as chairman of the Mechanics Section. Possibly all three men were also unwilling to serve in a higher role than Babbage, a man full of his own importance. Babbage remained as President and Donkin spoke up in the railway debate. For six days, members met in their chosen sections, seven groups representing every aspect of science from chemistry and mineralogy to zoology and botany.[15] Subjects under discussion during the six day conference ranged widely; papers were read on diabetic sugar, binocular vision, a new map of Mexico, crime in Newcastle and fish with four eyes, among many others. Several meeting rooms in the centre of Newcastle were used for lectures, including the Central Exchange.

It was a sociable conference, as well as being a technical and erudite gathering. The circus was in town, fountains were illuminated by gas lights, and fireworks lit the night skies.[16] Ladies were allowed to attend if they had a ticket, to sit in the galleries and listen to the lectures; a ball was held on the first evening and a Promenade on the Wednesday. Three thousand people attended the Promenade, a social evening with conversation and refreshments, held in the tastefully decorated Green Market – Mary and Bryan must have been there. On show during the week was an exhibition of models of the latest inventions, and

Mangiamele, another 'calculating youth', performed his mathematical feats to the amazement of all.[17] Celebrity-watchers waited in the street to catch a glimpse of Faraday or Sir John Herschel, and groupies followed Dr Whewell to the lecture rooms; such was the popular veneration for intellectual achievement.[18] Hannah Martineau, an outspoken social theorist of the day, was there.[19] She deplored the behaviour of some of the people present; as well as criticising the 'obtrusions of coxcombs', the 'conceit of third-rate men with their specialities' and Sir John Herschel's patronising comments on the presence of the fair sex at meetings, she felt ashamed by the ladies who could not sit still for more than half an hour and made sketches of the famous speakers under cover of their shawls or little parasols.

Dr Lardner's presence did not go unnoticed. It was reported that it was probably he who had started a rumour earlier in the year that Isambard Brunel's *Great Western* steam boat, on her maiden voyage to America, had broken her back and was lying helpless in mid-Atlantic; this apparent effort by Lardner to prove his case against steam locomotion to America caused him to be ostracised by many people at the conference.[20]

The Mechanics section was full of matters of interest to Donkin. Dr Lardner gave his paper on railway constants as well as the dreaded report on steam navigation, when he backed down somewhat and was supported by Babbage, leaving a sense of disappointment and some anger on both sides.[21] There were complaints from railway enthusiasts that Babbage, the Chairman, had cut short the session on the gauge of railway lines, which was particularly annoying when so many able men were present eager to hear about the important subject.[22] Clearly they were ignorant of the internal politics of the meeting. Mr Holtzapffel described new scales of measurement that he had invented, and the merits of stone versus cast iron and timber for supporting railway lines were discussed with vigour; opinions were expressed by both Donkin and George Stephenson on that subject.[23] A talk on isometric drawing (a method of graphically representing a three-dimensional object) was given by Thomas Sopwith, who also held forth on the subject of constructing geological models, and promoted his new 'levelling stave', a graduated, extending rod used by surveyors.[24] After one of the meetings, Sopwith walked to Newcastle's St. Mary's Square with Bryan Donkin, to show him his new buildings, noting afterwards that Donkin 'was much pleased with my writing cabinet and ordered one to be made like it'.[25] Later in the year, Donkin invited him to a four o'clock dinner before a meeting of the ICE, writing: '... if you feel any interest in that way, I will have much pleasure in showing you our factory'.[26] Sopwith took up the invitation and went to Bryan's Bermondsey manufactory with him, where he admired the 'very fine dividing engine which is capable of dividing an inch into 10,000 parts'. At dinner with the Donkin family (Mary and four of the younger Donkins), Sopwith enjoyed a discussion on phrenology and saw the writing cabinet that had been made in the Newcastle cabinet makers' workshop.

On the Friday of the British Association conference week, everyone took the day off to witness the opening of the Durham Junction Railway. There the main attraction was the new Victoria Bridge carrying two railway lines and a footpath over the Wear, its 160ft central arch then the largest in Europe in height and span.[27] The day was marked by a procession, watched by hundreds, and a big banquet.

Back at the conference, the phrenologist Dr Inglis read his paper on the analysis of the skull of Eugene Aram, an infamous murderer. His remarks on the correlation between the phrenological reading of the head and the man's character provoked comments about the authenticity of the skull and drew from the audience arguments for and against the importance and truth of phrenology – some denounced it as chimerical and absurd.[28]

Quite a number of the British Association members were also phrenologists, and some wondered whether to propose the formation of a phrenological section. But in spite of years of allegiance to the science, the phrenologists did not feel confident enough to press the point, for fear that their relatively small number and their contentious beliefs might leave them open to criticism. Instead, at rather short notice, they called a meeting of interested people at the end of the week, and the Phrenological Association was formed. [29]

Phrenological societies had of course been established for almost two decades, but it was felt that a wider approach should be adopted, to unify the groups and to bring 'this important branch of philosophy into the public eye to gain more respect and consideration for it'. It was decided that the new Phrenological Association, although an independent organisation, would meet annually at the same times and places as the British Association, partly to save money and time for those members who belonged to both. At a public meeting quickly announced at the conference to test the interest, five hundred people crowded into a room meant for fewer, and apparently hundreds were turned away. Two thirds were ladies, who braved the stuffy conditions to listen attentively; Mary Donkin would certainly have been among them, a proud sister when Bryan was called upon to chair the meeting. Speaking off the cuff, because of lack of time to prepare, ten phrenologists (including the education reformer Robert Owen and Professor Olinthus Gregory, a founder member of the Royal Astronomical Society) explained the principles and usefulness of phrenology to a rapt audience, some of whom had very little knowledge of the subject and who attended the meeting with a sense of curiosity for the unknown and the mysterious.

For the seventy year old Bryan, the British Association week must have been an exciting and stimulating event, if tiring. Other participants, too, surely revelled in the mingling of minds and the scientific and social interaction. There was criticism, though; as one journal editor put it: 'These meetings generally prove little more than travelling shows, for exhibiting the lions of the intellectual world'.[30] Why did the scientists merely read papers 'that could have been published long since in scientific periodicals, instead of bottling them up for a twelvemonth?' Dr Lardner came in for a slating: having insisted the previous year on the impossibility of trans-Atlantic steam navigation, and having been proved wrong, he now 'felt himself called upon to prove that he was still in the right … We shall wait patiently for his next antic.' Lardner was not the only scientist to lay himself open to the lash of the writer's tongue: the invention of a writing desk was ridiculed 'which had this unique disadvantage, that all the drawers could have their locks picked at the same time'. Another inventor was ridiculed because he 'occupied the time of the meeting by explaining an apparatus for cooking by gas!' Even if no great innovations were brought about by the BAAS meeting, forward steps had been taken, and knowledge was accumulating. During the conference, Donkin had been asked to join a research committee (with Dr Andrew Ure, Mr Cooper and Dr Michael Faraday), this time to report on the state of knowledge on the subject of the specific gravity of steam generated at different temperatures, an example of the many small projects that arose from discussions at the meeting.[31] The 1838 meeting brought benefits to the economy of the city of Newcastle, and played a part in bringing scientific ideas to the notice of ordinary people.

In mid February, before his election to the Fellowship of the Royal Society and the British Association meeting, Donkin had taken part in an experiment to determine the relative strengths of a brick beam and one of timber.[32] With Brunel, Frances Bramah, Field and about three dozen professional scientists and engineers, he watched with interest as a beam made of bricks, held together with Roman cement mixed with sharp, clean Thames sand and reinforced with iron tie-bars, was loaded with 'railway bars', adding to a container already holding over ten tons of scrap iron, which had hung suspended from the beam for two years without damage. The accumulated load of iron reached a total of over twenty two tons before the beam suddenly broke without warning. (There was no report of injuries.) Compared with Peter Barlow's table of the comparative strength of timber, it was found that even this strong construction was only a quarter to a half of the strength of a beam made of oak or fir. Detailed calculations made afterwards, taking into account previous experiments by Captain Brown, Brunel, Barlow and Telford, concluded (unsurprisingly) that the iron bars had played a significant part in the strength of the beam.

At the Society of Arts, Arthur Aikin gave a talk about the chattering of mill-stones.[33] Donkin had been asked for advice on this perennial problem. When grinding corn, one grindstone, called the 'runner', turned above a static stone at around 120 revolutions per minute, squashing the grain and producing flour. Sometimes, though, the process was upset by the stone running unevenly, setting up dangerous vibrations and causing a frightening chatter as the stones knocked violently together at one side.[34] Mr Aikin graciously acknowledged that he was indebted to Bryan Donkin for the 'very probable' explanation of the phenomenon. The use of plaster as a cement, which differed greatly in specific gravity from the

Buhr, and the variety of sizes of the pieces of stone held within the circular metal frame, meant that the weight was unequally spread across the stone, causing the stones to bump together at one side as the top stone rotated. The only remedy was to sort the pieces of stone carefully and lay them in the frame so that the cement would be evenly distributed.

By now, Bryan Donkin could have given up work altogether, but his expertise was still in demand, and he was asked for his opinion on 'a subject of very great importance'.[35] Francis Humphrys was an engineer, employed by John Hall and Sons of Dartford (Donkin's friend and brother-in-law), to design the engines made by the firm for the paddle steamer *Wilberforce*.[36] The *Wilberforce* went into service in 1837 between the Thames and the Humber, but in 1838 Isambard Brunel was called on to examine the slide valves in the engine.[37] Unable to go at the time, Brunel wrote to say that he had requested Donkin to take on the task and to make a report: 'I need hardly tell you that on mechanical subjects generally, Mr Donkin is one of the best and most cautious authorities, and in marine engines, I should at any time consider his opinion second only to that of Mr Field'. Donkin's report was highly favourable to the valves. Writing on behalf of his Great Western Steam Ship Company, Brunel thanked Bryan Donkin for his full and satisfactory report, and asked him to name his fee.[38] The two men had known each other since Isambard was a boy.

Collaboration with his brother-in-law's firm continued: an 'eight-horse steam engine was built for Donkin at John Hall's factory, in 1838, two years after Hall died.[39]

Work was still coming in and, in 1838, a drawing was sent to John Baradon, of 'a dredging-boat with machinery and engine as used on the River Yare below Norwich'.[40] Another drawing was needed of a paper mill in Baltimore: Donkin's reputation still held strong.[41]

The firm was still supplying tailor-made items for individuals, like the letter-copying press, drawn in 1839 'taken from one sent to Mr Warren'.[42]

At the Institution of Civil Engineers, Donkin was still enthusiastically taking part in debates. Steam engines were a constant subject for discussion; as someone who had grown up in their developmental stages and even patented his own idea for a steam wheel as far back as 1803, Donkin was keen to keep abreast and add his ideas. At a meeting in February 1840, he contributed his thoughts on the relative friction caused by engines of different construction, and its effect on performance.[43] The burgeoning interest in railways and their possibilities led to a torrent of ideas for the improvement of their speed and efficiency, and the 'Civils' were in the forefront of developments.[44] Their debate on 7 April 1840 was centred round the performance of several railway locomotives of American origin, which had been sent to England by their manufacturer, Mr Norris of Philadelphia, promising higher power, greater durability and less weight than the home-produced engines. Trials had taken place on the Grand Junction Railway between Birmingham and

58 *Bryan Donkin,* 1840, *aged* 72.

Liverpool in April and May 1839, with careful measurements made of the speed up and down gradients, with and without wagons attached. Detailed records were made of steam pressure, coal consumption, and wear and tear, and afterwards tabulated and analysed. Captain Moorsom reported to the Civil Engineers that out of twenty-one trials, only five had come up to expectation, in five others a doubt existed, and in the remaining eleven, 'the exact amount of duty was *not* performed'. Bryan Donkin was particularly interested to hear that the engines had managed to go round bends fast without falling off the tracks and remarked that the flanches on the wheels were all that kept them on the rails. He wondered whether there was some other part of the construction that was not shown in the model or by the description, which might account for the American engine's apparent success. Was there any provision made in English four- or six-wheeled engines to allow for a 'divergence from parallelism when rounding curves?' His comments provoked a lively discussion of methods for enabling wheels to remain on both straight and curved stretches of railway lines. It was clearly an important point that would need attention in the future.

These years were an exciting time for engineers. In a review of the state of the country's progress, the editor of *The Civil Engineer and Architect's Journal* looked back over the past year.[45] He singled out the subject of railways as having made the most progress: it was now possible to travel by rail from Birmingham to Preston, and several other lines, including the Newcastle to Carlisle, the London to Greenwich and the Manchester to Bolton railways had also been completed. There was not much to say about canals, because they had previously reached a high level of development. (Some canals were actually in decline after a hundred years of use, and suffering through competition with the speed and convenience of railways.) Many bridges had been completed and repairs made to several over the Thames; floating bridges powered by steam and running on chains on the river bed had been developed as a cheap method of ferrying vehicles and passengers across rivers in the South of England. The successful voyage to America by Brunel's steam-driven *Great Western* had shown the value and potential of steam navigation for closer contact with America and the longer-term advantages to trade. More iron-built steamers were now in use at sea and on the rivers. Direct links had been made between London and St. Petersburg and to the East. For some time, Trevithick had been carrying out a series of experiments in powering ships by means of a screw propeller at the stern, culminating in the launch of the new ship *Archimedean* in September 1838. Steam boats were still exploding though, mainly because of teething problems in an infant science.

It was reported, too, that the University of Durham, closely followed by King's College and University College in London, had been the first to introduce courses in civil engineering and mining. The hope was that the Sciences would now be considered on a par with the Arts, particularly in the awarding of doctorates. Certainly, civil engineering was becoming recognised as a profession in its own right and the civil engineers, led by the practitioners in the Royal Society and the British Association for the Advancement of Science, were making an impact on the country's infrastructure and industry.

19
Handing Over the Reins

When he turned seventy, Bryan's daughter Mary Ann and son John were both married with children; Bryan's first grandchild was Mary Ann's boy, Edmund, born in the same year (1830) as John's first children, twin girls, who unfortunately both died young. It was not long before Bryan's three youngest sons (Bryan, Henry and Thomas) started families too. None of the other girls ever married (although Maria had a surprise in store) and William, unusually for Donkin men, never found a wife. Of Donkin's five boys, four joined the firm and played a vital part in developing the business. As young men, John, Bryan and Thomas were all members of the Institution of Civil Engineers; Henry leant towards chemical engineering. Only wayward William proved unsuitable for a career in the Donkin business.

Engineering was John's chosen profession, as befitted the eldest son of Bryan Donkin. After studying French and German in Paris, he was taken on at the Donkin works, alongside his fellow pupils, Henry Palmer and William Gravatt. Early in his career he had proved himself to be adept at drawing and designing, and he soon became an important cog in the wheel of Bryan Donkin's business.[1] He rose to the trusted position of partner in the firm in 1824, joining his fellow engineer, John Wilks, Bryan's faithful and useful right-hand man, and contributed materially to the great degree of perfection reached by the paper-making machine. It was natural for John, at the age of twenty two, to follow his father's path to membership of the Institution of Civil Engineers. Together with William Gravatt, John Donkin spoke on one occasion to a meeting of the Institution about a variety of geological sections that they had obtained from Isleworth, Greenwich and London. Another time, he addressed the members on the best way of regulating the supply of water to mills, introducing his invention – gates for wide water wheels, which could be easily adjusted and reduced friction; his father contributed a drawing and description of the gate and Mr Cubitt said that the plan was simple and effective, reducing the friction to a tenth of the usual amount.[2] With his background knowledge, surely gained partly from his father's experiences of underground water, John described to the ICE the specialised techniques of sinking wells constructed of brick-lined iron or wood, and boring to a depth of up to 320 feet for water.[3]

This bright young man was elected Fellow of The Geological Society of London in 1834.[4] He also belonged to the Phrenological Association. John's responsibilities within the Company included planning paper mills and other establishments on the Continent and he accompanied his father to Europe to visit mills that were using the firm's machines; on one trip he sailed with his brother to Antwerp.[5] When his brother Bryan journeyed abroad to France, Italy and Germany, it was John who directed his movements.[6] Improvements to the manufacture of paper were John's concern, too: he took out patents in 1834 and1846.[7] In later life he took on, with some regret, a more administrative and commercial role in the firm, while his brothers Bryan and Thomas took the lead in technical matters.[8] The family must have been proud of him. John had married Caroline, the daughter of Benjamin Hawes in 1829.[9] They lived at 80 Great Surrey Street after his parents moved out but later brought up their family in a beautiful residence, Ormond House in the Old Kent Road, built not far from Bryan Donkin's factory in Bermondsey. Later they moved to a house named Roseacre at Bearsted, near Maidstone, and lived there for the rest of John's life.[10]

Donkin's second son Bryan went to a school near Windsor when he was seven or eight, and then on to a preparatory school in St Mary Cray, from Easter 1817.[11] His education, completed in London, Paris and Nantes, enabled him to speak French well, a great asset in his future career. He started work in the family firm at the age of nineteen, and in 1829 took on the task of superintending the setting up of a new mill near Nantes, staying there for about two years. John, Bryan Junior's older brother, arranged a European journey for Bryan in 1836, combining visits to mills with a full itinerary of sightseeing through Italy (Genoa, Naples, Rome and Milan) and via several places in Germany back to England through France. Bryan wrote a vivid description of the wonders he had seen, but he was disappointed by the climate in Italy, and although he found Italian girls were beautiful, he did not like the sound of their voices.[12] As a young man, Bryan lived with his parents at the Paragon, before marrying Emma Day (his sister Mary Ann's step-daughter) in July 1841, thus strengthening the bonds of the close-knit family. Bryan Senior and Bryan Junior worked alongside each other for many years, setting up new paper mills and machinery; like his father, the younger Bryan also carried out valuations and arbitrations.[13] He became a partner in the firm in 1840: he was truly a chip off the old block.[14]

Of William's early adulthood, little can be told. He must have been somewhat of a disappointment, and perhaps even an embarrassment to them all. After a rather shaky start in life, when he seemed to be an unhealthy youngster, and failed to fulfil his father's expectations as a teen-age student in Paris, William rather disappears from the family history during his middle years. An odd story appeared in *The Times* in 1830, which possibly throws some light on the mystery of his life.[15] A Commission of Lunacy was set up to enquire into the state of mind of Lady Charlotte Sherard; the enquiry was held at the Red Lion, Hillingdon.

For five years she had been resident in a lunatic asylum in Hillingdon. From the description of her erratic behaviour, it sounds as if she was a manic-depressive: she broke windows, suffered from delusions, and fancied that she could read people's thoughts. Although Lady Charlotte could be completely rational, she was not capable of looking after herself, because her mind constantly wavered from one thing to another. One of her claims was that she and a Mr William Donkin had a mutual agreement to marry; the very thought of him disturbed her sleep and she woke repeating his name. Could the jury, she asked, bring forward her marriage to Mr Donkin? A rather muddled letter from her to William Donkin was read out; in it she asked him to write, and mentioned that she had a lock of his hair. The jury called in the lady herself for an interview. She maintained that Mr Donkin had been a patient in the same house with her, a statement that her family solicitor maintained was without foundation, although 'there was a person named Donkin who had been introduced to her'; as far as the solicitor knew, Donkin had never made an offer of marriage to her. The unhappy lady was declared of unsound mind. The gentleman may or may not have been Bryan Donkin's son. He might have had some kind of liaison with Lady Charlotte. Why was he introduced to her? The lawyer may have been lying. The truth of the matter will never be known, but in the light of William Donkin's eventual fate, an element of doubt must remain.

A false start in his career was made by Henry, Donkin's fourth son. Perhaps unwilling at first to follow his brothers into the family business, he signed up to be apprenticed to his Uncle Henry, the Durham lawyer; but it did not work out, and instead, he joined the Donkin firm. In 1841 he and his brother Thomas were living together in Mead Row, Godalming, for a time, probably working for the progressive Thomas Sweetapple at his Catteshall paper mill.[16] The following year found him as ambassador for the Bryan Donkin Company in Italy. There he lived in San Marcello in Tuscany, working for Tommaso Cini, a wealthy landowner and engineer, who had established a large paper mill nearby, installing Donkin machinery.[17] Henry's task was to supervise the building of a huge water wheel, designed by Bryan Donkin in London for the extensive woollen and carpet-making mill that Cini was building.[18] The beautiful wheel was seventy six feet high with a width of only two feet and was carefully sheltered from the wind by walls that supported the canal supplying the water.[19] It was the second tallest vertical iron wheel ever built.[20] Parts were sent from England by boat. Henry's friendly relationship with Tommaso made the work congenial, and his thoughts of his fiancée – 'the charms and talents of my sweet Margaret' – as well as letters from his brothers, kept him in touch with home. In July 1843 Henry and Margaret married back in England, at St Oswald's in Durham; she was the youngest daughter of the late John Dunn, his Uncle Henry's Durham colleague.[21] After a quick visit to Sandoe following the wedding, the young couple returned to Tuscany and Henry started to build a house, ordering new furniture from nearby

59 *Water wheel for Tuscan mill,* 1842.

Florence. A project with paper machines in Lima was progressing well; the future looked rosy.[22] Then in the October, Margaret became ill and received costly medical treatment in the Grand Hotel in Florence, where they were forced to stay longer than expected; but she recovered. On 3 December 1844 Margaret gave birth to a little girl, named after her proud mother. But urgent letters reached Henry's Aunt Mary and his sister Maria (who was living in Sandoe) bringing the terrible news that Margaret had died three days after the birth.[23] Immediately, the family leapt into action, guided no doubt by their senior member, Bryan Donkin, and a decision was made: Maria would make the long journey to Italy to look after the baby.[24]

It was an irrevocable choice that shaped Maria's future. The thirty year old spinster immediately packed her bags and was ready to go before Christmas, but unpacked again to wait for a suitable time for her brother Bryan to travel with her. The two set sail from Folkestone on 2 March 1845, taking their time to cross Europe and stopping to take the opportunity of sightseeing in Paris, Turin, Genoa, Livorno and Pisa. Travelling across the Jura Mountains and the Alps in winter was no picnic; in places, the roads were almost blocked by snowdrifts of up to forty feet high, and at one point the partly-covered horse-drawn sledge carrying Maria and Bryan became stuck, teetering at an angle near the edge of a precipice. Sometimes they travelled at night, experiencing hurricane winds on a mountain summit. Driving rain, blizzards, miserable fog and bitter winds made their journey hazardous but they battled on in good spirits. Finally, they reached San Marcello after a journey of nearly two months, covering about a thousand miles. It was a life-changing experience for Maria Donkin. Plucked from her sociable gentlewoman's life in London and Northumberland, she endured the rigours of the voyage to Italy; after arriving at Henry's home, she took charge of the rather sickly baby's welfare and, helped by a nursemaid, became little Margaret's surrogate mother. She lived with Henry and the child in Italy for two years, until Henry's work there was finished and all three returned to London to join Bryan and Mary Donkin and other members of the family, living together at the Paragon. The tables were turned for Maria when Margaret grew up and married George Sloman: the couple looked after Maria in her old age.

Before leaving Tuscany, Henry had watched with interest the work being carried out on the Florence to Pistoia railway line, under the direction of Isambard Brunel … supposedly. In fact Brunel had left 'young Babbage' in charge.[25] Brunel, the chief engineer, had graced the project with very brief visits, apparently. Henry was kept up to date by Mr Sloan, the prosperous owner of a nearby copper mine and smelting works at La Briglia.[26] Henry's letter home spelt it out: the Italian workers were useless. It was more worthwhile to pay young English men £300 a year than to employ Italians at £60 or £70.[27] Sloan had told Henry that 'he perceived immediately that Brunel was a most talented, prudent, cautious and modest man.' Henry heartily disagreed. 'By this and other pretty speeches of said Sloan, I begin to think him a much bigger fool than I first took him for. As far as I can learn they have been committing a few blunders at the Briglia as to the building etc.'

Henry did not spend his lifetime immersed in work for the Donkin Company, but after working with his three brothers (John, Bryan and Thomas) broke away to take up a new career. Perhaps he had never really felt comfortable in the family business and now that his brothers were well established in the firm, there was no pressure on Henry to conform. Perhaps the loss of his young wife and the responsibility for his motherless child had unsettled him. His contented life in Tuscany and his willingness to make a home there had been cruelly upset. Two years after returning from Italy, Henry patented an 'antichlor' consisting of bisulphate of soda for use in the paper-making industry.[28] It was indeed widely used for several years, but was superseded by the cheaper and more effective hydro-sulphate. By 1861, the odd trio – Henry, his sister Maria, and the teenage Margaret – had moved out of the Paragon to Upper Tooting and Henry was a full-blown 'merchant in chemical products'.[29]

The youngest son of Bryan and Mary's family was Thomas, who played an important part in the Donkin firm all his working life, starting young. The design and supply of paper-making machines was his main work, from the busy years of the 1830s when business was booming. He married Sarah, the sister of Margaret Dunn (his brother Henry's late wife), and they lived in four different homes in South London. After his father's death, he filed three patents in four years, for improvements to the glazing of paper, for a wire-guiding apparatus to control the moving web on the paper machine (which could also be applied to machines for making fabrics) and for improvements to paper-making machinery.[30]

Mary Ann, the firstborn child of Bryan and Mary Donkin, grew up to be a caring young woman, spending much time away from home in her teens and twenties, living in Isleworth and helping to look after her mother's uncle, Matthew Stainton. Old Mr Stainton's generosity to Bryan Donkin in the past had not been forgotten; he had set Bryan on his feet by financing the mortgage on the Bermondsey factory, and later helped him out when funds were low. When Mary Ann was a teenager he was well into his eighties and had lost his sight, although he was 'no trouble'.[31] Also in Isleworth lived another relative, Mrs Robson, who was more troublesome; clearly dementia had taken hold of her, for she was losing her faculties and 'taking umbrage at some fancied neglect of being robbed'.

During her visits to Isleworth, Mary Ann made the acquaintance of her husband to be: they married in 1829, when Mary Ann was twenty nine years old. William Day was only twelve years younger than Bryan Donkin, and a widower with four children when he married Mary Ann. At the age of fourteen, he had been articled to Dr Cook, a surgeon in Colchester, and was destined to become an army surgeon after training at the London Hospital. Instead, having caught a fever on the wards, he returned to Colchester, married Dr Cook's niece and bought the private practice in Isleworth where he continued as a doctor for the rest of his life, gradually retiring, but attending his old friends until the last.[32] He was highly respected as a supporter of charities in his local area, including the local charity school, where 100 boys and 60 girls were educated.[33] There was great excitement in Isleworth in 1832, when it was learnt that King William would be passing through the village on his way to visit the Duke of Northumberland at nearby Syon House.[34] Plans were made and money was raised to give the Royal party a loyal welcome. On July 31st, a Tuesday, three triumphal arches of flowers and evergreens stood in the centre of the village and the doors and windows of the houses were bedecked with flowers, ribbons and garlands. A rowing race was held on the Thames; a steam boat and two bands took part in the festivities too. Dinner was provided for 500 poor children, and another 600 boys and girls enjoyed buns and cakes. The King and his entourage arrived at four o'clock and stayed for two hours; at the end of the event a select group of four men, one of whom was William Day, presented loyal addresses to His Majesty, who accepted them 'most graciously', declaring that he would never forget the unexpected and enthusiastic welcome he had received that day. It must have been an exciting day for Mary Ann, too.

Romance blossomed between William Day's daughter Emma (by his first marriage) and Bryan Donkin's son Bryan Donkin, Jun; by their union, William Day became both Bryan Junior's brother-in-law and his father-in law. William and Mary Ann had three children: Edmund (who studied as a lawyer), Albert (who followed his father's profession) and Alice. When William died, his funeral was well attended by local notables including the dowager Duchess of Northumberland.

The two other daughters of Bryan Donkin, Sarah and Jane, never married, and remain something of a mystery. When Jane was six, her father described her as 'among the middlings'.[35] Perhaps she blossomed as she grew. The two lived together with their parents until their father died. By the time Bryan's children were adults, there was money in the Donkin family, supplemented in the 1840s by interest from the judicious acquisition of shares in new railway companies. At least one of the Donkin ladies was rather fashionably dressed: Miss Donkin emerged from Lewis and Allenby in Regent Street on 4 November 1839, having purchased (for £2 6s. 6d.) a squirrel cape and half a yard of silk velvet at £10 a yard, perhaps to adorn a hat.[36]

The death in 1836 of Bryan's brother-in-law and fellow engineer was a sad loss. They had often worked together, since the time when Donkin became John Hall's apprentice and took over the paper machine project, and they had developed the canning process together. A few years before he died, John Hall suffered from kidney stones and travelled to France to be treated by the pioneer (Dr Civiale) of a new surgical procedure called lithotricity, an operation that took only minutes to perform, yet seemed to have successful and lasting effects, so much so that an account of the surgery was presented to the Royal Society.[37]

In London, there was still much for the socially-minded Bryan to do. Shrewd as he was, he became a director of the Victoria Life Assurance and Loan Company, probably encouraged by the influential Benjamin Hawes, its deputy chairman.[38] The company seems to have thrived with a philanthropic attitude coupled with solid business sense, an approach that would have appealed to Donkin. It advertised as its aims the ability to offer life insurance for sums as low as £50 'so as to extend more universally the important benefits resulting from a well-regulated system of life assurance'.[39] Loans or annuities of up to £200 could be advanced, provided that the borrower had a policy worth the required amount, and policy-holders could also receive a share of the profits. Donkin's involvement with the scheme continued until his death.

His work as an adviser continued, and he was called on to give his opinion at a Government Enquiry on the performance of steam boilers, as he had done at the Enquiry that took place after the disastrous explosion of the Yarmouth steam boat more than thirty years earlier. For years, there had been endless discussions about the behaviour and management of steam. In 1841 it seemed that there were fewer explosions of boilers in London, compared with elsewhere, a subject that exercised the minds of engineers.[40] The reason could be that because fuel was expensive in the capital, operators took more care; or, because of more sensible use of valves on Thames steamers – an improvement partly due to Donkin's advice in the Norfolk case. In general, the causes of explosions were now frequently discussed and remedies found. In a cross-examination, Donkin gave his opinions on several aspects of the problem, and said that he believed that, in most cases, unequal pressure on the tube inside the boiler, resulting from its not being completely cylindrical, was the cause of its collapsing.

On Donkin's home patch, the Surrey Dispensary gave medical help to the poor people of the area that lay between Vauxhall Bridge and eastwards towards Millpond Bridge, covering the streets around London Bridge.[41] Smallpox was on the increase and the poor lived in appalling conditions, sharing filthy, overcrowded rooms. Dr Aldis, one of the four physicians who practised at the Dispensary, suggested to its committee that ventilation in the houses was an important factor in preventing the spread of diseases. The Dispensary relied on the generosity of benefactors to keep the charity active; Bryan Donkin was a contributor, and in 1844 acted as one of the stewards at the anniversary dinner at the Bridge House Hotel, Southwark.[42] He also donated two guineas to the 'Baths and Washhouses for the Labouring Classes', a charitable organisation set up that year by a group of worthy gentlemen including the Governor of the Bank of England, the Lord Mayor of London, and the Bishop of London.[43] They believed that public health would be greatly improved if poor workers had access to clean water for bathing in and for washing their clothes.[44] William Hawes, the deputy chairman of the group, was the son of Benjamin Hawes.

Near Donkin's home were several schools.[45] The National and Parochial Schools for boys and for girls were supported by legacies and donations from parishioners,

Bryan Donkin among them. Bacon's Free School was established by Thomas Bacon (no relation of Donkin's one-time partner) with his father's bequest; it was built to educate and train between forty and sixty poor children of the parish. Bryan Donkin's son Bryan was later treasurer to the committee.[46] In addition, the Deaf and Dumb School, which was well supported by a numerous list of subscribers, trained the children to become useful members of society; the British and Foreign Bible Society School, which Donkin had helped to set up, offered a predominantly religious education, but was open to children of all denominations.

The hazards of London life in the mid nineteenth century were all too present, and too close for comfort on New Year's Eve 1845, when Donkin's friend John Farey was badly affected by a fatal fire at his home. Farey, the multi-talented engineer, was well known to Bryan. Donkin's matter-of-fact account of the disaster was typical of him:[47]

> Having offered Mr John Farey (after the disastrous fire at his house, by which he lost so much, and in which four lives were lost) some assistance in money to meet his present necessities, I today sent my son John with cheque of £100; he told John he would receive it as a loan.

Perhaps mindful of the ever-present threat of fire to his own premises, Donkin had already supported the fund for the relief of the people of Hamburg after a terrible fire there, 'unexampled in its extent and misery since the Great Fire of London'.[48] The quiet generosity and sympathy towards those less fortunate than himself was a hallmark of Bryan Donkin's life.

On 12 November 1845, Bryan Donkin was appointed as a Surrey magistrate.[49] In that capacity, one of his duties was to attend sessions to grant the renewal of victuallers' licenses and discuss complaints and other business of interest to the tradesmen of several parishes; on one day in March 1847 the magistrates, with Donkin among them, met at the Bridge House Hotel and two hundred and four licences were issued.[50] The meeting cannot have been the most exciting of activities, but is indicative of the still lively mind of Bryan Donkin at the age of very nearly seventy nine, as he settled into his retirement.

Numerous advertisements appeared in the newspapers at this time, promoting goods and services from medicinal aids to home helps and newly published books. The spiteful Sir James South, who had been a thorn in Donkin's side with his astronomical telescope, took advantage of this form of publicity to take another swipe at the Royal Society. Masquerading under the soubriquet 'a contributing Fellow of the Royal Society,' South forwarded to the President of the Royal Society an advertisement he had found in *The Times*; he drew the President' s attention to names of Fellows who were mentioned as having an interest in railway companies. South accused the Fellows, one of whom was Donkin, of using the prestige of their FRS to advertise the railway companies, while gaining shares in return. The insult was not taken seriously, and the storm in the teacup blew over.[51]. Sometimes advertisements for products included recommendations from users and notable figures; in his early eighties, Bryan Donkin allowed his name to be listed as giving approval to the Illuminated Glass Company, having tested the process on his astronomical telescope.[52]

In the early 1840s, committees of the Institution of Civil Engineers (where he was Vice President with Cubitt, Field and Palmer) and the London branch of the Phrenological Association (serving alongside phrenology experts Beamish, Combe and Deville) still occupied Bryan Donkin's time.[53] But in 1843, he decided to retire from the post of Vice President of the ICE, and resigned unwillingly from the Council too. The reason he gave was that his advanced age rendered exposure to the evening air dangerous.[54] For nearly twenty years, since the post of Vice President had been inaugurated, he had given his valuable assistance to the Institution, and the Council offered sincere expressions of regret and their thanks, and wished him health and happiness. At the extraordinary General Meeting of the Society of Arts on 1 June 1843, he was present when Prince Albert was elected President after the death of the Duke of Sussex.[55] Three years later, while still one of the sixteen members of the Council of the Royal Society, he was invited to the annual entertainment given by the President, the Marquis of Northampton. The Council, whose Secretary was Dr Peter Roget (at that time preparing his great work, the *Thesaurus*) enjoyed dinner together before joining the throng at a reception in the President's mansion to view an exhibition of inventions and new processes. Later in the evening Prince Albert graced the company with his presence, staying until midnight.[56]

Although nearing retirement, Donkin took out one last patent in 1845 (Patent No.10,932). [57] Great advances had been made in steam train design since their introduction in the previous decade, and Donkin was not alone in suggesting improvements to their design. His idea was for better wheels, and for 'mechanical contrivances' to enable railway carriages to cross from one line to another or into sidings. Unfortunately, he was too late: existing practice and health and safety regulations had ruled out the possibility of his method of switching lines.[58]

Forty years after the foundation of the Bryan Donkin Company, the firm was flourishing. In spite of competition, Donkin's Fourdrinier machines were still coming out of the factory, and mills still needed expert help to expand and repair their machinery and buildings.

Compound-plate printing was in its heyday during the 1840s, using printing plates engraved on Donkin's rose engine lathe. Many private manufacturers of small household goods, such as shoe polish, writing materials and wines, recognised compound-plate printing as an attractive method of safeguarding their products from forgery. Millions of pounds in tax from the sale of duty stamps were amassed by the Government for medicines; there is no doubt that compound-plate printing protected medicine duty labels from forgery for decades, and that in this field alone, the process must be considered a success.[59]

News of the spectacular printing method had reached the Continent too, and several printing companies had taken it up – Didot in Paris, and several in Germany, including Hänel, Naumann, Teubner and Hasper, as well as Haase in Prague.[60] More importantly, the need for the special machinery for printing anti-forgery revenue stamps arose in India. In 1845, the Company sent out the first machine to the Stamp Department in Calcutta, accompanied by William Brewitt from the Bermondsey works, to 'put it up' and set it working – he was given free passage and a good wage. An agreement was made between the Department of Stamps in Bengal and the Bryan Donkin Company to ensure that Brewitt was not out of pocket, and his family was provided for in his absence.[61] A second compound-plate printing machine followed three years later, and several more in subsequent years to Bombay and Calcutta, and to Hyderabad (where the Nizam owned four by the 1880s).[62] In addition, the complicated printing plates were being made and engraved at the works, together with small interchangeable parts for dating the plates and, in 1851, small machines for numbering the printed papers, to add even greater security than the compound-plate printing. Some of these items were sent under 'especial custody', following a robbery at the English Stamp Office.[63] Earlier, a shipment of compound plates for printing, with all their moveable parts, had been sent out to Bengal on the ship *Windsor*, under the special care of the Captain 'to whom you will make an allowance of £5 sterling when delivered in good condition'.[64] As late as 1922, a whole century after the production of the first compound-plate machine, a new one was ordered for the Stamp Office in London, which was in use for printing the duty labels that were stuck round the lids of medicines until 1941.

In 1844, a knowledgeable visitor, Andrew Ure, described his visits to Donkin's workshops. Donkin and Ure knew each other through the Royal Astronomical Society; Ure, ten years younger than Bryan Donkin, was a Scottish scientist, physician, geologist and tireless researcher. His praise for Donkin's workplace was fitting:[65]

> I have never witnessed a more admirable assortment of exquisite and expensive tools, each adapted to perform its part with despatch and mathematical exactness, though I have probably seen the best machine factories of this country and the Continent.

In 1846, Bryan Donkin Senior retired from business, assigning the lease of the factory to his three sons, the freehold being subsequently purchased by Bryan and Thomas.

20

Leaving the Legacy

Things had changed in Sandoe. The Cuthbert family had taken over Beaufront Hall from the Erringtons, and virtually rebuilt it in 1836. When William retired from his job there, Thomas, the youngest Donkin brother, had taken on some of the responsibility of land agent for the estate, making regular visits from Yorkshire to deal with the collection of rents around Sandoe, for many years.[1] He even rented land at Sandoe Green from Mr Cuthbert; although he had made his life in Yorkshire, he had a strong attachment to the family's Northumberland home. William was the only Donkin brother to stay in the Northumberland area where he had been born and brought up.

In his late seventies, Bryan was still able to make the long and arduous journey to Sandoe. In July 1843, he went for a long stay there with Mary Ann and her daughter Alice, fitting in a four-day visit to Tynemouth. In late February of the following year, his brother William (who had lived at the High House with their sister Mary for nearly twenty years) had a stroke, surviving for less than two weeks.[2] The funeral was held on 13 March 1844 and all the siblings attended. Bryan stayed on in Sandoe for nearly a week, then went to Alston for five days with his daughter Maria, returning to stay with Mary for a few days before travelling home to London on April 8th.[3] After William's death, the High House was sold to William Cuthbert of Beaufront; until then it had never been part of the estate, but privately owned by descendants of Henry Tulip and rented to a number of different tenants. Mary moved out after William died, but her busy social life continued in and around Sandoe, with dinner parties, visits and visitors. Mary kept in touch with the Erringtons as well as the newcomers to Beaufront, and had helped young Mr Rowland Stanley Errington (from Henry Errington's side of the family) to buy furniture when he moved into the area, making him a present of some of her china. She continued to write her diary, recording local and family matters until two years before her death at the age of eighty-three.

Of his seven siblings, only four were still alive at the end of 1848, the year when Bryan Donkin turned eighty: Mary, Ann and Jane in Northumberland, and his youngest brother Thomas in Yorkshire. Henry the lawyer had died that year. All Bryan and Mary's children were in their thirties and forties; all but John were to survive their parents.

Bryan was certainly slowing down by the time he was eighty. Old age and ill health were taking their toll, and he had found he no longer had the vigour to take such an active part in the Company, or to continue to attend meetings of the Societies where he had been a member for so long. He resigned altogether from the ICE in the year that he was eighty.[4] However, with his sons running the firm's activities at home and abroad, and a contented home life with Mary and his family around him, he must have felt fulfilled in his last years. Confidence based on honesty had been passed on.

The firm was still not only setting up new paper mills with their machinery, but also advertising for mill managers:[5]

> To paper-makers – WANTED – a thoroughly practical man as manager of a large paper mill erected by Donkin and Co. Must be well acquainted with the manufacture of fancy and other papers, cardboard and colours. Salary £200, and house etc free.

A later advertisement from Bryan Donkin and Co. was seeking a position on behalf of one of their employees: 'a person experienced in the management of both the manufacturing and commercial departments of paper mills at home and abroad'.[6]

A tremendous boost for the country – and in particular its industry and the Donkin Company's part in it – came in 1851, in the shape of the Great Exhibition. Springing from a pilot exhibition run in 1847 by the Royal Society of Arts and taken up with vigour by Prince Albert, the idea of a huge international showcase for manufactured products took hold like wildfire. The time was ripe for London to take centre stage; friendly confidence from other nations and commercial freedom, combined with ease of transport and security for property, ensured a warm welcome for all the countries of the world in this enormous enterprise.[7] Vacant ground was found in Hyde Park and design proposals were sought for the massive building needed to house the exhibition. The Committee (chaired by Donkin's friend William Cubitt) failed to agree on one and instead put forward their own design, for a monstrous brick structure with a dome – but the idea was rejected by the public, led by the local Nimbies, and Paxton stepped in with his glorious design of glass and ironwork. The financial arrangements and contracts were handled by the Royal Society of Arts, backed by donations from all parts of the community: not a penny was paid by Government funding. Regulations and restrictions for exhibitors were worked out and minor disagreements were overcome – about such things as the size of the space allotted to individuals, and special arrangements for unusual products. Duties were agreed for the police and the Metropolitan Fire Brigade; Messrs Schwepps were signed up to supply refreshments. Discounted rail travel and entrance fees were fixed and the opening ceremony was planned. No detail was overlooked; the Crystal Palace was

60 *The Great Exhibition,* 1851.

the first public building to provide toilets for ladies and gentlemen. After only sixteen months of intensive building and planning, the products of over 15,000 manufacturers from all over the world were ready, and everything was in place in the spectacular Crystal Palace for the grand opening by Queen Victoria on 1 May 1851.

The exhibits were divided into four sections: Raw Materials and Produce, Machinery, Manufactures, and Fine Arts (but no paintings), each with its committee; among the committee members of the Machinery section were the old gang: John Rennie, George Herschel, William Cubitt and Isambard Brunel. For each class within the sections was a set of 'jurors' who awarded medals for excellence: in the light of the myriad inventions and multiplicity of diverse artefacts, their brief was tough. In Class 17 of Section III alone, samples of every imaginable kind of paper, printing and bookbinding was on display: decorated and illustrated paper for drawing and writing, paper of every hue and texture; scrap books, card cases, books bound in Morocco or calf and sheep leather; inks for printing, colouring and marking, sealing wax for use in hot climates. There were machines to help the blind to write and for copying music, ornaments for decorating linen and damasks, metallic copy books with pencils, waterproof paper, security paper and paper of every size from foolscap to double elephant.[8] It was noted that the machine that made the great diversity of paper products possible was 'brought to a state of great perfection for Messrs Fourdrinier, by the ingenuity of Mr Bryan Donkin; upon this has been founded the various descriptions of paper-making machines which have since this time been introduced'.[9] By this time, 190 of Donkin's machines had been made, including 83 for Great Britain.[10] And there indeed, on the ground floor of the Exhibition building, stood an intricate model of one of Donkin's latest paper-making machines: 'an elaborate and beautiful model of a complete series of machines, with their appurtenances, for making paper, containing all the latest improvements which he has introduced into this important and valuable branch of manufacturing mechanism.'[11] For this, Bryan Donkin & Co. received the top award, a Council Medal. Oddly enough, Mr Fourdrinier also showed a model of the original patent paper machine, the two versions clearly illustrating the great advances that had been made since Donkin's early experiments.

Also featured in the show were numerous methods of printing, including the artistic products of the compound-plate printing machine first produced at Donkin's works in 1821, using the complex printing plates engraved on the 'rose engine' lathe designed by Bryan Donkin himself. It was noted that John Wilks, who later became Donkin's partner, was the inventor of the unique printing machine that printed the two-colour bank notes, tax stamps and decorative labels.[12] Without doubt, with his own experience of constructing unusual machines for printing, Bryan Donkin had a hand in its design and construction, and the machines were thereafter always built at the Donkin works. Aided by Robert Branston, the printer Charles Whiting, so well known for his top-quality work in colour printing and the only commercial printer in Britain to make use of the compound-plate machine and the rose engine engraving, was given high praise in the reports by the jury of the paper and printing section for his showcase of compound-plate printing, cameo embossing and relief engravings. Placed in the Fine Arts Court, between a plaster model representing 'The Peaceful Arts triumphant over War' and 'A Court Costume', the delicate printed work had clearly become accepted as far more than a method of security printing: compound-plate printing had been elevated to the status of an art form.[13]

At that time Whiting's printing plates were being engraved on the rose engine by Alfred Deacon, the successor to Robert Branston, who had his own business in the City, engraving in copperplate style on 'zinc and brass plates etc'.[14] No mere engraver, he had a go at building a difference engine, a piece of work that did

61 *Donkin's rose engine.*

not go unnoticed by Charles Babbage.[15] After Deacon retired (he died in 1886) rose engine engraving was carried out by two generations of the Kirby family. From 1848, the Donkin Company made big, engraved bronze printing plates and the compound-plate printing machines needed for printing from them, and sent them on the long journey by sea to India, where the bi-coloured images were printed at the top of large sheets of paper for use as legal documents. It was not until the early 1950s that the Bryan Donkin Company discovered that although the two-part plates were still in use, they were being clamped together on ordinary Wharfedale printing presses and inked in black only – what a waste of the hours of toil put in by the Kirby brothers, who had continued with the old methods of production in their secret room in the Donkin works! So the contract ceased. In any case, progress in printing methods eventually caused the demise of the ornate red and black compound-plate printed labels, even on the glass and pottery bottles of Stephens' Ink, remembered by schoolchildren and office workers of the 1940s. (The rose engine was restored in the 1980s and remains, an accolade to Donkin's expertise, in The Science Museum, London.)

Reminders of Donkin's collaboration with John Gamble in the food preservation business were on show in the south gallery of the 1851 exhibition, where John Henry Gamble had a display of cans of processed food, including three canisters of preserved mutton and vegetables from the original factory, dating from 1813.[16] Up-to-date samples from the huge range of Gamble's products were piled up: meat of all kinds, fish, eggs, milk, custard, oysters and many fine foodstuffs, 'the whole preserved so as to keep in any climate and for an unlimited length of time.' Described by the jury as 'very fine samples of preserved viands and vegetables' they gained a second-rank Prize Medal. Also among Gamble's exhibits, as witness to the heroism of the Arctic explorers and to Donkin's skill, was a can, one of a batch of meat brought back from the Arctic by Captain James Ross, after being abandoned in the ice for twenty six years.[17] Among the several hundred canisters of canned food from several countries were Ritchie & McCall's. Their method of preservation was based on the patent originally taken out by the infamous Goldner, whose horrible 'meat' had contributed to the death of many sailors, including John Franklin and his crew in the Arctic. His preserved foods were also exhibited, and gained high praise. By 1851 the art of canning had been mastered, and Ritchie & McCall, too, were awarded a Prize Medal for their excellence of material and preservation.

For Bryan Donkin, nearing the end of his time, the Great Exhibition reflected his life's achievements. Set amidst the vast collection of artefacts presented by the great manufacturers, inventors and artists of the day – great and small from every corner of the world – the Company's contributions were a tribute to their founder's skills and determination.

The work of the factory continued with vigour; Barnard William Farey (nephew of the steam expert, John Farey) had joined the Bryan Donkin Company in 1847 and experimented with improvements to steam engines for the firm; together with Bryan Junior, he patented improvements to the paper machine, which eased the measuring, marking and cutting of paper from the roll.[18] Farey was a real asset: 'an indefatigable scientific worker'. A double cylinder boiler for preparing the rags for paper-making had also been patented by him in 1849.

Bryan must have been sorry to hear of the death in 1853 of Thomas Tredgold Junior, the son of his friend of the same name. After his father's untimely death, the boy had been taken as an apprentice in the Bermondsey works and later sent out to Bombay as a civil engineer to the Stamp Office of the East India Company, where Donkin's compound-plate printing machines were in operation. There they printed the large bi-coloured duty stamps for legal documents, using the two-part printing plates sent by sea from London. Young Thomas Tredgold died in Bombay at the age of twenty eight.[19]

The unexpected death of John Donkin in 1854, from tuberculosis at the early age of fifty-two, was a dreadful sadness to everyone. It was said that he was esteemed for his urbanity and kindness of heart, and his family and wide circle of friends 'deeply regretted' his early death.[20] For the Company, it was a blow; John had been the king pin of the firm, and the impact of his death was surely not negligible. Fortunately, his brothers Bryan and Thomas were by then experienced in running the business, and with Barnard Farey now a partner, the firm was in safe hands in spite of the troubled times for some industrial areas. Disputes between engineers and machinists and their employers gave rise to large numbers

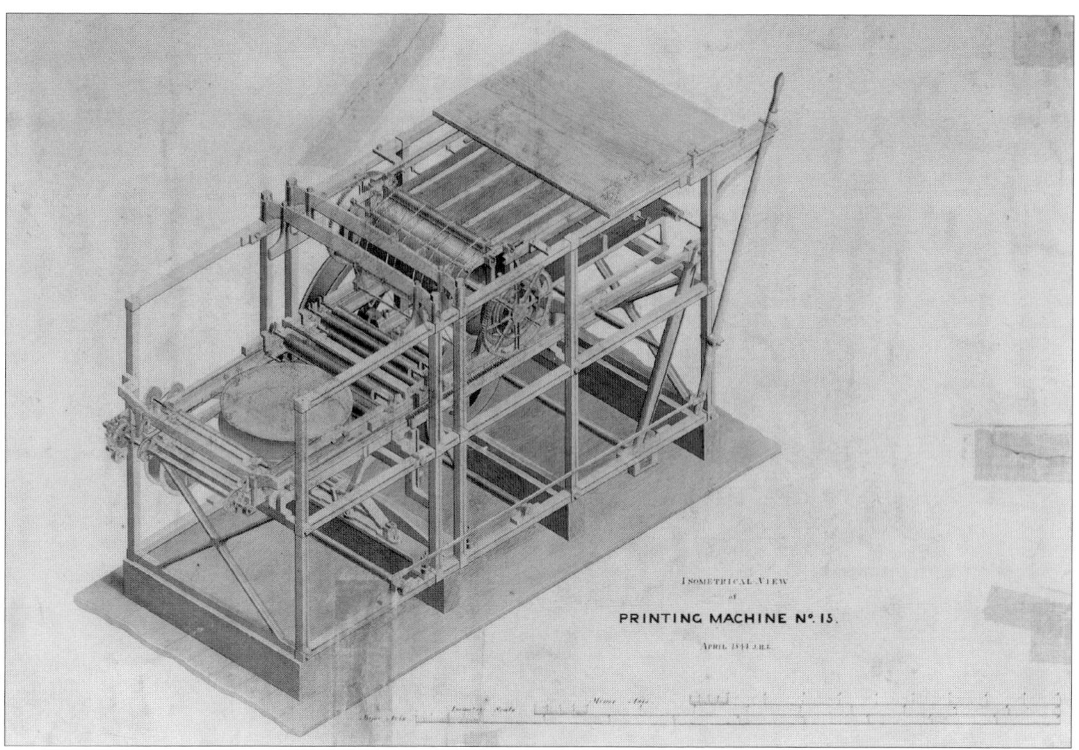

62 *Compound-plate printing machine,* 1844*: isometric view.*

of jobless workers in some towns: in London alone 4-5,000 were out of work in 1850.[21] It seems that, with its excellent reputation and under good management, the Bryan Donkin Company kept its head above water.

In the twilight of his life, Bryan Donkin was reintroduced to calculating machines when, in September 1854, Georg and Edvard Scheutz of Stockholm brought their second prototype to England. It was based on the same principles as Babbage's difference engine, but was much smaller and designed to be driven by a hand crank rather than a steam engine. Although they eventually secured some funding from the Swedish Government, the project had left them desperately short of money.[22] They found an enthusiastic sponsor in Count Pehr Ambjörn Sparre, who saw the sales potential of introducing their machine to the wider scientific market. He had held positions connected with the building of the Göta Canal and had been the superintendant of bank note production at Tumba. In this capacity, he was a frequent visitor to England and in his search for the most up-to-date printing presses and machinery, he had visited a number of the better engineering companies. Prominent among these was of course the Bryan Donkin Company, by now very well established, with an enviable reputation for precision and a strong history of commitment to scientific advancement. Furthermore, the Bryan Donkin dynasty of engineers was now entering its third generation, with the emergence of Bryan Donkin's grandson, the bright young man who would become universally known as the new Bryan Donkin Junior. Sparre made the necessary introductions and the young Donkin, then aged only nineteen, readily made space available at the Bermondsey factory. It was here that the calculating machine was first demonstrated to the British public by William Gravatt. Gravatt, the gentle giant, who had received a formal apprenticeship under Bryan Donkin's guidance, had gone on to make an illustrious career in canal and railway building up and down the country.[23] Now in his late forties, he was back in London, and with his 'well-known mathematical and mechanical acquirements', combined with his enthusiasm for scientific knowledge, he was the ideal man for the job. Bryan Donkin, the founder of the firm, had retired almost a decade earlier, but seeing his grandson working closely with Gravatt, one of his favourite pupils, would have brought great pride and pleasure to the old man's heart.

Very soon after the launch of the calculating machine at Bryan Donkin's factory, Gravatt secured space at the Royal Society, where he demonstrated the engine on many occasions.[24] Amongst the illustrious visitors were Michael Faraday and Charles Wheatstone, the noted physicist; impressed, Wheatstone introduced the inventors to Charles Babbage. At this first meeting Edvard and Georg Scheutz were somewhat taken aback: despite the failure of his own engine, Babbage took up their cause with great enthusiasm and gave tremendous help in promoting the merits of their invention.[25]

Once more short of money, Georg and Edvard appointed Bryan Donkin Junior as their London agent and returned to Stockholm satisfied that he and Gravatt, as joint custodians of the difference engine, would promote their interests. The engine remained at the Royal Society, where Gravatt devoted much of his time putting it through its paces. His work paid off handsomely when, at the end of June 1855, he and Bryan Donkin Junior demonstrated the machine for H.R.H. Prince Albert.[26] Sadly, it was too late for Bryan Donkin to witness the event.

Following this success, the Scheutz engine was taken from London to L'Exposition Universelle in Paris where, once again, Gravatt demonstrated its prowess. With support from Babbage, who was on first name terms with many of the French scientists on the committee, the inventors were awarded a Gold Medal.[27] Their creation was now receiving international recognition, and the sale of this engine to the Dudley Observatory at Albany, New York, gave the Scheutzes hope of a rush of orders from observatories around the world. Edvard Scheutz and Bryan Donkin Junior came to an agreement giving the Bryan Donkin Company the sole right of manufacture, with a sale price of each machine of £1,200: £400 to G. and E. Scheutz, and £800 to the Company. The British Government was approached as the obvious first customer, but after the expensive disaster of Babbage's failed venture, ministers were wary of committing more funds to mechanical calculation. The view was sought of the Royal Society; they were quick to advise that the Scheutz engine had the capacity to make calculations not only for the General Register Office (where it would be housed) but also for the Royal Observatory and the Nautical Almanac office. With this glowing report, the Treasury was convinced and, on 17 December 1857, the Bryan Donkin Company received an order to produce the first and only difference engine.

Nonetheless, there was still a major problem to overcome. In the months between the Paris Exhibition and the first Scheutz engine being shipped to the Dudley observatory, William Gravatt and Edvard Scheutz used the machine to produce a set of specimen tables. Dedicated to the work of Charles Babbage, the tables were printed in large numbers and distributed to serve as a promotional leaflet for the machine. However, Gravatt soon identified severe faults in the printing end of the machine; although faultless mechanical calculation was achieved almost instantaneously, the printer was prone to jamming. As with Babbage's project, the printer proved to be the weak link in the process. Gravatt spent many hours realigning its mechanism and without his expert help, the task might not have been completed. Armed with Gravatt's observations, the young Bryan Donkin improved and beefed up the printing unit of the machine now under construction. The engine was completed, with Bryan Donkin, Jun. feeling generally pleased with his work.[28] It was inspected by the Royal Society, and the taciturn Astronomer Royal, G.B. Airy, who had previously dismissed Babbage's work as 'humbug', declared of Scheutz's machine: 'Its execution is satisfactory in the highest degree, as might be expected from the well-known skills of the constructor'.[29] The Government paid the bill; but once in use, the inherent printing faults became increasingly apparent and no time or funding had been designated for further trials and development. The Bryan Donkin Company had lost £615, and the General Register Office went back quietly to the old method of producing tables.[30] The Scheutz difference engine was stored away, never to be used again.[31] Georg and Edvard could rightly claim for Sweden the honour of creating the first working calculating machine, and similarly, the Bryan Donkin Company had proved its prowess in engineering precision but, without an international market and the money it would bring for improvement and development, the project was doomed to fail. No more commercial difference engines were made.[32]

Bryan Donkin died at home on 27 February 1855, less than a month before his eighty-seventh birthday. The official cause of his death was 'natural decay from extreme age'.[33] His rewarding voyage through life had come to an end. He was buried in Nunhead Cemetery, London.

His sister Mary lived until 1858; Jane had died nine years before her, but Ann outlived all her siblings, reaching the great age of ninety four. 'The last of her branch of the very respectable family of that name, so long resident under the Stanley family … and sister to the late Bryan Donkin, esq, engineer, of London, died at Sandoe Cottage, on the Beaufront estate', wrote the *Gentleman's Magazine*.[34]

Because Donkin was no longer a member of the ICE when he died, no obituary (according to the rules) could be published in their annual publications. It happened that John died only a matter of months before his father, and the writer of John Donkin's obituary chose to include a heartfelt and complimentary tribute to Bryan, praising him as one who would be remembered with affection by those who had the good fortune to enjoy his personal acquaintance, and respected by the world for his uprightness of character and his 'general acquirements as an engineer, and more especially for the improvements introduced by him into the machinery for making paper, and for printing …'.[35] Another obituary singled out some of Donkin's achievements: he had prepared the heavy parts of the zenith micrometer which was made by Troughton for the Royal Observatory; his improvements to printing machinery had maintained his reputation; his preserved foods had added to the safety and comfort of many; he had enjoyed his great interest in astronomy, and he had made an important contribution to science by his dividing machine and his level. Most of all, Donkin's conquest over the difficulty that the original inventor of the paper-making machine had left to him, 'would alone place his name high in the list of useful inventors'.[36]

By the time of his death, Donkin had accumulated quite a collection of scientific instruments; it was said at the time that he had been a good judge of a telescope and owned two of the best that the noted instrument maker Tulley (the elder) had ever made.[37] It was well known that Bryan Donkin would never use an inferior piece of equipment. One of those telescopes was put up for sale at the rooms of the Royal Astronomical Society when Donkin died, at a price of £35.[38] Sixteen other items on sale included instruments made by Troughton – a micrometer, a mountain barometer, a sextant, a theodolite and a pentagraph. One of Donkin's own levels, together with a 30 inch transit was priced at £15; a Simms Y level and a Dollond dynameter were also offered. Together with astronomical instruments made by Simms, a small bust of Troughton was also found among his personal possessions.

Being a man of good sense and sound mind, Bryan had carefully thought out his will, first written almost exactly seven years before he died, when he finally retired from the business. He slightly amended it in a codicil in 1852. His family was well provided for; through hard work and patience, and despite troubled financial periods in his life, Bryan had become a man of means, owning stocks and shares, land and a well-appointed house. His chosen trustees dealt with his will – they were William Day (daughter Mary Ann's husband) and the two eldest brothers, John (who actually died before his father and would have been replaced) and Bryan. They held in trust for Mary the house with its stables, coach house and gardens, to sell if needs be. After Mary's death (or before, with her consent) they were to sell up and the proceeds were to be divided between the sons (or invested for their mother's benefit if she were still alive). Donkin's wife Mary, aged eighty-three when her husband died, inherited all the contents of the house, except the silver plate and linen, which were left to three of the daughters, Sarah, Jane and Maria, who were all still in their fifties and living in their own homes. The three girls were allowed to choose as many books and musical instruments from Bryan's collection as they wanted; the rest of the books and the scientific instruments ('philosophical and astronomical') were left to the sons. Everything else – investments, goods and chattels, effects and personal estate – were bequeathed by Bryan to the three trustees for payment of debts and expenses, the remainder to be held in trust for his sons. No detail of the disposal of his legacy was left in doubt. As an afterthought in the codicil, real estate owned by Bryan Donkin at Mountnessing in Essex passed to his wife until she died, and then to his three younger daughters. Mary Ann's situation as the eldest daughter, married to a well-to-do man already in his early seventies, was different from the spinster sisters'. She was bequeathed no specified items; instead 'as a mark of my affection and regard' she was given the sum of £100. Other bequests of the same value were given to Mary his wife, to William Day, and also to William Vanderwall, clerk to the Company 'as a mark of my regard'.

Bryan's son William did not figure in the will at all. Poor unfortunate William, whose life seems to have been such a disappointment, was still alive, but for many years had been living in Grove Hall, Fairfield Road, in Bow in East London. The once grand house, formerly a school, was now a 'Metropolitan Licenced House'; to put it bluntly – a lunatic asylum. The majority of the inmates were paupers, many of them ex-soldiers, but a small number of male private patients were also admitted.[39] The owner, Edward Byas, updated the building in 1864 by purchasing seven acres of adjoining land and building a good-sized dining room, a billiard room, a dormitory, several single bedrooms and a large bathroom for the male private patients. The atmosphere was orderly; some of the patients were allowed out beyond the gate; nearly all the soldiers were taken to play football and cricket in the park. Others went on trips to Crystal Palace and Kew Gardens, and a few even enjoyed trips to the theatre. To entertain the patients, some of the attendants had learnt to play musical instruments, and formed a band. The inspectors were happy with Grove Hall. Conditions there were relatively humane, but who knows what private torments William suffered? Surely his father, who had loved and worried about William, must have done what he could for him. As the crow flies, William's close-knit family was within easy reach, and perhaps they were able to visit him. Perhaps, though, William's mental affliction had somehow caused an irreparable rift: the truth is hard to guess. It fell to his brother Henry to sort out his affairs when poor William died intestate in April 1866.[40] There was little to deal with: the sum total of his effects came to under £300. The cause of his death was given as cerebritis, an inflammation of the brain tissue.

Six months after the death of the founder of the firm, a great misfortune struck.[41] On a Wednesday night, shortly after ten o'clock, a fire started at the factory, causing 'great excitement in the neighbourhood' and considerable loss of property. Fortunately no-one was hurt, but the incident must have caused consternation and distress to the family and workforce: Bryan would have been devastated. The Company came through the disaster, and went from strength to strength. In 1858, the directors of the firm (the two sons, Bryan and Thomas, and Barnard Farey), obtained a huge contract from the Russian Government for the erection of a complete paper mill at St Petersburg, for the manufacture of Russian bank notes and other papers.[42] Besides supplying the paper-making machinery, Donkin & Company supplied and installed a 2,000 horse power steam engine, an up-to-date water supply and a filtration system. The project took more than three years to complete, under the supervision of Bryan Donkin's grandson Bryan, who lived in St Petersberg for many months, enduring the bitter cold.[43] Richard Bowery, sent out with others from Bermondsey to set up the scheme, remained to become general manager, under the Ministry of State Papers.[44]

In Bermondsey, Barnard Farey invented his own steam engine, which was later extensively tested and developed by the youngest Bryan Donkin, grandson of the original Bryan. As Chairman of the Company, grandson Bryan took the firm into the age of gas, carving out a reputation for initiating the excellent systems of gas valves and exhausters that surged into the twentieth century. Thomas Donkin's son, Edwin Bryan, followed his father into the firm and developed the company's interests in the field of gas apparatus.

After a hundred years in Bermondsey, the workforce had grown to two hundred and twenty.[45] The factory moved north in 1902, to take advantage of resources in Chesterfield, Derbyshire – coal, iron and a convenient railway. Workers from the town joined the many skilled men who moved with the firm from London and made their home in Chesterfield, where the firm flourished for more than a century. The 'Donkin roundabout' near the works became a landmark for locals and the firm was one of the largest employers in the town, until it finally closed its doors in 2007, to be replaced by new dwellings and DIY stores. Donkin's rose engine, the geometric lathe that had engraved the printing plates for a century and a half, had been lifted through the roof from its secret garret twenty years earlier, and after restoration, eventually found a retirement home in the Science Museum in London.

It was a far cry from the early days, when Bryan plied his trade as a millwright, struggled with the first prototype of the paper machine, tinkered with pen nibs in a tiny room, and fiddled with boiled meat and tin cans in a cellar. How proud he would have been to realise the long-term impact of his inventions and the continued achievements of the firm, stretching into the twenty-first century! Improved versions of his paper machine, always known as the Fourdrinier, still dominate the paper-making scene. His important work for Telford and the Brunels, his excellent reputation amongst fellow engineers for precision in tool-making and machinery, and the great respect that he gained in his lifetime for efficiency, honesty and decency in business, must have given him personal satisfaction, but little of the lasting fame that he justly deserved. Never a man to blow his own trumpet, his concern was always to treat people fairly, to do a good job and to support his family.

63 *Compound-plate printing machine,* 1902

A few years after Bryan Donkin died, a large engraving was produced to accompany a book of biographies of the *The Distinguished Men of Science of Great Britain, living A.D.*1807-08.[46] One of the fifty-one scientists and engineers depicted was Bryan Donkin. In the illustration were also portraits of the Lunar Men and the luminaries of the 'age of wonder' – Banks, Herschel, Davy and their contemporaries.[47] Some of Donkin's friends and colleagues (Joseph Bramah, Henry Maudslay, John Rennie, Thomas Telford and more) were portrayed, as well as a few of the younger generation, including Isambard Brunel. Each one was a courageous thinker, whose innovations had brought change and progress: Donkin had certainly earned his place among them.

64 *Bryan Donkin's siblings and children.*

References

Notes and Abbreviations

Day Book: In chapters 11- 20, the 'Day book' is referred to (D1851/25). This large handwritten ledger gives details of sales by the Bryan Donkin Company, between 1824 and 1834.

Diaries and letters: many of Bryan Donkin's diaries and letters are available in both handwritten form and as transcripts. See the Derbyshire Record Office catalogue for collection D5029.

BD: Bryan Donkin
DRO: Derbyshire Record Office
NRO: Northumberland Record Office
ICE: Institution of Civil Engineers

Chapter 1: Foundations

1. Anthony Page, *John Jebb and the Enlightenment*, Westport U.S.A: Praeger, 2003, p.44.
2. Geoffrey Beard, *The Work of Robert Adam*, London: John Bartholemew & Son, 1978, pp.41-62 and plates.
3. Jenny Uglow, *The Lunar Men*, London: Faber and Faber, 2002; a detailed account of The Lunar Society and its activities.
4. BD diary, 1790 –1820, DRO: D5029/2/1.
5. Parish records of St John Lee, 1664 –1851 Part I, Hexham Library (microfiche).
6. Letters of attorney for a tenant, NRO: NR 672/A/10/1-75.
7. Lawrence James, *The Middle Class: a History*, London: Hachette Digital, Little Brown Book Group, 2006, p.152.
8. Uncle Donkin's diaries. There are two diaries, in a private collection: (1) 3 July-3 December, 1764 and (2) 26 March 1770-11 March 1771.
9. John Crawford Hodgson, *A History of Northumberland*, Newcastle-upon-Tyne: Andrew Reid & Co., 1897, Vol. IV, Hexhamshire, Part II, p.192.
10. John Donkin to BD, 18 April 1795.
11. List of subscribers, Richard Burn, *Ecclesiastical* Law, London: H.Woodfall and W. Strahan, 1763.
12. From a brief biography written by a member of the family – possibly Caroline Bedford – in 1854 or early 1855. Unpublished, in private collection. The reminiscences of Bryan Donkin's childhood come from the same source.
13. Joseph Banks, during his voyage to the South Seas with Captain Cook, had befriended a young Tahitian man, Omai, who subsequently spent several months in England and became a popular phenomenon in English society. On his return to Tahiti, Joseph Banks presented him several gifts to remind him of England, including an electrical machine. Kathleen Wilson: *A New Imperial History: Culture, Identity and Modernity in Britain and the Empire,* 1660-1840, Cambridge: Cambridge University, 2004, p.328.
14. Joseph Keithley, *The Story of Electrical and Magnetic Measurements*, New York: John Wiley & Sons, 1999, p.46.
15. Gerard L'Etrange Turner, *Nineteenth-century Scientific Instruments*, University of California Press, 1983, p.307.
16. Sylvanus Urban, *Gentleman's Magazine and Historical Review*, London: printed by D. Henry,

1878, pp.462-4.
17. Uncle Donkin's diary (2), 4 July1770.
18. D.W. Smith, 'The Hexham Riot', *Journal of the Northumberland & Durham Family History Society*, Vol. IV, N° 2 January 1980.
19. *An Historical, Topographical and Descriptive View of the County of Northumberland*, ed. Eneas Mackenzie, Berwick-on-Tweed: Mackenzie & Dent, 1825, p.299.
20. Uncle Donkin's diary (2) 13 June 1770 .
21. *The Times*, 19 October 1785.
22. Loose sheet, undated, found in accounts notebook in private collection.
23. *Newcastle Courant*, 16 March and 12 December 1789.
24. *Ibid*, 17 July 1799 John Donkin was named as a Trustee, together with James Liddell, in settling the estate of Adam Wilkinson of Brough in Westmorland.
25. *Newcastle Courant*, 4 July and 1 August 1778, 9 January and 24 July 1779.
26. *Ibid.*,20 December 1794.
27. See Chapter 5.
28. Will of John Donkin, 1793. He died in 1800.
29. Biographical note by a Donkin family member; and letter from Bryan's sister Mary to her niece Mary Ann. Both in private collection. Handwritten note on printed pamphlet from Royal Society (BD's obituary) 1855. Also: BD's sister Mary to her niece Mary, 9 January 1828, in private collection.
30. Sydney B. Donkin, 'Bryan Donkin, F.R.S., M.I.C.E. 1768-1855, *Transactions of the Newcomen Society*, Vol. XXVII, 1949-51, p.85.
31. Uncle Donkin's diary (2).
32. Uncle Donkin's diary (1).
33. H. Pollard, *John Wesley in Northumberland*, London: SPCK, 1949, p.6.
34. Uncle Donkin's diary (2), 4 July 1770
35. *Ibid.*, 2 September 1770.
36. *Thomas Bewick, a Memoir*, ('written by himself'), ed. Ian Bain, Oxford: Oxford University, 1979. Bewick's autobiography (particularly Chapters 1-3) and his engravings provide a detailed impression of the rural life of Northumberland.
37. *Ibid.*, pp.23-4.
38. NRO: 3410/Bell Collection.
39. *1800 Woodcuts by Thomas Bewick and his School*, ed. Blanche Circer, New York: Dover Publications, Inc.1962, plates 123 & 124.
40. *Ibid.*, plates 116, 118 & 124
41. Andrew Biggs Wright, *An Essay towards a History of Hexham*, Alnwick: W. Davidson, 1823, p.207
42. John Sykes, *Local Records, or, Historical Register of Remarkable Events*, Newcastle: printed for John Sykes, 1833, Vol. I, p.286. Henry Donkin, Bryan's brother, was a subscriber to this book.
43. Mr Wooler to John Smeaton, 19 July 1775. NRO: SANT/BEQ/1/4/1.
44. NRO: SANT/BEQ/1/4/1 January 1777.
45. John Millington, *Elements of Civil Engineering*, Philadelphia, USA: J. Dobson, 9, p. v.
46. M.A. Richardson, *The Local Historian's Table Book of Remarkable Occurrences,* Newcastle: M.A. Richardson, 1841, p.233.
47. *Newcastle Courant*, 14 December 1779.
48. University of Newcastle: Structural Images of the North East, online. The buildings were demolished in 1997.
49. NRO: ZHE 68.
50. Wright, pp.27-8. There were thirty two inns and public houses in and around Hexham by 1823.
51. *Newcastle Courant*, 3 September 1796.
52. R. Beilby and T. Bewick, *A General History of Quadrupeds*, Newcastle: S. Hodgson, R. Beilby & T. Bewick, 1792, p.55.
53. John Donkin's evidence in the petition for re-building Hexham Bridge, 27 February 1873. NRO: SANT/BEQ/1/4/1.
54. John Smeaton to Mr Pickernell, 6 June 1782, *Reports of the late John Smeaton, FRS*, London: M. Taylor, 1837, p.343.
55. John Smeaton to Mr Donkin (John), 7 February 1784. ICE: John Smeaton letter books, 1724-92, Vol.II, SM/ML/2/58-64,

56. *Ibid.*, p.18.
57. E.C. Ruddock, *The Foundations of Hexham Bridge*, Dept of Architecture, Edinburgh University, Sept 1977.
58. John Smeaton to John Donkin, 10 March 1785, ICE: Smeaton's Machine Letters II, p.118.
59. Jenny Uglow, *Nature's Engraver; A Life of Thomas Bewick*, London: Faber & Faber, 2006. Bewick's life story is expertly told in this biography.
60. *Bewick, Memoir, op. cit.*, p.xii.
61. See Chapter 7.

CHAPTER 2: FATHER'S FOOTSTEPS

1. Date on BD's Latin book, in private collection.
2. Nicholas Hans, *New Trends in Education in the Eighteenth Century*, London: Routledge, 3rd edn, 2001, p.109.
3. V. Sackville-West, *Knole and the Sackvilles*, London: Earnest Benn, 4th edn, 1958, p.172.
4. *The Letters of Horace Walpole*, ed. Peter Cunningham, London: Richard Bentley, 1857, p.347.
5. Richard Greville-Temple Temple, *The Greville Papers*, ed. William James Smith, London: John Murray, 1853, Vol. IV, pp. 275-7.
6. Sackville-West, pp.174-84.
7. Kent History and Library Centre, Maidstone, (KHLC) U269/A50 Sackville Papers.
8. Sackville-West, p.185.
9. The KHLC holds the copious archives of Knole, including items U269/A47/3 and U269/A50, which are mainly accounts. Numerous bills and other records are kept in U269/A293/1, and others in the U269 series.
10. Mary Donkin to her brother, BD, 29 July 1791.
11. Sackville-West, p.186.
12. KHLC, U269, Sackville papers.
13. *The Penny Cyclopaedia for the Diffusion of Useful Knowledge*, London, Charles Knight & Co., 1841, Vol. XXI, p.145.
14. Letter and draft agreement from R.Whitfield (solicitor) to Bryan Donkin, 27 February 1792, DRO: D/1851/21.
15. R.H. Clapperton, *The Paper-making Machine: its Invention, Evolution and Development*, Oxford: Pergamon, 1967. p.302.
16. John Dunkin, *The History and Antiquities of Dartford*, London: John Russell Smith, 1844, pp.301-3.
17. *Ibid.*, p.260.
18. *Ibid.*, p.295.
19. *Ibid.*, p.322.
20. BD's Recipe Book, 1797-1820, DRO: D5029/2/1.
21. BD's Old Note Book, DRO: D5029/2/3.
22. *Reports for the Society for bettering the condition ... of the Poor*, ed. Sir T. Barnard, London: Becket, 1798, pp.92-4
23. *Biographical Dictionary of Civil Engineers*, ed., A.W. Skempton, London: Thomas Telford, 2002, p.188.
24. Bill, from Mr Brames, 1797, DRO: D5029/33/13.
25. BD's notebook of accounts, 1804-06, DRO: D5029/2/6.
26. BD's Recipe Book, 1795-1820, DRO: D5029/2/1, 21 March 1800.
27. BD's Recipe Book, 27 September 1800.
28. Newcastle Courant, 25 January 1800.
29. Will of John Donkin, 1 October 1793.
30. Thomas Donkin to his brother BD, 11 December 1802, in private collection.
31. *The Farmer's Magazine*, London: Rogerson & Tuxford, 1858, pp.425.
32. E. Mackenzie, *A Descriptive and Historical Account of the Town and County of Newcastle*, Newcastle upon Tyne: Mackenzie and Dent, 1827, p.509. William Ingham was a prominent figure in the medical world. He was instrumental in raising money for a improvements and extensions to the Infirmary in Newcastle, and is known to have received a cheque for £500 from the Duke of Northumberland as the first subscription to the venture.
33. Ann Donkin to her brother BD, 27 June 1805, in private collection.

34. *The Athenaeum*, conducted by J. Aitkin, London: Longman, Hurst, Rees and Orme, M.D., July-December 1808, Vol.1V, p.65.
35. *Journal of Natural Philosophy, Chemistry and the Arts* (Nicholson's Journal), London: Printed for William Nicholson by W. Stratford, 1803, Vol.VI, p.86.
36. DRO: D5029/33/16/17 & 18.
37. The Technical Section of the Paper Makers' Association, *Paper-making: a general Account of its History, Processes, and Applications*, Kenley, Surrey: 1949, printed by William Clowes & Sons, pp.15-16.
38. R.L. Hills, *Papermaking in Britain,* 1488-1988*: A Short History*, London: Athlone, 1988, p.55.
39. *The Universal Magazine*, March, April, May and June, 1762, Vol.XXX, London: John Hinton, 1762. The articles in the magazine came from a translation of Joseph de Lalande's *Art de faire le Papier*, Paris, 1761.
40. Hills, p.58.
41. *Ibid.*, p.34.
42. *Ibid.*, p.59.
43. *Ibid.*, p.61-2.

CHAPTER 3: TRIALS AND TRIUMPHS

1. Ernst Völker, *The Great Dream*, Heidelberg: Gebr. Bellmer, 1998, pp.9-14.
2. R.H. Clapperton, *The Paper-making Machine: its Invention, Evolution and Development,* Oxford: Pergamon, 1967. Clapperton is an extremely well-researched and detailed source of information about the development of the paper-making machine; he had access to material that is no longer available. Many references to the subject in this chapter are from his book.
3. John Gamble, 'The Origin of the Machine for Making Endless Paper, and its Introduction into England', in *Journal of the Society of Arts*, London: George Bell, 1857, Vol.V, p.238.
4. *Ibid.*, 237-9.
5. Clapperton, p.20.
6. Christine Richardson, *James Brindley: Canal Pioneer*, Burton-on-Trent: Waterways World, 2004, p.1.
7. Samuel Smiles, *Lives of Boulton and Watt*, London, John Murray, 1865, p.294.
8. Thomas Crump, *The Age of Steam*, London: Constable & Robinson Ltd, 2007, p.104.
9. Gamble, p.238.
10. Minutes of Proceedings of the Committee to whom was referred the Bill entitled 'An Act for prolonging the Term of certain Letters Patent assigned to Henry Fourdrinier and Sealy Fourdrinier for the Invention of Making Paper by Means of Machines, ordered to be printed 10 August 1807, pp.6-7.
11. Like Clapperton, Hills explains the Robert's machine at length. Richard L.Hills, *Paper Making in Britain,* 1488-1988, London: Athlone, 1988, p.94-9.
12. *Minutes of Proceedings*, 1807, p.7.
13. *Ibid.*, p.8.
14. Clapperton, p.29.
15. James Strachan, 'Notes on the Evolution of the Fourdrinier Paper machine,' *The World's Paper Trade Review*, 27 March 1931, p.1145.
16. BD's Account book, 1804-06, DRO: D5029/2/6.
17. Ann Donkin to BD, 27 June, 1805, in private collection.
18. Joan Evans, *The Endless Web: John Dickinson & Co. Ltd*, London: Jonathan Cape, 1955, p.10.
19. Prospectus of the Patent Machine for Making of Wove Paper, London: Whittingham and Rowland, printers, 1813.
20. Hills, p.103.
21. *Minutes of Proceedings*, 1807, p.11.
22. DRO: BD diary, 1809-10, D5029/1/1: transcript D5029/1/8.
23. BD diary, 1 March 1805, in private collection.
24. Certificate in private collection; on every appraisement carried out, the client had to pay stamp duty, on a rising scale from 2s 6d for a judgment of under £50, to £1 on £500: *The Statutes of the United Kingdom of Great Britain and Ireland*, ed. John Raithby, London: George Eyre & Andrew Strahan, 1816, p.498.
25. See Chapter 4.

26. See Chapter 5.
27. BD Diary, 1810-12, D5029/1/2; transcript D5029/1/9.
28. Clapperton, p.62.
29. *Prospectus of the Patent Machine for making of Wove Paper*, London: Whitham & Rowland, printers.1813. 'This Prospectus is printed upon extra large, thick Post, manufactured by a Machine erected at Mr Buttanshaw's Mill, West Peckham, Kent.' DRO: D029/5/2 (Buttanshaw was a client of Bryan Donkin.)

CHAPTER 4: EBB AND FLOW

1. Southwark Local History Library and Archive, Richard Horwood's map, 4th edn, *c.*1831.
2. Michael Finlay, *Western Writing Implements in the Age of the Quill Pen*, Carlisle: Plains, 1990, p.3.
3. *Ibid.*, pp. 44-5.
4. Henry Bore, *The Story of the Invention of Steel Pens*, London: Perry & Co, 1892, p.30.
5. Sir Daniel Keyte Sandford, Thomas Thomson and Allan Cunningham, *The Popular Encyclopaedia*, Glasgow: Blackie, 1836, p.733.
6. *People, Pens and Production*, ed. Brian Jones, Studley, Warwickshire: Brewin, 2013, pp. 26-7.
7. *The Boston Mechanic and Journal of the Useful Arts and Sciences*, eds. 'Several practical men', Boston: Light & Stearns, 1835, Vol.IV, p.148.
8. 'Donkin's Patent Pens' advertisement, engraved by Rowe & Walter, 1808, in private collection.
9. SLHLA: *Poor Rate book for the parish of St Mary, Bermondsey*, PR 1809-11.
10. Documents in private collection.
11. Draft of auction notice and invoice in DRO: D5029/4/18.
12. DRO D5029/6.
13. Ian McNeil, *Joseph Bramah: A Century of Invention* 1749-1851, Newton Abbot: David and Charles, 1968, pp.134-5.
14. *Ibid.*, p.139.
15. Documents in private collection.
16. G.E. Roe, *Writing Instruments*, G.E. Roe: 1996, p.9.
17. M. Cooper, *Journal of the Writing Equipment Society*, No.28, 1990, p.6.
18. Asa Briggs, *Victorian Things*, London: Batsford, 1988, pp.186-7
19. BD's recipe book 1797-1820, DRO: D5029/2/1.
20. *Encyclopaedia Britannica*, 3rd edn, Edinburgh: printed for A. Bell & Colin Macfarquar, 1797, Vol. IX, Part I, p.237.
21. David Harris, 'Early Portable Copying Machines', *Journal of the Writing Equipment Society*, No.76, pp.10-11.
22. J.H. Andrew, 'The Copying of Engineering Drawings and Documents', *Newcomen Society Transactions*, 1980, Vol. 53, pp. 1-15.
23. BD's Recipe book, DRO: D5029/2/1.
24. Luke Hebert, *The Engineer's and Mechanic's Encyclopaedia*, London: Thomas Kelly, 1836, Vol. II, pp.792-794.
25. *The Times*, 20 December 1800.
26. Hebert, p.794.
27. BD's diary, 24 January 1810, DRO: D5029/1/1.
28. BD's diary, 30 October 1812 DRO: D5029/1/2.
29. BD's diary, 26 April 1813. D5029/ 1/3.
30. Eric Shanes; *The Life and Masterworks of J.M. Turner*, New York: Parkstone International, 2012, p.51.
31. Jonathan Jones, *The Guardian*, 8 December 2001.
32. Deidre Le Faye, *Jane Austen's Letters*, Oxford: University Press, 2011, p.222, Jane Austen to Cassandra Austin, 24 May 1813.
33 David Coke and Alan Borg, *Vauxhall Gardens: A History*, London: Yale University Press, 2011.
34. A Memoir of Zerah Colburn; written by himself, Springfield: G. & C.Merriam, 1833, pp.36-42.
35. John Mortimer, *Zerah Colburn, the Spirit of Darkness*, Bury St. Edmunds: Arima, 2005, p.18.

CHAPTER 5: STRENGTH TO STRENGTH

1. Report of meeting, in private collection.
2. *Manual of the System of the British and Foreign School Society of London*, London: Longman & Co.,

1816: a full account of the ethos of the elementary schools and the methods of teaching reading, writing, arithmetic and needlework.

3. *Report of the Select Committee of the House of Commons appointed to inquire into the Education of the Lower Orders ...*, London: printed for Gale & Fenner, 1816, pp.336-7.
4. BD's diary. 18 October 1809, DRO 5029/1/1.
5. BD's diary, 14 May 1811. DRO: D0529/1/9/2. All other 1811-12 diary entries come from this source.
6. BD's balance sheet, DRO: D1851/22.
7. *Summer Excursions into Kent*, London: William S. Orr & Co, 1847, p.183.
8. Paul Clements, *Marc Isambard Brunel*, London: Longmans, Green & Co.,1970, pps.81-2.
9. *The Penny Magazine*, London: Charles Knight, 1832, Vols. I-II, pp.257-8.
10. Martin Worth, *Sweat and Inspiration*, Stroud: Sutton 1999, p.40.
11. *Mechanics' Magazine*, ed. J.C. Robertson, London: Robertson & Co., 1817, Vol.XLVI, p.304.
12. 'Memoir of Richard Trevithick', *Mechanics Magazine, Museum Register, Journal and Gazette*, 2 January-26 June 1848, XLVI, reprinted from *Civil Engineers Journal*, Vol.11, p.94.
13. Alfred E. Beach, 'A Plan for a Small Brick Tunnel and Peculiar Method of Laying it in The River'. *The Pneumatic Dispatch*, New York: American News Co., 1868, p.58.
14. *The Boston Magazine*, Boston: Gilbert & Dean, 1803, Vol.I, p.151.
15. John I. Hawkins, 'Account of the Mode and Progress of an Experiment for the purpose of ascertaining the Practicability of constructing Cylinders of brickwork, and of depositing them through the Water, on a given spot in the River Thames, at Rotherhithe, with a view to the formation of a Tunnel for Foot Passengers, from Shore to Shore.' *Repertory of Arts, Manufactures and Agriculture*, London: J. Wyatt, 1814, Vol. XXIV, pp.18-26: Hawkins and Wyatt's full account of their plan.
16. Richard Lunniss & Jonathan Baber, *Immersed Tunnels*, Boca Raton, FL, USA: Taylor & Francis, 2013, p.6.
17. Drawing, DRO: D1851/P/4/1.
18. Richard Beamish, *Memoir of the Life of Sir Marc Isambard Brunel*, London: Longman, Green and Roberts, 1862, pp.103-16.
19. *Edinburgh Encyclopaedia* (American Edition), conducted by David Brewster, Philadelphia: Joseph & Edward Parker, 1832, p.8.
20. Paul Clement, *Marc Isambard Brunel*, London: Longmans, Green & Co., 1970, p.49.
21. Drawing, DRO: D1851/P/4/2.
22. BD to Henry Maudslay, 18 July1811. Copy in Science Museum, ref. Field 2/1, Swindon.
23. BD's diary, 10-14 June 1811.
24. BD's diary, 7 November 1811.
25. *The Star*, 6 November 1811.
26. 'Woolf's Patent Steam Engine', *Quarterly Papers on Engineering*, III, London: Johan Weale, 1845, p.38.
27 H.W. Dickinson & Arthur Titley, *Richard Trevithick: the Engineer and the Man*, Cambridge: University Press, 2011 (First edn 1934), p.255.
28. See Chapter 6.
29. See Chapter 7.
30. BD's diary,13 April 1812. The repercussions continued well into May.
31. BD's diary, 25 April 1812.
32. *The Edinburgh Annual Register for* 1812, Edinburgh: John Ballantyne & Co., p.149.
33. BD's diary, 16 May 1812.
34. John Donkin to his brother William (BD's nephews), 22 November 1812, in private collection.
35. Gunther Buttmann, *The Shadow of the Telescope: A Biography of John Herschel*, London: Trinity, 1974, p.6.

CHAPTER 6: HONOURABLE MENTION

1. Sir John Sinclair, Bart, *The Code of Health and Longevity*, London: MacMillan, 1818, p.164.
2. BD diary 'Old Note Book, B.D. Sr.', 1797-1820 , D5029/2/3.
3. Malcolm Summers, *Nicolas Appert*, 1749-1841, Oxford: printed by Parchments, 2009, p.15. Further information on Appert's life comes from this source.

4. *Ibid.*, p.74.
5. Tom Quinn, *The Military's Strangest Campaigns and Characters*, London: Robson, 2006, p.75.
6. Nicholas Appert, 'Method of Preserving Animal and Vegetable Substances for Several Years', *The Tradesman*, London: Sherwood, Neely and Jones, Vol. VI, 1811, p.303.
7. Gordon L. Robertson, *Food Packaging: Principles and Practice;* Florida, USA: CRC, 2006, p.123.
8. *All the Year Round*, a weekly journal conducted by Charles Dickens, London: Chapman & Hall, 1863, Vol. X, p.466.
9. Summers, p.124.
10. Archibald Clow and Nan L.Clow, *The Chemical Revolution*, London: Blatchworth, 1953, p.574.
11. *The Repertory of Arts, Manufactures and Agriculture*, CXII, London: J.Wyatt, Sept. 1811, pp.193-6.
12. Alexander Tilloch, *Philosophical Magazine*, London: Richard Taylor, 1809, Vol. XXXIII, p.208.
13. *Journal of the Society of Arts*, November 1868, XVI, p.745.
14. *Retrospect of Philosophical, Mechanical, Chemical and Agricultural Discoveries*, ed. John Wyatt, London: Sherwood, Neely & Jones, 1812, VII, p.240.
15. BD's diary, 1812. D5029/1/9/2 Experiments and developments were recorded in his diaries by Donkin from April 1812.
16. BD's notebook, 1797-1820, DRO: 5029/2/1.
17. A Retired Officer of the East India Company's Service, *The Friend of Australia*, London: Smith, Elder & Co., 1836, pp.78-9.
18. Donkin Hall & Gamble Prospectus, 1813: 'Messrs Donkin, Hall and Gamble beg leave …'. Three page brochure.
19. BD's diary, 1 July 1813, DRO: D5029/1/3.
20. Summers, pp.136-9.
21. *Ibid.*, pp.182-3.
22. *Ibid.*, pp.140-95.
23. *The Times*, 6 March 1815.
24. *The Times*, 15 August 1815.
25. Otto von Kotzebue, *A Voyage of Discovery*, London: Longman, Hurst, Rees, Orme and Brown, 1821, Vol.I, pp.18-20.
26. Retired Officer, p.77.
27. Captain Basil Hall, *Patchwork*, London: Edward Moxon, 1841, Vol. II, pp.20-2.
28. *The Times*, 3 November 1818.
29. *Encyclopaedia Britannica*, ed. W. Smellie, Edinburgh: Archibald Constable, 1824, Vol.IV, Supplement, p.339.
30. Maurice James Ross, *Polar Pioneers*, Montreal: McGill-Queens University, 1994, p.119.
31. James P. Delgado, *Across the Top of the World*, Vancouver: Douglas and Macintyre, 1999, p.57.
32. Edward Pelham Brenton, N*aval History of Great Britain, from* 1783-1822, London: H. Colburn, 1837, p.323.
33. *Maritime Empires: British Imperial Maritime Trade in the Nineteenth* Century, eds. David Killingray, Margaret Lincoln & Nigel Rigby, Woodbridge, Suffolk: Boydell, 2004, p.87.
34. Retired officer, p.78.
35. Sir John Ross, *Narrative of a Second Voyage in search of a North West Passage*, London: A.W. Webster, 1825, p.108
36. Philip Parker King, Robert Fitzroy & Charles Darwin, *Narrative of the Surveying Voyages of His Majesty's Ships, the Adventure and the Beagle*1839, Vol.I, p.227.
37. Francis Moore, *The Age of Intellect*, London: William Hone, 1819, p.1320.
38. *The English Cyclopaedia of Arts and Sciences*, ed. Charles Knight, London: Bradbury, Evans & Co, 1866, p.392.
39. John Wilson, *John Franklin*, Montreal: XYZ, 2001, p.121.
40. George Dodd, *The Food of London*, London: Longman, Brown, Green and Longman, 1856, p.286.
41. Edmund Burke, *The Annual Register*, London; Longman, Brown, Green and Longman, 1853, p.3.
42. Owen Beattie and John Geiger, *Frozen in Time*, London: Bloomsbury, 2004. The book describes the course of the Franklin expedition, and exhumation and testing by the authors of three bodies found in graves in the ice..
43. William Battersby, 'Identification of the probable source of the lead poisoning observed in

members of the Franklin expedition', *Journal of the Hakluyt Society*, online, September 2008, pp.1-10.

44. Norman Chevers, M.D., *A Treatise in Removable Mitigable Causes of Death*, Calcutta: Bishop's College, 1852, I, p.293 (footnote).
45. Burke, p.3.
46. Charles Knight, *Arts and Sciences*, London: Bradbury, Evans & Co, 1866, p.392: a general account of the history of preserved food that glosses over Goldner's faults.
47. *Hansard's Parliamentary Debates*, 1852, Vol. CXIX, London: Cornelius Buck, pp.438-60.

CHAPTER 7: MAKING IMPRESSIONS

1. Michael Twyman, *Printing* 1770-1970, London: British Library, 1998, p.6.
2. *Ibid.*, pp.50-2.
3. T.C. Hansard, *Typographia*, London: Baldwin, Cradock & Joy, 1825, pp.689-92.
4. *Ibid.*, p.694.
5. BD's Recipe book, DRO: D5029/2/1.
6. *Oxford Dictionary of National Biography*, ed. H.C.G. Matthew & Brian Harrison, Oxford: University Press, 2004, Vol.III, p.372.
7. Joseph Mason, 'The Bacon-Donkin Printing Machine, Norfolk and the Origin of the Rotary Press', *The Journal of the Norfolk Industrial Archaeology Society*, Vol.IX, No.1, 2011, pp.3-12.
8. BD's diary, 6 / 7 October 1809, DRO: D5092/1/1.
9. *Ibid.*, 11 November 1809.
10. Drawings, DRO: D1851/P/2/1 & 2.
11. B&D *Prospectus of a Machine for facilitating and improving The Art of Printing* 1814, *for which Letters Patent have been granted to R.M.Bacon of Norwich and Bryan Donkin, of Bermondsey*, Cambridge: printed by the machine at the University Press, by John Smith, 1814, p.6. DRO: D5029/9/1.
12. Prospectus, p.11.
13. Document in private collection.
14. BD's diary, 16/17/18 February 1814, DRO: D5029/1/3.
15. From the above Prospectus: 'Some of the first Impressions from a Stereotype plate taken by Bacon & Donkin's printing machine at the University Printing Office, Cambridge, before the Gentlemen of the Syndicate. 28 February 1814'. DRO: D5029/9/1.
16. Description by R.M. Bacon of the Bacon and Donkin printing machine in The *Norwich Mercury* 3 *December* 1814, quoting an extract from *The Times* 29 November 1814.
17. Abraham Rees, *The Cyclopaedia, or Universal Dictionary*, London, Longman, Hurst, Rees, Orme & Brown, 1819, Vol.XXXIV, p.3T2 and Plate III.
18. *Bury and Norwich Post*, 7 December 1814, quoting from the Prospectus published by Donkin and Bacon.
19. Hansard, pp.700-1.
20. BD's diary, 17 February, 1814.
21. BD to unknown recipient, 28 October 1816, DRO: D1851/7.
22. Lesley Howsam, *Cheap Bibles: Nineteenth Century Publishing and the BFBS*, Cambridge: University Press, 2002, p.88.
23. Mason, p.8.
24. BD's letters to his wife Mary, family members, Bacon and others, 1816-17, DRO: D5029/3/12. Transcripts of letters of these dates are from this source.
25. Howsam, pp.88-90.
26. Mason, pp.6-7.
27. BD's diary, 30 August 1816. DRO: D5029/1/5.
28. Rees's *Cyclopaedia*, Vol. XXXIV, p. STE.
29. Karl-Eugen Kurrer, H*istory of the Theory of Structures*, Hoboken, N.J. USA, John Wiley & Sons, p.312.
30. Diary entries and letters between Bryan Donkin, and Bacon, Wilkin and both solicitors, elucidate the sorry state of affairs for Bryan, from May 1816 into 1817, DRO: D5029/1/5 (diary) & D5029/3/18/2-3 (letters).
31. BD to Simon Wilkin, 3 August 1816.
32. BD to Maria Dobson, 9 September 1816.

33. BD's diary, 11 &12 September 1816, and BD to Maria Dobson, 19 September 1816.
34. BD to Maria Dobson, 9 September 1816.
35. See Chapter 10.
36. Cambridge University Library: UA Pr.V8: *Minutes of Syndicate*, 13 Nov 1846.
37. *Exhibition of the Works of Industry of All Nations: Reports by the Jurors*, London: Spicer Bros., 1851, p.413.
38. James Moran, *Printing Presses: the History and Development from the Fifteenth Century to Modern Times*, Berkeley and Los Angeles: University of California, 1973, p.107.
39. *Reports by the Juries on the Subjects in the Thirty classes into which the Exhibition was divided*, London: printed for the Royal Commission by William Clowes & Sons, 1852 (Presentation Copy), p.413.
40. Hansard, p.837.
41. Hansard, p.699.
42. BD to Charles Brightley, 15 July 1818, DRO: D5029/3/18/3.
43. BD to Charles Brightley, 2 September 1818.
44. C.H. Timperley, *A Dictionary of Printers and Printing*, London: H. Johnson, 1839, p.879.
45. Full details of the development and process of compound-plate printing are to be found in *Compound-plate printing: A Study of a Nineteenth Century Colour Printing Process*, Maureen Greenland (PhD thesis), University of Reading 1996. Details not otherwise referenced are from this source.
46. *Dictionary of National Biography*, p.940-43.
47. Drawings, DRO: D1851/P/2/8-10.
48. For details of the arguments for and against the Congreve method, and Perkins's, see Greenland, *Compound-plate Printing*, pp.41-4 & 188-90.
49. *The London Journal of Arts and Sciences*, London: Sherwood, Neely & Jones, 1820, Vol.I, pps.102-8
50. References regarding work carried out at the Excise Office at the Bryan Donkin factory and by his men are to be found in the Day Book, pp.21, 81-92, 99-100, and 347-57.
51. Day Book, pps.143-50.
52. Sketch of the motions of the Congreve Press, 1835, DRO: D1851/P/2/7.
53. Day Book, p.247.
54. *Sixteenth Report of the Commissioners of Enquiry into the Collection and Management of the revenue arising in Ireland, Scotland, etc.*, Ireland: Stamp Revenue, ordered to be printed 4 February 1828, Appendix No.9, pp.69-71.
55. DRO: D1851/P/2/5.
56. *Ibid.*, p.11.

CHAPTER 8: BODY AND MIND

1. *Cambridge Illustrated History of Medicine*, ed. Roy Porter, Cambridge: University Press, 3rd. edn, 2006, p.126.
2. *Ibid.*, p.6.
3. *Ibid.*, p.41.
4. Mary Donkin's diary, 19 March 1847, in private collection.
5. *Medieval Medicine: a Reader*, ed. Faith Wallis, Toronto: University Press, 2010, pp.113 & 367.
6. *Ibid.*, pp.30 & 428.
7. Elizabeth Bennion, *Antique Medical Instruments*, London: Sotheby Parke Bernet, 1979, p.48.
8. Mrs Isabella Beeton, *The Book of Household Management*, London: S.O.Beeton, 1861, p.1065.
9. Mary Donkin's diary, 24 June 1830.
10. *New Monthly Magazine*, London: Henry Colburn, 1820, Vol. XIII, p.249.
11. Andreas Michalson & Manfred Roth, *Medicinal Leech Therapy*, Stuttgart: Georg Thiemer, 2007 (translated from Blutegelthaerapie by Suzyon O'Neal Wandrey, 2006), pp.8-9.
12. Mary Donkin's diary, 20 February 1824.
13. *Ibid.*, 7 July 1837 & 22 December 1842.
14. *Cambridge Illustrated History*, p.124.
15. *Ibid.*, p.134.
16. Mrs Beeton, p.1084.

17. Frances Moore, *The Age of Intellect or, Clerical Showfolk and Wonderful Layfolk*, London: William Hone, 1819, p.175. William Hone was a satirist. 'Frances Moore' was probably a pseudonym.
18. Mary Donkin to her brother BD, 29 July 1791, in private collection.
19. *The Quarterly Review*, London: J. Murray, 1815, p.365.
20. Sir Walter Scott, *The Complete Works of Sir Walter Scott, with a Biography*, New York: Conner & Cooke, 1833, pp.31, 551.
21. Graham's questionable remedies are detailed by Lydia Syson: *Doctor of Love: James Graham and his Celestial Bed*, Richmond, Surrey: Alma, 2008.
22. Poem, anon *from Guide to Gilsland*, Robert Ward, Dumfries: Anderson and Son, 1860, p.8.
23. *Ibid.*, pp.4-13.
24. A.B. Granville, M.D., F.R.S., *The Spas of England*, London: Henry Colburn, 1841, pp.306 & 313.
25. *Ibid.*, p.315.
26. *Ibid*, p.321.
27. *Cambridge Illustrated History*, p.309.
28. BD's recipe book, DRO, D5029/2/1.
29. *The Age of Intellect*, p.116.
30. John Abernethy, *The Surgical Works*, London: Longman, 1811, pp.15-16.
31. Mary Donkin's diary, 5 May 1828.
32. BD to Mary Ann, 8 June 1815, DRO: D1851/Box 19/ item 4, 1815.
33. Ray Merrill, *Introduction to Epidemiology*, London: Jones & Bartlett, 2010, p.27.
34. *Edinburgh Medical and Surgical Journal*, London: Longman, Hurst, Rees,& Orme; and John Murray, 1805, Vol.I, p.513.
35. BD to James Swann, 27 May 1817, DRO: D5029/3/18/2.
36. *Ralph Fletcher*, 'Medico-chirurgical Notes and Illustrations, Part I,' *Medico-Chirurgical Review*, ed. James Johnson, M.D. New York: (republished) Richard & George S.Wood, 1831, Vol. XV, p.364.
37. P.V. Renouard, *The History of Medicine* (first published 1856), translated by Cornelius G. Comegrys, Philadelphia: Lindsay & Blakiston, 1867, p.x.
38. Robert M.L.Winston, *The Human Mind*, London: Transworld, 2003, pp.23-4.
39. Derek Hodson & Bob Prophet, 'A bumpy start to science education', *New Scientist*, London: IPC magazines, No.1521, 14 August 1986, p.26.
40. John Timbs, *Knowledge for the Times: A Manual*, London: Lockwood & Co, 1864, pp.254-5.
41. BD to W. Stark, 21 September 1816, DRO: D5029/3/18/1.
42. BD to Mr Gold, 23 Jan 1817, DRO: D5029/3/2.
43. BD to his wife Mary, 16 November 1816, DRO: D5029/3/18/1.
44. Engraving by J. Egan, after a painting by W. Yellowlees.
45. Michael Twyman, *Printing* 1770-1970, London: British Library, 2nd edn, 1998, p.52.
46 BD to Mr König, 24 January 1817, DRO: D5029/3/18/2.
47. BD to Mr König, 7 February 1817, DRO: D5029/3/18/2.
48. BD to Mr Barton, 20 February 1817, DRO: D5029/3/18/2.
49. *The Age of Intellect*, pp.117-18.
50. George Man Burrows & Anthony Todd Thomson, *The London Medical Repository*, Vol. XIII, p.4.
51. BD to Spurzheim, 31 July 1818, in private collection.
52. BD to Spurzheim, 3 November 1818, DRO: D5029/3/18/3.
53. BD to Spurzheim, 29 December 1818. DRO: D5029/3/18/3.
54. e.g. BD to his son William, 29 December 1818, DRO: D5029/3/18/3.
55. Combe to BD, 22 June 1821, in private collection.
56. Mary Donkin's diary, 1 October 1835, in private collection.
57. *Encyclopedia of Romanticism (Routledge Revivals) Culture in Britain*, 1780s-1830s, ed. Laura Dabundo, Oxford: Routledge, 2009, p.455.
58. Winston: p.36.
59. *Ibid.*, pp.15-16.
60. *The Phrenological Journal*, London: A. Spotiswoode, 1841, p.191.
61. *Ibid.*, p.338.
62. O.S. & L.N. Fowler, *New Illustrated Self-Instructor in Phrenology and Physiology*, London: W. Tweedie, 1867.

63. Steven Weisler & Slavoljub P. Milekic, *Theory of Language*, Massachusetts: Institute of Technology, 2000, p.281.

Chapter 9: Connections

1. Margery Purver, *The Royal Society: Concept and Creation*, London: Routledge, 2013, pp.82, 95-8.
2. John Hill, M.D. *A Review of the Works of the Royal Society of London*, London: R.Griffiths, 1751.
3. Max Louis Kent, *British Enlightenment and the Spirit of the Industrial Revolution: the Society of the Encouragement of the Arts, Manufactures and Commerce*, Ann Arbor, MI, USA: Proquest Information and Learning Company, 2008, p.190.
4. RSA membership election letter, 31 October 1804; in private collection.
5. John Smeaton, *Reports of the late John Smeaton, FRS, London*:. M.Taylor, 1837, Introductory remarks to 2nd edn, p.xxi-xxii.
6. Sydney B. Donkin 'Bryan Donkin, F.R.S., M.I.C.E. 1768-1855', *Transactions of the Newcomen Society*, Vol. XVII, 1949-1951, p.93.
7. J.M. Thomas, *Michael Faraday and the Royal Institution; The Genius of Man and Place*, New York: Taylor & Francis, 1991, p.192.
8. BD's diary, 30 June 1813, DRO:D5029/1/3.
9. BD's diary, 1813, D5029/1/3.
10. Richard Beamish, M*emoirs of the Life of Sir Marc Isambard Brunel*, London: Longman, Green, Longman & Roberts, 1862, pp.131-9.
11. *Repertory of Arts, Manufactures and Agriculture*, London: J.Wyatt, 1811, Vol. XIX. pp.346-7.
12. William Pole, *A Treatise on the Cornish Pumping Engine*, in two parts, London: John Weal, 1844, p.41.
13. The nice Mr Phillips unfortunately later went bankrupt, still owing the Fourdriniers between £2,000 and £3,000, thereby contributing to their downfall. *House of Commons Papers*, Report from the Select Committee on Fourdriniers Patent, Vol.20, 1 June 1837, p.4.
14. William Henry Bayley Webster, *The Recurring Monthly Periods and Periodic System of the Atmospheric Actions*, London: Simpkin & Marshall, 1857, pp. 42-8.
15. 'Biographies of Geologists', *Essays on the History of Geology*, ed. George Willard White & Claude C. Aubritton, North Stratford, NH, USA: Ayer, p.289.
16. BD to Westgarth Forster, and to Mrs Patterson, 4 June 1816, DRO: D5029/3/18/1-3.
17. *Monthly Magazine*, London: Sherwood, Gilbert & Piper, 1819. Vol. 47, March 1819, p.160.
18. BD to Mr Hutchinson. 13 January, 1817, DRO: D5029/3/18/1-3.
19. *Morning Chronicle*, 26 May 1817.
20. Alexander Tilloch, *Philosophical Magazine*, London: printed by R. Taylor & Co, 1806, Vol.XXV, p.191.
21. BD's diary, 13 May 1806, in private collection.
22. Joseph Wickham Roe, *English and American Tool Builders*, Yale: University Press,1919, reprinted Read Books, 2010, pp.33-5.
23. Skempton, p.436.
24. *Ibid.*, pp.185-6.
25. *The Monthly Magazine*, London: R. Phillips, 1820, Vol.L, p.369.
26. Skempton, p.188.
27. John Booker, *Essex and the Industrial Revolution*, Essex County Council, 1974, p.129.
28. *Minutes of the Proceedings of the Institution of Civil Engineers*, London. ICE, 1867. Vol. XXVI, pp.565-75.
29. See Chapter 15.
30. *The London and Edinburgh Philosophical Magazine and Journal of Science*, London: printed by R. and J.E. Taylor, 1834, Vol.IV, pp.394-5.
31. British Library: Additional manuscripts, *Babbage Letters*, Vol.VI (37183), nos. 415 & 418.
32. Ian McNeil, *Joseph Bramah: a Century of Invention 1749–1851*, Newton Abbot: David and Charles, 1968, p.175.
33. Skempton, p.156.
34. E.g. Report of meeting in *Morning Post*, 27 January 1837, mentioning BD in the Chair.
35. *Morning Chronicle*, 11 February 1823.
36. Hermione Hobhouse, *The Crystal Palace and the Great Exhibition*, London: A.& C.Black, 2002, p.76.

37. *Proceedings of the Royal Society of London*, London: Taylor & Francis, 1863, Vol.XII, p.iv.
38. Thomas Telford to BD, 31 December, 1832, in private collection.
39. Lecture IV, 'On the Progress of Civil and Mechanical Engineering during the Present Century', William Fairbairn, *Useful Information for Engineers*, London: Longman, Green, Longman & Roberts, 1860, p.211.

Chapter 10: Full Steam Ahead

1. BD to Henry Donkin, 4 June 1816, DRO: D5029/3/18/1.
2. BD to his brother Henry, 4 June 1816, DRO: D5029/3/18/1.
3. BD to his brother Henry, 4 January 1817, DRO: D5029/3/18/2.
4. Boulton and Watt to Donkin, 14 November 1815, in private collection.
5. BD to Thomas Telford, 5 September 1816, DRO: D5029/3/18/1.
6. BD to his brother Henry, 21 September 1816, DRO: D5029/3/18/1.
7. *The Mariner's Mirror*, London: Society for Nautical Research, 1964, p.68.
8. John Leather, *The Gaff Rig Handbook*, London, Allard Coles Nautical, 2012, p.99.
9. BD to wife Mary, 30 September 1816, DRO, D5029/3/18/1.
10. BD to his brother Thomas, 4 January 1817, DRO: D5029/3/18/2.
11. *The Civil Engineer and Architect's Journal*, 1839, Vol. II 1839, London: H. Hooper & others, pp.9-11.
12. *The Civil Engineer and Architect's Journal*, London: R. Groombridge, 1843, Vol.VI, p.16.
13. Walter Elliott, 'Description of a steam engine used upon the Caledonian Canal', *Minutes of Proceedings*, London: Institution of Civil Engineers, 1842, p.149.
14. *Transactions of the Newcomen Society for the Study of the History of Engineering and Technology*, Newcomen Society, 1956, Vol. XXVII, p.9.
15. Elliot, p.149.
16. 'Thirteenth Report of the Commissioners for making and maintaining the Caledonian Canal', *House of Commons Papers*, London: Ordered by the House of Commons to be printed, 24 May 1816, p.9.
17. Elliot, p.150.
18. 'Nineteenth Report of the Commissioners for the Caledonian Canal', *House of Commons Papers*, 1822, Vol. VIII, p.25, Appendix D.
19. A.W. Skempton, *Biographical Dictionary of Civil Engineers*, London: Thomas Telford, 2002, p.189.
20. BD to Mary Donkin, 28 October, 1816, DRO: D5029/3/18/1.
21. BD to his sister Ann, 16 November 1816, DRO: D5029/3 18/1.
22. BD to his wife Mary, 16 November 1816, DRO: D5029/3/18/1.
23. H.H. Lamb, *Climate, History and the Modern* World, London: Routledge, 2nd edn, 1995, p.298.
24. BD to Robert Hutchinson, 13 January 1817, DRO D5029/3/2.
25. Angus M. Gunn, *Encyclopaedia of Disasters*, Westport, USA: Greenwood, 2008, p.99.
26. BD to Mary Donkin, 25 November 1816, DRO: D5029/3/18/1.
27. BD to his brother Henry, 1 January 1817, DRO: D5029/3/18/2.
28. BD to Fenton, Murray & Wood, 30 September 1815, DRO: D1851/Box 19/item 4, 1815.
29. BD to one of his sisters, 25 December 1816, DRO: D5029/3/18/1.
30. R.H. Clapperton, *The Paper-making Machine: its Invention, Evolution and Development*, Oxford: Pergamon, 1967, p.75.
31. BD to one of his sisters, 25 December 1816, DRO: D5029/3/18/1.
32. BD to daughter Maria, 1 January 1817: D5029/3/18/2.
33. BD to his brother Henry Donkin, 1 January 1817, DRO: D5029/3/18/2.
34. BD to his brother Thomas, 4 January 1817, DRO: D5029/3/18/2.
35. Alex Werner, 'Scaling London's early 19th Century Docks, Bridges and Manufactories: Charles Dupin's Writings and Technological Exchange' *Documents pour l'Histoire des Technique*, 19, 2e semestre, 2010, p.2.
36. *Report from the Select Committee appointed to consider the means of improving and maintaining the Foreign Trade of the Country*, London: House of Commons, 1823, pp.19-20.
37. *Ibid.*, pp.3-4.
38. 'The West India Dock Sheds', *Survey of London*, ed. Hermione Hobhouse, Vols. XLIII & XLIV, London: Royal Commission on the Historic Monuments of England, 1994, p.305.
39. Sir David Brewster, *The Edinburgh Encyclopaedia*, Philadelphia USA: Joseph Parker, 1st American edn., 1832, Vol.XVII, p.245.

40. Rev. C.C. Clarke, *The Hundred Wonders of the World*, 8th edn, London: T. Hansard, 1817, p.636.
41. George Dodd, *An Historical and Explanatory Dissertation on Steam Engines and Steam Packets*, London: James Asperne, M. Richardson & Co; R. Ackermann; N. Hailes, 1818, p.xiii.
42. Richard Beamish, *Memoir in the Life of Marc Isambard Brunel*, London: Longman, Green & Roberts, 1862, p.141-2.
43. Dodd, p.xiv.
44. R.B. Watts, *The Margate Steam Yachts' Guide*, London: printed by Joseph Mallett, 1820, p.12-13.
45. *The Repository of Arts, Literature, Fashions, Manufactures ... etc*, London: R. Ackerman, 1819, 2nd series, Vol.VIII, Plate III and p.62.
46. Henry Maudslay, *To the Proprietors of The London Engineer Steam Yacht'*, London: printed for Henry Maudslay by Strahan & Spottiswoode, 1819.
47. BD to Maria, 19 Sept 1816, DRO: D5029/3/18/1.
48. Clarke, p.637-8.
49. BD to his brother Thomas, January 4th 1817, DRO: D5029/3/18/2.
50. *Morning Chronicle*, 17 April 1818.
51. *The New Monthly Magazine and Universal Register*, London: H. Colburn, 1817, Vol.VII, p.368.
52. BD to his brother Henry, 12 April 1817, DRO: D1851, Box 19, item 12.
53. Dodd, 1818, p.xxiv.
54. *The Monthly Magazine; or British Register*, Vol. XLIII, Part I, London, printed by J. Adlard. 1817, p.381.
55. *Report from the Select Committee on Steam Boats, etc.*, London: House of Commons, June 24, 1817, pp.5-10.
56. Francis Trevithick, *Life of Richard Trevithick*, London: Spon, 1872, Vol.I. p.200.
57. *Fifth Report of the Select Committee on the Roads from London to Holyhead ... Steam boats, etc*, London: printed by the House of Commons, 12 June 1822, p.124-9.
58. BD to Thomas Telford, 7 February 1817, DRO: D5029/3/18/2.

CHAPTER 11: INNOVATIONS

1. *Morning Chronicle*, 30 September 1822. Great Surrey Street changed its name to Blackfriars Road in 1829; information from London Metropolitan Archives.
2. Charles Babbage, *On the Economy of Machinery and Manufactures*, London: Charles Knight, 1832, pp.77-8.
3. (The late) Charles Holtzapffel, *Turning and Mechanical Manipulation*, London: Holtzapffel, 1850, Vol.I, p.843
4. *Cyclopaedia of Useful Arts*, ed. Charles Tomlinson, London: J.S.Virtue, 1852, p.861.
5. Day Book, pp.8, 579 & 588. See Chapter 16.
6. Day Book, p.574
7. Day Book, p. 59.
8. Day Book, pp.69, 66.
9. Day Book, pp.80 & 107.
10. V.H. Hewitt & John Keyworth, *As Good as Gold: Three Hundred years of British Bank Note Design*, London: Trustees of the British Museum and the Governor and Company of the Bank of England, 1987, pp.54-5.
11. *Minutes of Proceedings*, Session 1842, Institution of Civil Engineers, London: ICE, 1842, p.166-7.
12. *Transactions of the Society at London for the Encouragement of Arts, Manufactures and Commerce*, 1820, Vols.XXXVII-XXXVIII, p.x.
13. *Ibid.*, p.116.
14. *Ibid.*, p.234.
15. Charles Babbage, *On the Economy of Machinery and Manufactures*, London: Charles Knight, 1833, p.39.
16. *The Times*, 2 June 1819.
17. *London Journal of Arts and Sciences*, London: Sherwood, Neely and Jones, 1820, Vol.I, p.5.
18. 'An Account of some Experiments made in 1823 and 1824, for determining the Quantity of Water flowing through different shaped Orifices, by Bryan Donkin, esq, F.R.A.S., V.P. Inst. C.E, Transactions' in *Transactions of the Institution of Civil Engineers*, Vol. I, London: John Weale, 1836, Vol. pp. 215-18.

19. *Mechanics' Magazine*, New York: Printed for the Proprietors, D.K.Minor & George C.Schaeffer, 1837, Vol.IX, No.5, April 1837 (from Transactions of the ICE), pp.273-5.
20. Zachary Alden Smith, *Renewable and Alternative Energy Resources: a Reference Handbook*, Katrina D. Taylor, ABC-It CLIO, 2008, p.164.
21. *The Banker's Magazine*. ed. J. Smith Homans, New York: J. Smith Homans, 1855, Vol. IV, p. 693.
22. Patent and Drawings, DRO: D1851/P/4/13-14, dated 7 Nov 1823.
23. BD to Mrs Maria Dobson, 6 March1817, DRO: D5029/3/18/2 diary 1817.
24. John Loudon McAdam, *Report of the Select Committee on the Highways of the Kingdom, from Remarks on the Present System of Roadmaking*, London: Longman, Hurst, Rees, Orme and Brown, 1821, pp.61-96.
25. *Ibid.*, p.98.
26. Sidney M. Levy, *Public-private Partnerships*, Reston, Virginia, USA: American Society of Civil Engineers, 2011, p.85.
27. *A Paper on Pavements, read before the Institution of Civil Engineers, on the Construction of Carriageway Pavements*, by Bryan Donkin, Civil Engineer, 1824. DRO: D5029/7/2.
28. Sir Henry Parnell, *A Treatise on Roads ... made use of by Thomas Telford, Esq. On the Holyhead Road*, London: Longman, Rees, Orme, Brown, Green & Longman, 1833, pp. 92 & 98.
29. *Minutes of Proceedings of the Institution of Civil Engineers*, ed. Charles Manby, London: ICE, 1852, Vol. XI, pp. 100-102.
30. *A Treatise on the Steam Engine*, John Farey, London: Longman, Rees. Orme, Brown and Green, 1827.
31. R*eport from the Select Committee on the Law relative to Patents for Inventions*, London: House of Commons, 12 June, 1829.
32. A.W. Skempton, *Biographical Dictionary of Civil Engineers*, p.223.
33. *Newton's London Journal of Arts and Sciences*, London: Newton & Son, 1857, Vol.I, p.67.
34. Elizabeth H. Oakes, *A-Z of STS Scientists*, New York: Facts on File, Inc, 2009, p.125.
35. *Transactions of the Society of Arts, Manufactures and Commerce*, London: sold by the Housekeeper at the Society's House, 1823, Vol.XLI, pp.124-160, & Plate XI.
36. Day Book, p.139.
37. Day Book, p. 32.
38. Thomas Webster and Mrs William Parkes, *An Encyclopaedia of Domestic Economy*, New York: Harper and Brothers, 1855, p.307. The word 'britska' or ' brizka' originates from the Polish word 'bryczka', or 'little cart', but it was far from little: it was a long, four-wheeled horse-drawn vehicle with seats facing to the front and back, and big enough for a bed. Isambard Kingdom Brunel commissioned one to sleep in when travelling long distances.
39. Letter (10 December 1833) from John Lewthwaite to *The Nautical Magazine*, London: Simplon & Marshall, 1834, Vol.III, p.48-9.
40. Day Book, p.126.
41. Sir Robert Christison, a noted Scottish surgeon, was asked in 1831 to provide a harpoon to kill whales quickly; he produced one charged with prussic acid which was used in 1833 with such appalling effects that the sailors refused to repeat the process. *Principles and Methods of Toxicology*, ed. A. Wallace. Hayes, New York: Informa Health Care, inc., 2008, fifth edition, p.25. In 1835, an American, Dexter N. Chamberlain tried to patent the use of prussic acid in harpoons, but was told that the idea was not new. *Journal of the Franklin Institute*, Philadelphia: Franklin Institute, 1836, Vol. XVII, p.200.
42. Day Book, pp.67 & 75.
43. Day Book, p.142.
44. *Iron: An Illustrated Weekly Journal for Iron and Steel*, ed. Sholto Percy, London: Knight & Lacey, 1824, pp.15 & 34; also Day Book, p.133.
45. Day Book, p.282.
46. See George Escol Sellers, *Early Engineering Reminiscences* 1815-40, ed. Eugene S. Ferguson. Washington: Smithsonian Institution, 1965
47. Sellers, pp.127-130. Subsequent paragraphs relate to this source.
48. Drawing of 'Mr Delarue's press', DRO: D1851/P/2/6.
49. Sellers, p.30.
50. *Ibid.*, p.116.
51. *Ibid.*, pp.122 & 125.

Chapter 12: Home from Home

1. Much of the unreferenced information about the lives of the brothers and sisters in Sandoe comes from Mary Donkin's unpublished diary, in private collection.
2. BD's diary, 28 April 1806: in private collection.
3. *Sotheran's York Guide*, printed by T. Wilson and R. Spence, York, for H. Sotheran & Son, 1803, p.82. On the return journey, the London Post Coach, or Mercury (late Paul Jones) set out from the Black Swan, in Coney Street, York, every morning at five o'clock, arriving at the Saracen's Head, Snow Hill, London, 'next day to dinner'.
4. Mary Donkin's diary and family letters give a good idea of her activities and family events. Documents in private collections.
5. Notes by a family member from Swinburne Collection, NRO: ZSW/60-672.
6. Robert Forster, *History of Corbridge and its Antiquities*: Newcastle upon Tyne: J. Beall, 1871, p.881.
7. William Holt Beaver & Charles Taylor, *The Literary Panorama*, London: Cox, Son and Baylis, 1807, p.1295; and *An Alphabetical Arrangement of the Leading Shorthorn Tribes*, London: J. Thornton, 1881, p.72.
8. George Coates *The General Short-horned Herd-book*, Otley: W. Walker, at the Wharfedale Stanhope Press, top of the Market-place, 1822.
9. *The History of Improved Short-horn or Durham Cattle, and of the Kirklevington Herd, from the notes of the late Thomas Bates*, Newcastle-upon-Tyne: Robert Redpath, 1871, p.294
10. J.C.Loudon, *The Gardener's Magazine*, London: Longman, Rees, Orme, Brown and Green, 1830, pp.383, 522 & 631.
11. *Local Collections or Records of Remarkable Events* ... 1840, Gateshead-on-Tyne: printed by William Douglas, 1841, p.48.
12. Eneas Mackenzie, *An Historical, Topographical and Descriptive View of the County of Northumberland*, Newcastle upon Tyne: Mackenzie & Dent, 1825, p.300.
13. William Hutton, *The History of the Roman Wall*, 1813, reprinted Newcastle upon Tyne: Frank Graham, 1990, p.55.
14. See Chapter 1.
15. Information from the present owner and personal observations.
16. NRO: William Donkin to Sir John Swinburne, Swinburne Collection, 1801: ZHE 68.
17. *The Poll Book of the Contested Election for the Southern Division of the County of Northumberland*, Newcastle: printed for and by John Hernaman, 1852, p.66.
18. *An Appeal to the Poor Miner, and to every Nobleman, Gentleman and Tradesman in the Kingdom who feels Interested in the Miner's Fate*, London: Longman, Hunt, Hurst, Rees, Orme & Co., 1818. pp.31-2
19. NRO: 309/b1.
20. NRO: 309/G/XI, Account book, 1836.
21. Thomas Donkin to BD, 11 December 1802, in private collection.
22. Tithe award for Sandoe Township, 6.May 1849 (1839 survey) NRO: DT408.
23. Edward Jacob, *Reports of Cases argued and determined in the High Court of Chancery*, London: Joseph Butterworth & Son, 1828, p.405-6.
24. NRO: Letters and accounts, ZSW/536, 1828.
25. NRO: Cellar book, ZSW/309/b1.
26. NRO, ZSW/565, December 1822. This source gives many instances of William's work with John Errington quoted below.
27. *The Catholic Miscellany and Monthly Repository of Information*, London: Sherwood & Co.,1827, pp.223-4.
28. Among the many accounts of this episode are: Valerie Irvine, *The King's Wife: George IV and Mrs Fitzherbert*, London: Hambledon & London, 2005, and *Harper's New Monthly Magazine*, New York: Harper & Brothers, June 1856, Vol. XIII, No.73, pp.202-5.
29. C. Allyn Pierson, *And this our Life*, Bloomington IN, USA: iUniverse, 2008, pp.237-238.
30. Arthur Aspinall, *The Correspondence of George, Prince of Wales*, London: Cassell, 1971, p.189.
31. Charles Lawndale, *Memoirs of Mrs Fitzherbert*, London: Richard Bentley, 1856, p.122.
32. Dr Kelly, *Registers of Hexham Christenings* 1752-1851, Hexham Library, Local Collection, 929.3. These are records transcribed from parish registers, noting a John Donkin baptised in Hexham 1793, 'son of John Donkin, schoolmaster.'

33. BD to one of his sisters, 25 December 1817, DRO: D5029/3/18/1.
34. Mary Donkin's diary. Evidence of life at Sandoe, and family matters, is mainly from this source.
35. BD's Recipe book, 1797-1820, DRO: D5029/2/1 Try it! Use approx 4 teasp. ground ginger, roll the mixture into small flattened balls and spread out on a baking tray. Bake for about 15 mins. at gas mark 6 - 200° C.
36. *The Quiver: an Illustrated Magazine for Sunday and general Reading*, London: Cassell, Petter and Galpin, 1869, p.395.
37. *The Examiner, a Sunday Paper*, London: John Hunt, 1826, p.569.
38. William and Robert Chambers, *Chambers's Edinburgh Journal*, Edinburgh: William and Robert Chambers, 1849, Vol.XI, No.309, p.344.
39. *Local Records, or Historical Register of Remarkable Events,* Newcastle: John Sykes, 1833, Vol.II, pp.381-382.William Parson and William White, *History, Directory and Gazateer of the Counties of Durham and Northumberland,* Newcastle: W. White & Co, printed at the Leeds Mercury Office, 1827, Vol.I, p.187.
40. *The Royal Kalendar, and Court and County Register for England and Scotland,* London: Longman & Co, printed for William Stockdale, 1818, p.250.
41. Charles Abbot, *Reports of the Select Committee ... into the State of the Public Records of the Kingdom*, London: House of Commons, 1800, pp.255-6.
42. Sylvanus Urban, *Gentleman's Magazine*, July-December 1816, London: Nicholls, Son and Bently, 1817, Vol.LXXXVI, part 2, p.139.
43. Abbot, p.256.
44. William Parson and William White, *History, Directory and Gazateer of the Counties of Durham and Northumberland,* Newcastle: W. White & Co, printed at the Leeds Mercury Office, 1827, Vol.I, p.187.
45. Abbot, p.203.
46. Durham Probate Records DPR: I/3/1849/A75
47. Among the books to which Henry subscribed were: *A Topographical Dictionary of England* (1811); *An Essay on the Study and Composition of Biography* (1813); *A Glossary of North Country Words* (1825); *Historical Account of Newcastle-upon Tyne* (1827); *Memoirs of Count Borwalski* (1833); and *Captain John Ross's Narrative of his Second Voyage* (1835).
48. Sylvanus Urban, *Gentleman's Magazine*, London: William Pickering, 1838, Vol.X, July-December 1838, p.527
49. John Sykes, *Local Records, or Historical Register of Remarkable Events*, Newcastle, T. Fordwich, 1866, pps, 351-2.
50. William Hutchinson, *The History and Antiquities of the County Palatine of Durham*, Durham: G. Walker, 1817, p.756.
51. *Monthly Notices of the Royal Astronomical Society*, London: RAS, printed by George Barclay, 1857, p.95.
52. David Lansley, *Wilfred Dodgson of Shropshire*, London: White Stone, 2011, p.10.
53. Thomas Donkin to BD, 11 December 1802, in private collection. See Chapter 2.
54. *Monthly Magazine*, Vol. 27, Part I, for 1809, London; printed for Richard Phipps, 1809, p.625.
55. *Ure's Dictionary of Arts, Manufactures and Mines*, ed. Robert Hunt, London: Spottiswoode, 1897, p.114.
56. A Lady, the wife of a Naval Officer, *An Account of the Celebration of the Jubilee*, Birmingham: R. Jabet, 1809, p.183.
57. Lansley, p.11.
58. Edward and James Weatherby, *The Racing Calendar for the Year* 1815, London: C.H. Reynel, 1816, Vol.XLIII, p.433.
59. Electoral Roll of East Riding of Yorkshire, 1834.
60. J.T. Shearham and T. Whellean, *History and Topography of the City of York, the East Riding, etc.*, Beverley: John Green, 1857, Vol.2, p.668.
61. *Declaration of the Freeholders and Inhabitants of the County of York*, York: Printed at the Gazette-office, by John Wolstenholme, 1819.
62. Ames Chandler, *England in* 1819*: The Politics of Literary Culture and the Case of the Romantic Historicism*, Chicago, University of Chicago, 1999.
63. Michael Andrew Žmolek, *Rethinking the Industrial Revolution*, Leiden, The Netherlands: Koninglijke Brill NV, 2013, p.610.

64. Joyce Lee Malcolm, *Guns and Violence: The English Experience*, Harvard, USA: University Press, 2009, p.188.

Chapter 13: Master and Man

1. Southwark Local History Library: 'Surveys ... of the Parish of St Mary Magdalene, 1833-36, shelf mark 912; and *Minutes of Evidence, Central Criminal Court*, London: George Hebert, 1839, Vol. XII, p.893.
2. Diagram of the Donkin works 1827: DRO: D5029/8/9/1.
3. William Woodfall, *An Impartial Report of the Debates that occur in the two Houses of Parliament*, London: T. Chapman, 1799, Vol.II, p.519.
4. BD's notebook 1804-06, DRO: D502/2/6.
5. *Mechanics' Magazine*, Vol.IX, Knight & Lacey 1828, p.204.
6. Samuel Smiles, *Industrial Biography: Iron Workers and Tool Makers*, J. Murray, 1901, p.295.
7. BD's diary, 11 May 1813, DRO: D5029/29/1/10.
8. *The Parliamentary Debates from the Year 1803 to the Present Time*, London: T. Hansard, 1812, Vol. XXI, p.702.
9. Petition, 1814: To the Honourable House of Commons of the United Kingdom of Great Britain and Ireland in Parliament assembled. In private collection.
10. *The Pamphleteer*, printed by A.J. Valpy, Chancery Lane, 1814, pp.218-42.
11. *Ibid.*, p.222.
12. See Chapter 9.
13. *The Pamphleteer*, p.237.
14. *Penny Cyclopaedia*, London: Charles Knight, 1833, Vol.I, p.195.
15. See Chapter 12.
16. *First Report of the Select Committee on Artizans and Machinery*, London: House of Commons, February 23rd, 1824, pp.33-4.
17. *Ibid.*, pp.34-42.
18. *First Report*, p.35.
19. *Ibid.*, p.35.
20. *Ibid*, p.38.
21. *Mechanics' Magazine*, London, W.A. Robertson, 1839, Vol. XXXI, pp.335-6.
22. Day Book, p.185.
23. *First Report*, p.37.
24. *Ibid.*, p.41.
25. *Ibid.*, p.38.
26. *Ibid.*, p.42.
27. Hansard: '*Resolutions of the Select Committee on Artizans and Machinery*', House of Commons debate, 21 May 1824, pp.1-2.
28. *First report*, p.37.
29. *Mechanics' Magazine*, London: Knight & Lacey, 1825, pp.177-8.
30. *Mechanics' Magazine*, London: Knight & Lacey, 1826, pp.458-9.
31. *Mechanics' Magazine*, London: Knight & Lacey, 1827, p.460.
32. *The London Mechanics' Register*, London: Gifford & Co, 1826, Vol.3. pp.92-3.
33. Mabel Phythian Tylecote, *The Mechanics' Institute in Lancashire and Yorkshire before* 1851, Manchester: University Press, 1957, pp.54-6.
34. *The Kaleidoscope or, Literary and Scientific Mirror*, Liverpool, E. Smith & Co.1824, p.320.
35. Thomas Gill, *The Technical Repository*, London: T. Cadell, 1823, Vol.III, p.214.
36. *The Philosophical Magazine and Journal*, ed. Andrew Tilloch and Richard Taylor, London: Richard Taylor, 1823, Vol.LXI, January to June 1823, p.133.
37. *The New Monthly Magazine*, London, Geo. Whittaker, No.378, February 1823, Part 1 of Vol.LV, p.321.
38. *Ibid*, p.312.
39. Thomas Joseph Pettigrew, *Medical Portrait Gallery; Biographical Memoirs of the most Celebrated Physicians, Surgeons, etc.*, London: Fisher, Son and Co.,1840, p.10.
40. *Monthly Notices of the Royal Astronomical Society*, London: George Barclay, 1839, Vol.6, February, 1844, p.42. Richard Peckover Harris was on the board of the Thames Tunnel in 1823, but he was in his mid forties, and his son of the same name was only eight.

41. *Encyclopaedia of Romanticism: Culture in Britain, 1780s-1830s*, ed. Laura Dabundo, London: Routledge, 2014, p.172.
42. John Fletcher Clews Harrison, *The English Common People*, Beckenham, Kent: Croom Helm, 1984, pp.249-50.
43. Brian Brenchley Wheals, *Theirs were but Human Hearts*, Buckinghamshire: H.S.Publishing, 1984, p.107.
44. *Ibid.*, p.103.
45. Day Book, p.523.
46. Day Book, p.416.

CHAPTER 14: FAR AND WIDE

1. R.H. Clapperton, *The Paper-making Machine: its Invention, Evolution and Development,* Oxford: Pergamon, 1967, pp. 43-4.
2. The Day Book always records the sales by using the former sizes, based on the maximum width of paper produced; this measurement will be used here. The width of the wire in centimetres was respectively 113 and 143.5.
3. *Ibid.*, p.317.
4. Joseph Mason, 'The Bacon-Donkin Printing Machine: Norfolk and the Origin of the Rotary Press', *The Journal of the Norfolk Industrial Archaeology Society*, Vol.IX, No.1, 2011, p.9.
5. BD's diary, 18 February 1809, and 13-17 November 1809. DRO: D5029/1/1.
6. BD's diary, 29 May 1813, DRO: D5029/1/1.
7. BD to unknown paper maker, 5 May 1817, DRO: D5029/3/18/2.
8. Mason, p.9.
9. Day Book, p.31.
10. Edith Brill, *Old Cotswold*, Newton Abbot: David and Charles, 1968, p.153.
11. Alfred Henry Shorter and Richard Leslie Hills, *Studies on the History of Papermaking in Britan*, Aldershot, Variorum, 1993, p.193. A huge paper mill still operates on the site today.
12. Day Book, p.35.
13. Day Book, pp. 39, 53-4.
14. Pamela Sharpe, *Population and Society in an East Devon Parish*, Exeter: University of Exeter, 2002, p.87.
15. Day Book, pp.12 & 16.
16. *The Law Journal for the Year* 1832-39, London: E.B. Ince, 1839, p.33.
17. Day Book, p.3.
18. *Letters from Settlers in Upper Canada*, London: printed by Marchant, Fenchurch Street, 1839, p.4.
19. *The Industrial Resources of ... The Tyne, Wear and Tees*, ed Sir W.G. Armstrong *et al*, London: Longman, Green, Longman, Roberts and Green, 1864, 2nd edn, pp.265-7.
20. Clapperton, p.127.
21. Day Book, p.35.
22. *Reports of the Commissions, First Annual Report of the Poor Law Commissioners for England and Wales.* London: Charles Knight, 1835, Vol. I, pp.316-7. The Commissioners' thorough and compassionate accounts give details of the effect of the Poor Law on families and their working conditions.
23. Letter from Edmund Ashworth, Turton, near Bolton, *Reports of the Commissioners*, 1835, p.344.
24. *Ibid.*, p.346.
25. 'Employment of Children Commission', *Chambers' Edinburgh Journal*, ed. William & Robert Chambers, London: W.S. Orr & Co., 1844, Vol.VII, p.130.
26. *Exhibition of Works of Industry of all Nations,* 1851*: Report by the Juries*, London: William Clowes & Sons, 1852, p.427.
27. J. Munsell, *A Chronology of Paper and Paper-making*, London: Turner & Co., 1857, p.50.
28. *The Photographic News*, ed. William Crookes, F.C.S., Vol.I, London: Cassell, Petter and Galpin, 1859, p.281.
29. *Reports of the Juries, Exhibition of the Works of All Nations*, 1851, London: W. Clowes, 1852, Presentation copy, p.427.
30. Joel Munsell, *A Chronology of Paper and Paper-making*, Albany, USA: J. Munsell, 1870, 4th edn, p.71.

31. Day Book, pp.175-80.
32. Day Book, pp.45-8.
33. Léger's younger sister Félicité was an attractive but rather waif-like girl, who caught the eye of Bernardin St Pierre; he was a writer whose works were published by Pierre Francois Didot. Bernardin St Pierre, at the age of fifty seven, married the twenty-year-old Félicité; there were rumours that he was cruel to her, which caused a scandal in the family. The marriage lasted eight years and Félicité died of consumption in a damp cottage in Essonnes. Agnes M. Duclaux, *The French Procession*, London: T. Fisher Unwin, 1909, pps.83-5.
34. Day Book, p.45
35. Day Book, p.19.
36. Day Book, pp. 49 & 132.
37. *Reports of the Juries*, p.427.
38. Day Book, p.459. *The World's Paper Trade Review*, London: Stonhill & Gillis, 1893, Vol. XX, p.70.
39. Magloire Nayral, *Biographie Castraise ou Tableau Historique, Chroniques et Antiquités Castraises*, Castres, 1837, Vol.IV, pp.35-6.
40. Day Book, pp.183-5.
41. Day Book, p.209.
42. *Bulletin des Lois du Royaume de France*, Paris: L'Imprimerie Royal, August 1835, Vol.X, p.449.
43. Day Book, p.209.
44. *London Journal of Arts and Sciences*, London: Sherwood, Gilbert and Piper, ed. W. Newton, Vol. III, 1836, p.122.
45. *Ibid.*, p.121. Perpigna himself took out a patent in 1835, for 'a peculiar preparation applicable to meat, and by the agency of which it may be preserved without taint for a considerable time'. He also represented James Perry, a London pen and penholder maker, who became one of England's largest manufacturers.
46. *London Journal of Arts and Sciences*, ed. William Newton, London: Sherwood, Jones & Co., 1825, Vol. IX, p.219.
47. Document in private collection.
48. Friedrich Oehler & Rheinhold Bocket, *The European Economic and Cultural Region of Bavaria*, Bad Wörishofen: Holzmann, 1995, p.60.
49. Day Book, pp.9, 257-66, & 278.
50. Drawing, 'Machine for drying paper for Messrs Rauch', Heilbronn, Wurtemberg, 1823, DRO: D1851/P/1/14.
51. *Reports of the Juries*, p.427.
52. Day Book, p.194.
53. *Annali di Giurisprudenza*, Turin: Societa di Avvocati e di Causidice, Vol.1, p.605.
54. Day Book, p.187.
55. Day Book, pp. 15 & 94.
56. Clapperton, p.96.
57. Plan and elevation of the paper mill at Klippan, drawing, 1830, DRO: D1851/3.
58. Drawing, plan and elevation of paper machines, machine house and water wheel at Klippan, DRO: D1851/P/5/4.
59. Day Book, p.586
60. Clapperton, p.122
61. Day Book, p.587.
62. DRO: D1851/P/5/17. There are numerous drawings of machinery sent to the Klippan mill in the D1851/P/5 series.
63. John Bidwell, *American Paper Mills*, 1690-1832, New England, U.S.A: Dartmouth College Press, 2013, p.220.
64. *Rag Paper Manufacture in the U.S.* 1801-1900, A.J. Valente, Jefferson, North Carolina: McFarland, p.94.
65. *Ibid.*, pp. 69 & 468.
66. Ewen Jardine, 'Scottish Paper Makers and the First Fourdriniers in America', *The Quarterly, Journal of the British Association of Paper Historians*, No.86, April 2013, p.15.
67. Jardine, p.16.
68. It is possible that another Donkin Fourdrinier paper machine was ordered for the Saugerties Mill in 1839; Bidwell, p.220.

69. *Ibid.*, p.221
70. Marjorie Fellows Block, *Saugerties*, Chicago, U.S.A: Arcadia Press, 2010, pp.8 & 78-9. Barclay sold out to the Sheffield family.
71. Valente, p.94
72. Bidwell, p.li.
73. Clapperton, p.319.
74. Patent No.5934, 1830, DRO: D5029/4/15, and drawing, D1851/P/1/38-39, 1835.
75. *The Athenaeum*, London: J. Lection, January-December 1831, p.154. 'Drawing and description of an improved gate for wide water wheels presented by Mr B. Donkin to the Institution of Civil Engineers, January 25th, 1831.
76. DRO:D1851/P/1/31, 1835.

CHAPTER 15: LINKS

1. Day Book, p.455.
2. Day Book, p.574.
3. *Mechanics' Magazine*, ed. M. Salmon, London: W.A. Robertson, 1839, Vol.XXX, p.8.
4. *Mechanics' Magazine*, ed. Sholto Percy, London: M. Salmon, 1832, Vol.XVI, p.258.
5. John Guest, *Relics and Records of Men and Manufactures at or in the Neighbourhood of Rotherham*, Rotherham: printed by A. Gilling, 1866, pp.48-9.
6. Newspaper advertisement, in private collection.
7. Day Book, pp. 495-505.
8. W.A. Provis, *An Historical and Descriptive Account of the Suspension Bridge constructed over the Menai Strait*, London: Ibotson & Palmer, 1828, pp.11-13
9. Sean C. Dooley, *The Development of Material-adapted Structural Form*, thesis 2004, Appendix A-02, pp.A53-4.
10. *Transactions of the Royal Institution of Naval Architects*, ed. E.J. Reed, London: Secretary's Office, 1860, p.161.
11. *The Tradesman*, London: Sherwood, Neely and Jones, 1811, Vol. VI, p.504. This gives a description of an iron bridge recently built over the River Merrimack in America.
12. House of Lords: *The Sessional Papers*, 1801-33, Vol.CXXXIX, 1822, Paper No.121, 'Report from Committees of the House of Commons, on Holyhead roads, harbours etc.', p.336.
13. James Hamilton, *London Lights*, London: James Murray, 2007, p.135.
14. 1819 report.
15. Dooley, p.A55.
16. *The Penny Cyclopaedia*, London: Charles Knight & Co 1842, Vol.XXIII, p.334.
17. Minutes of Evidence of the Select Committee of the House of Commons into the London to Holyhead road (Menai Bridge) April 1819, p.257.
18. House of Lords: *Sessional Papers*, p.337.
19. Charles Stewart Drewry, *A Memoir of Suspension Bridges*, London: Longman, Rees, Orme, Green and Longman, 1832, pp.58-60.
20. Provis, pp.35-6.
21. John Hickling, *The Illustrated Handbook of North Wales*, London: Whittaker & Co.,1850, pp. 47-50.
22. Thomas Telford, *The Life of Thomas Telford*, written by himself, ed. John Rickman, London: James & Luke Hansard & Sons, 1838, pp.574-5.
23. George John Bennett, *The Pedestrian's Guide through North Wales*, London: Henry Colburn, 1838, p.372.
24. *Mechanics' Magazine*, London: Knight and Lacey, Vol.VIII, 1828, p.135.
25. *Ibid.*, p.151.
26. Thomas Telford to BD, 1 April 1821, in private collection.
27. Thomas Telford to BD, 9 October 1823, in private collection.
28. ICE: Telford Papers, T/GC 229-35.
29. Day Book, p.3.
30. Day Book, p.31; see also Alexander Gordon, *A Treatise on Elemental Locomotion*, London: Thomas Tegg & Son, 1834, pp.234-6.
31. Paul Clements, *Marc Isambard Brunel*, London: Longmans, 1970, p.81.
32. Diary of I.K.Brunel, 24 April 1814, University of Bristol Library, Special Collections: Brunel Collection: DM1306/2/2/1, folio 13.

33. *Transactions of the Society of Arts*, London: Society of Arts (sold by the Housekeeper at the Society's house in the Adelphi), 1826, Vol. 44, pp.75-6.
34. I.K. Brunel's diary, DM1306/2//2/1, folio 14.
35. I.K. Brunel's diary, DM1306/2/2/1, folio 16.
36. Drawing in private collection.
37. Clements, p.101.
38. *Ibid.*, pp.116-17.
39. *Ibid.*, p.108.
40. *Ibid.*, p.110.
41. *Ibid.*, p.103.
42. Day Book pp.101-5.
43. Annabel Gillings, *Brunel*, London: Haus, 2006, p.15.
44. Day Book, pp.293-4 (August 1832-May 1833).
45. R. Angus Buchanan, *Brunel: The Life and Times of I.K.Brunel*, London: Hambledon Continuum, 2006, p.28.
46. William Peace to John Donkin, DRO: D5029/15/5, undated.
47. Comment on a letter from Mr Thomas Deakin, engineer, Blaenavon Ironworks, in *Mechanics' Magazine*, London: Knight and Lacey, Vol.VIII, 1828, p.442.
48. Clements, p.148.
49. Sylvanus Urban, *Gentleman's Magazine*, London: printed by J.B. Nichols & Sons, 1828, Vol. XCVIII, Part 2, p.79.
50. Benson Bobrick, *Labyrinths of Iron*, Sittingbourne: Quill, 1986, p.72.
51. G.F. Cruchley, *New Guide to London: A Handbook for Strangers*, London: G.F. Cruchley, 1866, p.117.
52. Alfred E. Beach, *The Pneumatic Dispatch*, New York: American News Co., p.67.
53. Cruchley, p.118.
54. Michael Worth, *Sweat and Inspiration*, Stroud: Sutton, 1999, pp.190-1.

Chapter 16: Onward and Upward

1. BD: Council member, Astronomical Society 1824-26, 1833-35, 1840-41, 1844; Vice President 1845 & 1846.
2. Obituary of BD, *Memoirs of the Royal Astronomical Society*, London: RAS, 1857, Vol.XXV, pp.147-8.
3. Anita McConnell, *R.B. Bate of the Poultry*, 1782-1847, London: Scientific Instrument Society, p.35.
4. *Reports from the Committees, Session 14 July-20 October* 1831, London: House of Commons, 1831, p.73.
5. J. William Rosenthal, *Spectacles and other Vision Aids*, San Francisco: Norman, 1996, p.118.
6. Iwan Rhys Morus, *Bodies/Machines*, London: Berg, 2002, p.52.
7. Letter from John Fulton, employee of R.B. Bate, 13 August 1835, in private collection.
8. McConnell, *R.B.Bate*, p.19.
9. Day Book, p.8.
10. Henry Kater to The Commissioners of Weights and Measures, 12 January 1825, in *Mechanics Magazine*, London: Knight and Lacey, Vol.3, 1825, p.387.
11. Day Book, p.8.
12. Edward Troughton, 'An account of the method of Dividing Astronomical and other Instruments by Ocular Inspection', *Philosphical Transactions of the Royal Society of London*, London: Printed by W. Bulmer & Co.,1809, p.106.
13. Day Book, pp.98 & 108.
14. Charles Holtzapffel, *Turning and Mechanical Manipulation on the Lathe*, London: Holtzapffel, 1856, Vol.II, p.652.
15. *Ibid.*, p.654.
16. George Escol Sellers, *Early Engineering Reminiscences*, 1815-40, Washington DC, USA: Smithsonian Institute (US National Museum), 1965, p.121-2.
17. Norman Atkinson, *Sir Joseph Whitworth: The World's Best Mechanician*, Stroud: Sutton, 1996, p.102.
18. Day Book. p.225.

19. 'Mr Baily's Report on the Description of the new Standard Scale and Apparatus', *Memoirs of the Royal Astronomical Society*, London: J.Weale, Vol.8, 1835. Francis Baily's report is very long and detailed: subsequent allusions to the subject are mostly from this source.
20. Anita McConnell, *Instrument Makers to the World: a History of Cooke, Troughton and Simms*, University of York, 1992, p.36.
21. Baily's report, p.79.
22. Baily's report, p.119
23. *Sharpe's London Magazine*, London: T.B. Sharpe, No.89, 10 July 1847, p.162.
24. BD to his daughter Jane in Sandoe, 17 October 1834, in private collection.
25. Mary Donkin's diary, 28 October & 15 November 1834.
26. Baily's report, p.91.
27. Several books have been written on the subject, including: Margaret A. Boden, *Mind as Machine*, Oxford: University Press, 2006; Ian Watson, *The Universal Machine*, New York: Copernicus, 2012; R .J. Hyman, *Charles Babbage: Pioneer of the Computer*, Princeton, USA: Princeton University Press, 1982; J.M. Dubbey, *The Mathematical Work of Charles Babbage*, Cambridge: Cambridge University Press, 2004.
28. Charles Babbage, *A Letter to Sir Humphry Davy, Bart, on the Application of Machinery to the Purpose of Calculating and Printing Mathematical Tables, from Charles Babbage, Esq., M.A.*, London: J. Booth, 1822.
29. *Cyclopaedia of Useful Arts*, ed. Charles Tomlinson, London: printed by W. Clowes, 1868, Vol. I, p. 271.
30. Babbage to Rennie, 11 April 1829, British Library, Babbage Additional Manuscripts: Letters, Vol. III, 37184, p.252.
31. *Arcana of Science and Art*, London: John Limbird, 1833, p.28.
32. Babbage letters, Vol.III, Babbage to BD, 8 April 1829, p.249.
33. *Ibid.*, BD to Babbage, 22 April 1829, p.266.
34. Babbage to BD, 3 January 1830, British Library: Babbage Additional Manuscripts: Letters, Vol. IV, 37185, p.8.
35. *Ibid.*, Babbage to BD, 19 February 1830, p.64; BD to Babbage, 20 February 1830. p.64.
36. *Ibid.*, Babbage to BD, 31January 1831, p.454.
37. BD to Babbage, 2 February 1833, British Library: Babbage Additional Manuscripts: Letters, Vol. VI, 37187, p.503.
38. *Ibid.*, Several letters between Babbage and Donkin, February-June 1833.
39. *Ibid.*, BD to Babbage, 3 April 1833, p.465.
40. G. & E. Scheutz, *Specimens of Tables, Calculated, Stereo-moulded and Printed by Machinery*, London: Longman, Brown, Green, Longman and Roberts, 1857, p. viii. See also Chapter 20.
41. McConnell, *Instrument Makers*, p.7.
42. *Ibid.*, p.17.
43. Anita McConnell, *Astronomers at War: The Viewpoint of Troughton and Simms*, NASA Astrophysics Data System: Science History Publications, 1994, p.219.
44. Day Book, p.248.
45. Rev. R. Sheepshanks, *A Letter to the Board of Visitors*, London: G. Barclay, 1854, p.23.
46. 'Royal Annual Grant to Sir J. South for the Promotion of Astronomy', *Philosophical Magazine*, Vol.VIII, July-December 1830, p.231.
47. Sheepshanks, p.12.
48. McConnell, *Astronomers at War*, p.220.
49. Sheepshanks, p.21.
50. Eleanor Mennim, *Transit Circle: the Story of William Simms, 1793-1860*, Ann Arbor: Michigan University Press, 1992, p.49.
51. Day Book, pp.579-80 .

CHAPTER 17: GOING STRONG

1. B.L.Vulliamy, *Some Considerations on the Subject of Public Clocks*, London: B.McMillan, 1828; private circulation, not for sale. Vulliamy wrote his own account of the building of the church clocks in London.
2. BD to Benjamin Vulliamy, 17 November 1829, *Ibid.*, pp.27-8.
3. Timothy Bramah to Benjamin Vulliamy, 17 November 1829, *Ibid.*, p.26.

4. Mr Vulliamy to A. Milne, 13 January 1847, in *A Portion of the Papers relating to the Great Clock for the New Palace of Westminster*, London: printed by William Clowes, by order of the House of Lords, 1848 (for private circulation only), p.34.
5. Day Book, p.31.
6. ICE: T/LL.6: report of experiments on 22 February 1825.
7. Later account of the planning and results of the Liverpool and Manchester railway enquiry: *The Quarterly Review*, London: John Murray, 1868, Vol. CXXV, pp.287-90.
8. The building of George Stephenson's Liverpool and Manchester railway is vividly recounted, with illustrations, by Samuel Smiles in Chapter XI of *The Story of the Life of George Stephenson*, London: John Murray, 1862.
9. *The Annual Biography and Obituary*, London: Longman, Rees, Orme, Brown & Green, 1831, Vol. XV, p. 441.
10. *Acts relating to the London and Birmingham Railway*, London: George Eyre and Andrew Spottiswoode, 1837.
11. *Ibid.*, p.330.
12. Day Book, pp.1-2, 615.
13. *Passages from the Life of a Philosopher*, Charles Babbage, London: Longman, Green, Longman, Roberts & Green, 1864, pp.323-6
14. *The Penny Cyclopaedia*, London: Charles Knight, 1842, p.487.
15. A. W. Dickinson and Arthur Titley, *Richard Trevithick: the Engineer and the Man*, Cambridge: Cambridge University Press, 2011 (first published 1934), p.48.
16. Elijah Galloway, *History of the Steam Engine, from its First Invention to the Present Time*, London: Cowie & Co, 1826: list of patents, pages unnumbered.
17. Walter Hancock, *Narrative of Twelve Years' Experiments (*1824-1836*)*, London: John Weale, 1838, p.48.
18. Minutes of the Select Committee on Mr Goldsworthy Gurney's case, *Reports from Committees*, 1834, London: William Clowes, ordered to be printed by the House of Commons, 1834, p.53 (p.223 of *Reports*).
19. *The Repertory of Patent Inventions*, London: W.Simpkin and R.Marshall, 1833, pp.244-9.
20. 'Report of the Result of an Experimental Journey upon the Mail Coach Line of the Holyhead Road, in Lieutenant Colonel Sir Charles Dance's Steam Carriage, on the first of November 1833', *Journal of the Franklin Institute*, ed. Thomas P. Jones, New York: Franklin Institute, Vol. VIII, 1834, pp.198-9.
21. *Mechanics' Magazine*, London: W.A.Robertson, 1839, Vol.XXXI, pp.420-421. Maceroni ended up penniless.
22. William Matthews, *Hydraulia: an Historical and Descriptive Account of the Water Works of London*, London: Simpkins, Marshall & Co., 1835, pp.407- 8.
23. Day Book, p.67.
24. *Ibid.*, pp.436-8.
25. Matthews, pp.427-8.
26. J.D. Mather. *Two Hundred Years of British Hydrology*, London: Geological Society Special Publications 225, 2004, p.3.
27. Day Book, p.24.
28. Jason Birkett and John Lester, *Microbiology and Chemistry for Environmental Scientists*, London: E. and F. Spon, 2nd edn 1999, p.4.
29. Day Book, p.467.
30. A.W. Skempton, *Biographical Dictionary of Civil Engineers*, London: Thomas Telford, 2002, p.189.
31. *Mirror of Parliament*, ed. John Henry Barrow, Vol.V, London: Longman, Orme, Brown, Green and Longmans, 1838, p.270-7.
32. Pippa Drummond, *The Provincial Musical Festival in England*, 1784-1914, Farnham, Surrey: Ashgate, 2011, p.269.
33. Richard, Earl of Mount-Edgcumbe, *Musical Reminiscences*, London: John Andrews, 1834.
34. Bryan Donkin Jnr, to his sister Maria Donkin, 27 June 1834, in private collection.
35. Bryan Donkin to his daughter Maria, 27 June 1834, in private collection.
36. Charles Burney, *An Account of the Musical Performances in Westminster Abbey*, London: Duff and Hodgson, 1834, p. xxxviii.

37. *Musical Reminiscences*, pp. 232-3.
38. *Reports of Cases argued and determined in the Court of the Exchequer*, Philadelphia, USA: T & J.W. Johnson, 1854, Vol. I, pp. 864-7.
39. *The Repertory of Patent Inventions*, London: J.S. Hodson, 1838, Vol.VIII, pp.46-8.
40. *Ibid.*, pp.51-9.
41. A.D. MacKenzie *The Bank of England Note: a History of its Printing*, Cambridge: CUP Archive 1953, pp.32-3.
42. *The Phrenological Journal and Miscellany*, Edinburgh: John Anderson Jun. Vol.VI, 1833, pp.78-9.
43. Drawing of Mr Oldham's press, DRO: D1851/P/2/3.
44. Day Book, pp.98 & 108.
45. *Minutes of proceedings of the ICE*, London: printed for the Institution, 1837, p.22.
46. *Memoirs of the Royal Astronomical Society*, London: J.Weale, 1838, Vol.X, pp.319-24.
47. *Dictionary of National Biography*, originally ed. Leslie Stephen, 1891, New York: Adegi Graphics LLC, 2001, pp.217-8.
48. Lieutenant Frome, *Outline of the Method of Conducting a Trigonometrical Survey*, London: John Weale, 1840, p.21.
49. Day Book, p. 385.

CHAPTER 18: THREE SCORE AND TEN

1. BD's election certificate, Royal Society: EC 1838/01.
2. Royal Society: JBO/48, p.683.
3. Information from Royal Society Journal books.
4. Royal Society: Journal Book, JBO/47, 1834.
5. Alan S. Weber, *Nineteenth Century Science: A Selection of Original Texts*, Peterborough, Ontario: Broadview, 2000, p.172.
6. *Journal of the Society of Arts*, London: Bell and Daldy, Vol.XII, p.125.
7. William Simms's election certificate, Royal Society: EC/1852/11.
8. Marie Hall, *All Scientists Now: The Royal Society in the Nineteenth Century*, Cambridge: University Press, 2002, p.4.
9. Richard Holmes, *The Age of Wonder*, London: Harper Press, 2008, pp.435-7.
10. Charles Babbage, *Reflections on the Decline of Science in England*, London: printed for B. Fellowes, p.214.
11. Hall, p.185.
12. *Report on the Seventh Meeting of the British Association*, London: John Murray, 1838, pp.xxi-xxii.
13. Mary Donkin's diary, 14 August 1838.
14. Charles Babbage, *Passages from the Life of a Philosopher*, London: Longman, Green, Longman, Roberts and Green, 1864, pp.326-7.
15. Sylvanus Urban, *Gentleman's Magazine*, London: William Pickering, Vol. X, July–December, 1838, pp. 423-7.
16. Numerous articles were written in magazines in 1838 and 1839 about this important event in the life of Newcastle.
17. *Gentleman's Magazine*, 1838, pp.428-30.
18. *The London and Westminster Review*, New York: Jemima M.Lewer, 1838, p.141.
19. Hannah Martineau & Maria Weston Chapman, *Hannah Martineau's Autobiography*, Cambridge University Press, 1877, p.137.
20. Martineau & Chapman, p.136. Hannah Martineau knew Dr Lardner, because she had been asked to write an article for his publication, the *Cabinet Cyclopaedia.*
21. Babbage, p.328.
22. John Herepath, *The Railway Magazine*, London: Wyld & Son, 1839, Vol.V, p.244.
23. *Ibid.*, p.428.
24. *The Civil Engineer and Architect's Journal*, October 1837-December 1838, London: published for the proprietor, M. Hooper et al, 1838, pp.349-50.
25. Thomas Sopwith: Diaries 1-12, 9 September 1834, NRO: 00504.
26. BD to Thomas Sopwith, DRO: D1851/Box 19/item 2, 1839.
27. *Gentleman's Magazine*, 1838, p.429
28. *Ibid.*, p.427.
29. *The Phrenological Journal*, London: Simpkin, Marshall & Co, Vol.XII (Vol.II of the new version)

1839, pp.29-32.
30. *The Civil Engineer and Architect's Journal*, 1838, p.348.
31. *Report of the Eighth Meeting of the British Association*, London: John Murray, Vol.VII, p.xxi.
32. *The Civil Engineer and Architect's Journal*, 1838, pp.135-6.
33. *Mechanics' Magazine*, London: W.A. Robertson, 7 April-29 September 1838, Vol.XXIX, p.402.
34. *Magazine of Science*, London: William Brittain, 1843, Vol.IV, p.270.
35. Isambard Kingdom Brunel to (probably) Francis Humphrys, 28 November 1838, in private collection.
36. Edward Humphrys, 'On Surface Condensation in Marine Engines', *Proceedings of the Institution of Mechanical Engineers*, London: The Institution, Vol.XVI, p.99.
37. *Ibid.*, Letter from I.K.B as above.
38. Isambard Kingdom Brunel to Bryan Donkin, 20 November 1838, in private collection.
39. Steam engine, drawing, DRO: D1851/P/38.
40. Day Book, p.614.
41. Day Book, p.601.
42. Letter copying press, 1839, drawing, DRO: D1851/P/2/11.
43. *The Civil Engineer and Architect's Journal*, London: published for the Proprietor, 57, King Street, Westminster, 1840, Vol. III, p.282.
44. *Ibid*, p.347.
45. *The Civil Engineer and Architect's Journal*, 1838, pp.v-vii.

Chapter 19: Handing over the Reins

1. Obituary of John Donkin, *Transactions of the Institution of Civil Engineers*, 1854, Vol.II, p.131.
2. *The Athenaeum*, London: James Holmes, 1831, p.154.
3. *The Farmers' Register*, ed. Edmund Ruffin, Petersburg, Virginia: Ruffin, 1838, Vol.V, p.178.
4. *Proceedings of the Geological Society of London*, London: Geological Society of London, Vol. II, No.39, p.128.
5. BD's daughter Maria's diary, 5 May 1843.
6. Bryan Donkin, Jnr. writing from Florence to his sister Maria, 14 June 1836; in private collection.
7. Patent dated 25 November 1834, for 'an improved mode of constructing cylinders of ... wire web', recorded in the *London Journal of Arts and Sciences*, ed. W. Newton, London: W. Newton, 1842, p.349; patent dated 15 October 1846, for a 'process of bleaching paper, linen and other manufactures in which chloride of lime is employed', *London Journal of Arts and Sciences*, 1846, p.302.
8. Obituary, *Transactions of the Institution of Civil Engineers*, 1854, Vol.2, p.131.
9. Caroline's brother – Benjamin Hawes Junior, M.P., later knighted – married Sophia, the daughter of Marc Brunel.
10. The house was later inhabited, for a short while at the beginning of the 20th century, by the poet Edward Thomas.
11. BD to Mr R. Rowell, Chelsfield, near St Marys Cray, Kent, DRO: D5029/3/18/2.
12. Bryan Donkin, Jun. to his sister Maria, 14 June 1836. In private collection.
13. Obituary, *The Engineer*, London: Morgan Grampian, 1893, Vol. LXXVI, December 1893, p.525.
14. Harry J. Donkin, *Bryan Donkin & Co: Some Notes on the history of an Engineering firm during the last Century* 1803-1903. D5029/30/1.
15. *The Times*, 29 July 1830.
16. Thomas Sweetapple patented improvements to paper machines in 1839: *Repertory of Patent Inventions*, London: J.S.Hodson, Vol. XI, January–June 1839, p.62.
17. *Minutes of Proceedings of the Institution of Civil Engineers*, London: published by the Institution, 1853, p.151.
18. Drawing of Tuscan water wheel, DRO: D1851/P/4/3; also illustrated in the Newcomen Society's *Transactions* 1949-1951, p.88 & plate 22.
19. Henry Donkin to his brother Bryan, 20 September 1842; in private collection.
20. Terry S. Reynolds, *Stronger than a Hundred Men: a History of the Vertical Water Wheel*, Baltimore, U.S.A.: Johns Hopkins University Press, 1983, pp.307-8.
21. *Morning Post*, 8 July 1843: 'Henry Donkin (3rd son of Bryan Donkin, esq.) of San Marcello, Tuscany,, on 6th inst, at Battersea Church, married Margaret Louisa, youngest daughter of the late John Dunn, esq of the City of Durham.'

22. Henry Donkin to his brother Bryan, 15 October 1843, in private collection.
23. Mary Donkin's diary, 18 December 1844 and Maria Donkin's, 14-18 December 1844, both in private collection. An extract from the Register of Baptisms in the City of Florence, 24 April 1845 records the birth of Margaret Sarah Julyan Donkin as December 3rd, 1844, a date confirmed in Maria Donkin's diary.
24. Maria's diary records her journey and her life for the next few years.
25. Henry Donkin to his brother Bryan, Jnr. 29 Sept 1845, in private collection.
26. *Handbook for Travellers in Northern Italy, Part II*, London: John Murray, 1858, 7th edn, p.443.
27. Henry Donkin to his brother Bryan, Jnr., 29 September 1845, in private collection.
28. Thomas Richardson, *Complete Practical Treatise on Acids, Alkalies and Salts*, London: H. Baillière, 1867, Vol. 2, p.186.
29. Census 1861.
30. Thomas Donkin's patents were: for glazing paper, 1856; for wire guiding, 1858, and for improvements, 1860.
31. BD to his sister Ann, 2 August 1818, DRO: D5029/3/18/3.
32. *Gentleman's Magazine*, Vol. 44, 1856, pp.92-3.
33. George James Aungier, *The History and Antiquities of Syon Monastery, the Parish of Isleworth and the Chapelry of Houndslow*, London: J.B Nichols & Sons, 1840, p.182.
34. *Ibid*, pp.240-1.
35. BD to his sister Ann, 2 August 1818, DRO: D5029/3/18/3.
36. Receipt, in private collection.
37. *The Dublin Literary Gazette*, Dublin: printed by John S. Folds, 1830, January-June 1830, pp.339-40.
38. Arthur Scratchley, *Industrial Investment and Immigration*, London: John W. Parker, 1851, p.46.
39. *Stamford Mercury* 1838–1855, adverts for Victoria Life Assurance and Loan Company.
40. *The Civil Engineer and Architect's Journal*, London: Published for the Proprietor, Vol. 4, 1841, p.321.
41. *First Report of the Commissioners for Inquiring into the State of Large Towns and Populous Districts*, Vol.I, 1844, pp.111-17.
42. *Morning* Post, 23 March 1844.
43. *Morning Post*, 14 June 1844.
44. *The Lancet*, ed. Thomas Wakley, pub. London: John Church, 1844, p.177.
45. G.W. Phillips, *The History and Antiquities of the Parish of Bermondsey, London:* J.Unwin, 1841, pp.91-8.
46. London Metropolitan Archives: A/BFS/ 49 & 56
47. Bryan Donkin's Journal, 1January 1845; quoted in notes made by Caroline (Bryan Donkin's granddaughter) in private collection.
48. *Morning Post*, 2 May 1842.
49. *Ibid.*
50. *The Era*, 7 March 1847.
51. *Morning Post*, 24 November 1845
52. *Hampshire Advertiser*, 4 August 1849.
53. *Morning Post*, 24 January 1840 and *Worcestershire Chronicle*, 21 April 1841.
54. *Minutes of the Proceedings of the Institution of Civil Engineers*, ed. Charles Manby, London, ICE, 1845, Vol. IV, p.9.
55. *Morning Post*, 2 June 1843.
56. *Morning Post*, 24 March 1846.
57. Patent No.10,932, 11 November 1845. *Civil Engineer and Architect's Journal*, ed. William Laxton, London: R.Groombridge & Sons, 1846, Vol. 8, p.392.
58. Patent No.10932, Sydney B. Donkin, *Bryan Donkin, F.R.S.* Paper read at the I.C.E., 8 March 1950, p.93.
59. Maureen Greenland, *Compound-plate Printing: a Study of a Nineteenth-Century Colour-printing Process*, PhD thesis, Reading University, 1996, p.327.
60. Dr Karl Falkenstein, *Geschichte von Buchdruckerkunst*, Leipzig: B.G. Teubner, 1840, p.370.
61. British Library, India Office Records, IOR /E/4/783.
62. Greenland, p.91.
63. British Library: IOR/E/4/812.

64. British Library: IRO/E/4/791.
65. Andrew Ure, *A Dictionary of Arts, Manufactures and Mines*, Vol.II, D.Appleton & Co, New York, 1844, p.938.

CHAPTER 20: LEAVING THE LEGACY

1. Document in private collection.
2. Mary Donkin's diary, 25 February 1844.
3. Mary Donkin's diary, 13 March–8 April 1844.
4. *Minutes of the Proceedings of the Institution of Civil Engineers*, 1855, Vol.XIV, pp.130-1.
5. *The Times*, 7 October 1848.
6. *The Times*, 27 September 1854.
7. *Official Descriptive and Illustrated Catalogue of the Great Exhibition of the Works of Industry of all Nations*, 1851, London: Spicer Brothers, Stationers, and W.C.Clowes and Sons, Printers, 1851, Part 1, p.1. (Introduction by Henry Cole.) Subsequent references to the arrangements and organisation are from this source.
8. *Ibid*, pp.537-9 .
9. *Ibid* p.539.
10. *Reports by the Juries*, London: printed by Authority of the Royal Commission by W. Clowes & Sons, 1852, Vol.III, p.938. There are several editions of the report: this edition was presented to the Government of Bavaria. Twenty three out of the 190 paper-making machines made before 1851 went to France, 46 to Germany, 22 to Northern Europe, 14 to Italy and Southern Europe, two to America and one to India.
11. *Reports by the Juries*, Presentation copy, London: printed for the Royal Commission by William Clowes, 1852, p.198. (This is a different edition from the Presentation copy above.) The machine was exhibited as Number 130 of the exhibits in section C (Papers and Printing) of Class VI (Manufacturing and Tools).
12. *Reports of the Juries*, London: printed by Authority of the Royal Commission by W. Clowes & Sons, 1852, Vol.III, p.886. (Presented to the Government of Bavaria.)
13. *Official Descriptive and Illustrated Catalogue*, p.150. Whiting's work was shown in case No 123, in Section IV, Fine Arts, Class 30, Sculpture, Models and Plastic Art.
14. Advertisement in *The Atheneum*. Part I, 25 February 1854, London: J. Lection, 1854.
15. Brian Randell, 'A Mysterious Advertisement', *Annals of the History of Computing*, New York: Springer International, Vol V (1), January 1983, pp.60-3.
16. *Official Descriptive and Illustrated Catalogue*, p.28. Exhibit No. 12, Section 1, Raw Materials, Class 3: 'Substances used as food'.
17. *Reports of the Juries*, presentation copy, p.68.
18. Obituary of B.W. Farey: *Minutes of the Proceedings of the Institution of Civil Engineers*, London: ICE, 1888, Vol. 94, p.299.
19. Sylvanus Urban, *Gentleman's Magazine*, London: John Bowyer Nichols & Sons, 1853, Vol.XL, July-December, 1853, p.321.
20. Obituary of John Donkin, *Transactions of the Institution of Civil Engineers*, 1854, Vol.2, p.131.
21. *Chelmsford Chronicle*, 16 June 1850.
22. Michael Lindgren, *Glory and Failure*, translated by Craig G. McKay, Massachusetts Institute of Technology, 1990, p.186.
23. Obituary, *Proceedings of the Royal Society*, London: Royal Society, 1868, Vol.XVI, p.vii. Gravatt died at the age of 59, from 'an accidental administration of a dose of morphia'.
24. *Proceedings of the Royal Society*, London: Royal Society, 1854, Vol. VI, p.166.
25. Ian Watson, *The Universal Machine: From the Dawn of Computing to Digital Consciousness*, New York: Copernicus, 2012, p.36.
26. *Illustrated London News*, 30 June 1855.
27. Margaret A. Boden, *Mind as Machine: a History of Cognitive* Science, Oxford: University Press, 2006, Vol.1, p.32.
28. Michael Lindgren, *Glory and Failure*, Linköping, Sweden, 1990, p.224.
29. Michael Lindgren, *Glory and Failure*, 1987, p.130.
30. *Ibid.*, p.225
31. *Ibid.*, p.232.

32. *Ibid.*, p.289.
33. Bryan Donkin's death certificate.
34. Sylvanus Urban, *Gentleman's Magazine*, London: John Henry & James Parker, July-December 1858, Vol.V of new series, p.314.
35. *Proceedings of the Royal Society*, London: Royal Society, 1855, Vol.VI, pp.586-9.
36. Edward Walford, *Hardwicke's Annual Biography for 1856*, London: Robert Hardwicke, 1856, pp.453-4.
37. *Ibid.*, p.254.
38. *Monthly Notices of the Royal Astronomical Society*, London: printed by George Barclay, 1856, Vol. XVI, November 1855 – July 1856, p.203.
39. *Reports from Commissioners: Lunacy; Lunatic Asylums; (Ireland), Lunacy (Scotland)*, London: House of Commons, 1864, Vol. XXIII, Session February–July 1864, pp.57-8.
40. Letters of Administration . . . . . the personal Estate and Effects of William Donkin, 12 May 1866, Principle Registry, General Register Office, Somerset House, London,
41. *Liverpool Mercury*, 28 August 1855.
42. Harry J. Donkin, *Bryan Donkin and Co: Some Notes on the History of an Engineering Firm during the Last Century,* 1803-1903, Chesterfield: Bryan Donkin Company, 1912, p.15.
43. Alan Crocker, 'Bryan Donkin Junior at St Petersburg in 1859', *The Quarterly*, Britsh Association of Paper Historians, No.69. January, 2009, pp.1-11.
44. Harry J. Donkin, p.15.
45. Bryan Donkin Company Ltd, *A Brief Account of Bryan Donkin, F.R.S. and the Company he Founded*, Chesterfield, 1953, p.16.
46. William Walker Junior, *Memoirs of the Distinguished Men of Science of Great Britain, Living A.D.* 1807-8, London: W. Walker & Son, 1862.
47. Richard Holmes, *The Age of Wonder*, London: Harper, 2008.

Index

Note: page numbers in *italics* refer to illustrations.